The Open University

MST209 Mathematical methods and models

Block 1

Contents

The Open University, Walton Hall, Milton Keynes, MK7 6AA.

First published 2005. Second edition 2008.

Edited, designed and typeset by The Open University, using the Open University T_EX System.

Printed and bound in the United Kingdom by Charlesworth Press, Wakefield.

ISBN 978 0 7492 5281 6

1.1

UNIT 1 Getting started

Study guide for Unit 1

This unit reviews material that you will need as a basis for your study of MST209. You should have covered most of it in previous courses.

The only non-text study for this unit involves the use of the computer algebra package for the course. All the computer activities appear in Section 7. These can be studied when you have finished each section.

The time you will require to study this unit will depend on how familiar you are with the material that it contains. Most sections begin with a short diagnostic test. If you find that you can answer the test question(s) correctly, then it is probably safe to progress directly to the next section — you can always return to re-read a section if the need arises, and you can further check your knowledge by trying the other exercises. If you choose not to study a subsection in detail, do check for any new ideas introduced, and make sure that you look at those. (New terms are set in bold type.)

Because this unit reviews a large amount of material, it is longer than other units in the course; so, even if the material is not new, you may find that there is a good deal to cover in one week. If you do not have time to study the whole unit, make sure that you are familiar with the material in Sections 2 and 3 and Subsections 5.1, 5.2 and 6.1, as this material is particularly important. You can always use this unit later to revise other topics when you find you need them.

The unit is structured so that it is natural to study the material in the order in which it appears in the text. However, you can if you wish leave study of Section 4 until last.

Introduction

The main purpose of this unit is to review ideas that you should have met before, and that you will need as a basis for your study of MST209. The unit focuses mainly on mathematical techniques, but also covers some examples involving skills in the application of mathematics. The use of mathematics to investigate questions arising in non-mathematical contexts is broadly referred to as 'mathematical modelling'. In this course, the study of mathematical techniques will quite often be separated from their use in models, as this enables you to practise the mathematical methods before you go on to use them. However, the methods introduced in the course are chosen because of their wide application in modelling.

The unit contains a number of 'standard formulae': for example, for the solution of a quadratic equation, for expanding $\sin(a + b)$ and $\cos(a + b)$, and for the derivatives and integrals of standard functions. It is helpful if you are able to remember such formulae, but not essential; they are all given in the course Handbook. You *do* need to be aware that the formulae exist, however, and to be able to find them in the Handbook and to apply them.

The computer algebra package for the course can be used to help with much of the work in this unit, and the unit reviews how this is done. However, the majority of the unit concentrates on how the mathematical techniques can be performed 'by hand'; that is, without use of a computer (or calculator). This is because, in the long run, a familiarity and confidence with using common mathematical formulae and techniques by hand will speed up your study, and because it is not always convenient to resort to a computer. (Having said that, the computer remains a valuable tool, both for checking hand calculations and for addressing problems too complicated or time-consuming to be worked on by hand.)

Generally, we advise you to first attempt all exercises without using a computer, unless they are specifically marked as computer activities.

Section 1 starts by reviewing some basic points about numbers. Sections 2 and 3 cover a number of important standard functions: linear, quadratic, logarithmic and exponential functions in Section 2, and trigonometric functions in Section 3. All these functions occur frequently. These sections also remind you of some important mathematical techniques: for example, for manipulating algebraic expressions, for solving a quadratic equation, and for manipulating expressions involving functions such as sin and cos. Section 4 covers some basic ideas about complex numbers.

Sections 5 and 6 discuss the fundamental concepts of calculus: differentiation and integration. It is important that you understand what these ideas are, and how they arise in models. These sections also provide plenty of exercises on performing basic calculus operations by hand, as being able to do this quickly will stand you in good stead for the rest of the course.

Note, however, that the computer algebra package for the course can be used to find most derivatives and many integrals.

The final section shows how the computer algebra package for the course may be used in many of the techniques in the unit.

1 Numbers, measurement and accuracy

This section covers some fundamental terminology and notation relating to numbers.

Diagnostic test 1.1

Do Exercise 1.1 on page 9, and check your answers with the solutions given on page 53. If you are happy with your answers, you may proceed directly to Section 2.

We distinguish various types of number. The **integers** are the positive and negative whole numbers, together with zero:

$$\ldots, -4, -3, -2, -1, 0, 1, 2, 3, 4, \ldots .$$

We denote the set of all integers by $\mathbb{Z}$. These are fine for counting, but insufficient for measuring lengths, for example. Non-integer quantities can sometimes be represented exactly, for example as fractions (such as $\frac{7}{3}$) or roots (such as $\sqrt{5}$). Often in this course, however, decimals will be used. In decimal notation, we can sometimes express a number exactly, but frequently we need to approximate. We may write a number correct to a particular number of **decimal places**, as in, for example,

$\frac{7}{3} = 2.33$ (to two decimal places),

$\sqrt{2} = 1.4142$ (to four decimal places).

For large or small numbers we extend decimal notation by 'taking out' powers of 10, as in, for example,

3.414×10^6 (for $3\,414\,000$),

3.42×10^{-7} (for $0.000\,000\,342$).

In this course we shall use the convention that a non-zero number is expressed in **scientific notation** as

$\pm b \times 10^c,$

where $1 \le b < 10$ and c is an integer.

> Other conventions for scientific notation exist; for example, choosing b to satisfy $0.1 \le b < 1$.

If 3.414 is quoted to an accuracy of three decimal places, then $3.414 \times 10^6 = 3\,414\,000$ almost certainly is not. It is, however, accurate to four **significant figures**. That is, giving a number to 'so many decimal places' indicates its *absolute* level of accuracy, while to 'so many significant figures' indicates the accuracy *relative* to the size of the number itself.

Many numbers cannot be represented exactly by a decimal, but any such number can be approximated arbitrarily closely by a decimal. For example, taking more and more decimal places, the number π is

3.1, 3.14, 3.142, 3.1416, 3.14159, 3.141593, 3.1415927, ...

Any number that can be approximated arbitrarily closely by a decimal (or is actually equal to one) is called a **real** number. We denote the set of all real numbers by $\mathbb{R}$. Those real numbers that can be expressed exactly as a fraction (such as $\frac{337}{1149}$) are referred to as **rational** numbers, and those that are not equal to any such fraction (such as π and $\sqrt{2}$) are called **irrational**.

Sometimes one wishes to reduce the accuracy to which a number is given. For example, a calculator may give you the result of some calculation to an accuracy of ten significant figures, while the assumptions on which the calculation was based justify quoting the result only to three significant figures.

> Rationals have either a terminating or a recurring decimal representation; irrationals do not. For example, $\frac{3}{2}$ has the terminating decimal representation 1.5, whereas $\frac{4}{3}$ has the recurring decimal representation $1.333\,333\ldots$.

The process of reducing the number of significant figures or decimal places to which a number is expressed is referred to as **rounding**. To express 3.141 59 to three decimal places, we simply take the number expressed to three decimal places that is closest to 3.141 59, which is 3.142. It is usual to make clear that a number is accurate only to some specified level by writing, for example, '3.142 (to three decimal places)'. The process of rounding is straightforward except in one case. The number 4.15, for example, is equally close to 4.1 and 4.2. To round 4.15 to one decimal place we shall use a standard, if arbitrary, convention, in which 5 is always rounded *up* for positive numbers. So 4.15 is expressed as 4.2 (to one decimal place). For negative numbers, 5 is rounded down: for example, -4.15 is expressed as -4.2 (to one decimal place).

The choice of how accurately to express some real number depends on circumstances. If the number represents a measurement, you may know how accurately the measurement was made. For example, using a tape measure (see Figure 1.1) to measure a length carefully, one might hope to measure it to the nearest millimetre, and would express the measurement as, for example, 1.274 metres (to three decimal places).

When considering problems arising from the real world, we shall generally quote numbers to relatively few significant figures. When discussing numerical methods, a larger number of significant figures will be used. The number of significant figures used will depend on the context.

Figure 1.1   A tape measure

If we know that a real number x is 1.274 to three decimal places, then x lies between 1.2735 and 1.2745; that is, x lies in the **interval**

$$[1.2735, 1.2745].$$

This 'closed interval' notation represents the set of real numbers between 1.2735 and 1.2745, inclusive of the endpoints. We can actually say slightly more, for we know that x is not 1.2745, since that would round up to 1.275. So x is in fact in the interval

$$[1.2735, 1.2745),$$

which represents the set of real numbers between 1.2735 and 1.2745, with 1.2735 included, but 1.2745 *not* included. Other, similar, 'round bracket' notations are also used.

Note the *round* bracket on the right.

$[a, b]$ means all real numbers x between a and b, with a and b both included.

that is, $a \leq x \leq b$

$[a, b)$ means all real numbers x between a and b, with a included and b excluded.

that is, $a \leq x < b$

$(a, b]$ means all real numbers x between a and b, with a excluded and b included.

that is, $a < x \leq b$

(a, b) means all real numbers x between a and b, with a and b both excluded.

that is, $a < x < b$

The interval $[a, b]$ is sometimes referred to as a **closed** interval, the interval (a, b) as an **open** interval, and the intervals $[a, b)$ and $(a, b]$ as **half-open** intervals. As you will see later, interval notation is useful in expressing domains of functions and in discussing the accuracy of calculations, and sometimes it is important to be able to say whether or not the endpoints are to be included.

It is common scientific practice to quote measurements with 'error bounds'.

We might write, for example,

$$y = 32.62 \pm 0.08 \, \text{m}$$

to indicate that the observed measurement of y is 32.62 m, but this can be expected to be accurate only to within an **error bound** of 0.08 m; that is, the actual value of y may lie anywhere between $32.62 - 0.08 = 32.54$ m and $32.62 + 0.08 = 32.70$ m, inclusive (i.e. anywhere in the interval $[32.54, 32.70]$). Such error bounds may not fit exactly with expressing y to a particular number of decimal places or significant figures (see Exercise 1.1(b)). We can also express the information that y is within 0.08 m of 32.62 m by writing

$$-0.08 \le y - 32.62 \le 0.08,$$

or more succinctly by writing

$$|y - 32.62| \le 0.08.$$

Remember, $|x|$ is a non-negative number with the same magnitude as x. So, for example, $|5.72| = 5.72$, while $|-3.8907| = 3.8907$.

We refer to $|x|$ (read as 'mod x') as the **modulus** (or **magnitude** or **absolute value**) of x.

Exercise 1.1

(a) Express the following numbers in scientific notation.

(i) 64 823.5   (ii) 0.000 073

(b) Suppose that we know that a measured value y is

$$y = 127.683 \pm 0.006 \, \text{m}.$$

(i) Give an interval in which the number y must lie.

(ii) To how many significant figures can we give y with certainty?

(c) Suppose that the number x satisfies the condition

$$|x - 2.763| < 5 \times 10^{-4}.$$

What is the smallest interval in which this condition tells you that x must lie? To how many decimal places can we give x with certainty?

Note that in this course we use the convention of placing a * against not-to-be-missed exercises.

2 Some standard functions

Functions play a central role in mathematics. After a brief look at some general ideas about functions (in Subsection 2.1), this section reviews some key classes of functions (linear, quadratic and exponential). These form part of a 'library' of standard functions, central both to building models and to solving more complicated mathematical problems (such as differential equations). The section also looks briefly at how such functions may be combined.

2.1 Functions, variables and parameters

Diagnostic test 2.1

If you are familiar with each of the following terms (and the distinction between them), you may proceed directly to Subsection 2.2. If not, it is advisable to read this subsection.

(a) Continuous model, Discrete model.

(b) Variable, Parameter.

(c) Domain, Image set.

Consider the following example. At midday on 1 June, a reservoir contains 2×10^6 cubic metres of water. Each day, 25 000 cubic metres of water are removed from the reservoir, while only 3400 cubic metres flow into the reservoir, and it is expected that these conditions will continue for 50 days. If there are no other factors affecting the quantity of water in the reservoir, then there is a daily net reduction of 21 600 cubic metres of water. Assuming that the rate of reduction is exactly the same at all times, this means that the quantity of water in the reservoir reduces by $21\,600/(24 \times 60) = 15$ cubic metres each minute. Suppose that, at a time t minutes after midday on 1 June, the reservoir contains V cubic metres of water. Then we might use the equation

$$V = 2 \times 10^6 - 15t \quad (t \in \mathbb{R},\ 0 \leq t \leq 72\,000) \tag{2.1}$$

to model the quantity of water in the reservoir for the 50 days $(= 72\,000$ minutes) after midday on 1 June. The letters V and t represent measurable quantities. We call V and t **variables**. Here, V depends on t, and we call V the **dependent** variable and t the **independent** variable.

A different way to approach the same problem is to form a **recurrence system** as follows. Denote the volume of water in the reservoir at the end of minute i as V_i. The initial volume of water is 2×10^6 cubic metres, and we denote this as V_0. Then (using the above arithmetic) we see that

$$V_0 = 2 \times 10^6, \qquad V_{i+1} = V_i - 15 \quad (i = 0, 1, 2, \ldots, 72\,000). \tag{2.2}$$

You may have met such recurrence systems before, and recognize that (2.1) is the **closed form** solution.

Equations (2.2) relate two variables: volume (V_i) and time (i). However, in (2.2) the independent variable i is constrained to take only *integer* values (between 0 and 72 000), while in (2.1) the independent variable t may take *any real* value (between 0 and 72 000). We call (2.1) a **continuous** model, while (2.2) is a **discrete** model.

A **function** is a process that can be applied to each of a specified set of input values to produce an output value. One example is 'given t between 0 and 72 000, calculate $2 \times 10^6 - 15t$'. If we denote this function by f, then we can write Equation (2.1) as $V = f(t)$. The **domain** of a function is the set of permitted input values. The function f associated with Equation (2.1) has as domain the set of real numbers t with $0 \leq t \leq 72\,000$; that is, the interval $[0, 72\,000]$. If we were to associate Equations (2.2) with a function g, say, then g would have as domain the set consisting of those integers i between 0 and 72 000. The **image set** of a function is the set of output values. The function f associated with Equation (2.1) has as image set the set of values of $2 \times 10^6 - 15t$ for $0 \leq t \leq 72\,000$; that is, the interval $[920\,000, 2\,000\,000]$.

In this course we shall usually be concerned with continuous models, and with functions whose domain is $\mathbb{R}$, or a part of $\mathbb{R}$ such as an interval. We may specify such a function, say f, by writing it in a form such as

$$f(t) = 2 \times 10^6 - 15t \quad (0 \leq t \leq 72\,000),$$

where the expression $2 \times 10^6 - 15t$ on the right-hand side gives the *rule* or *formula* that specifies the function, and the bracketed conditions indicate its domain.

Since in MST209 we are almost always concerned with continuous models, we shall usually omit '$t \in \mathbb{R}$' from the bracketed conditions.

To define a function, a process must produce a unique output value for each allowed input.

So, for example,

$$f(x) = \pm\sqrt{x} \quad (x \geq 0)$$

does *not* define a function f, since $\pm\sqrt{x}$ does *not* specify a *unique* value (given x).

We write $\pm\sqrt{x}$ to denote the positive and negative square roots of x because, by convention, $\sqrt{x}$ denotes only the positive square root.

Now consider a generalization of the situation described by Equation (2.1). Suppose that the reservoir initially contains V_0 cubic metres of water and that the net loss per minute is L cubic metres. Then we have

$$V = V_0 - Lt \quad (0 \leq t \leq 72\,000). \tag{2.3}$$

We now have an equation involving several letters, with differing roles. Assuming that we want to use (2.3) to describe how V will change with time t, we continue to call t the independent variable and V the dependent variable. The quantities V_0 and L do *not* depend on t. They may, however, take different values in different uses of (2.3) — in an application to a different reservoir, for example. We call V_0 and L **parameters**. Whatever the values of the parameters V_0 and L, Equation (2.3) gives a similar form of relationship between V and t: for example, the independent variable t appears in a similar way in any of the expressions $12\,000 - 5t$, $300 - 6.6t$ and $14 - 2t$.

In this course we shall often be concerned with relationships between variables, and it will be convenient to use language and notation that blur the abstract idea of a function. For example, we may write $V = V(t)$, rather than introducing a separate symbol (such as f) for the function relating V to t, and say 'V is a function of t'. Then, for example, $V(3)$ denotes the value of V when $t = 3$.

Exercise 2.1

Suppose that, at midday on 1 May, a reservoir is at 60% of its capacity. The forecast for the next 50 days suggests that $30\,000\,\text{m}^3$ of water will be removed each day for consumption, while only $15\,600\,\text{m}^3$ will be added to the reservoir each day, so that on average the quantity of water in the reservoir reduces by $(30\,000 - 15\,600)/(24 \times 60) = 10$ cubic metres each minute. Crisis measures will be introduced when the reservoir falls to 20% of its capacity.

The notation m^3 is shorthand for 'cubic metres'.

Let V (measured in m^3) be the volume of water t minutes after midday on 1 May, and let C (measured in m^3) be the reservoir's overall capacity. The volume of water can be modelled using

$$V = V_0 - 10t \quad (0 \leq t \leq 72\,000),$$

with a suitable choice of V_0.

Determine a suitable expression for V_0, and hence use the model to obtain an expression in terms of C for the time at which crisis measures will be needed (according to this model).

2.2 Linear functions

Diagnostic test 2.2

Read the description of the problem below, and do Exercise 2.2. Then do Exercise 2.3 on page 13, and check your answers with the solutions given on page 53. If you are happy with your answers, you may proceed directly to Subsection 2.3.

A **linear function** relating y to x is one of the general form

$$y = mx + c,$$

where m and c are constants. The graph of such a function is a straight line (hence the term 'linear'), as in Figure 2.1. The constant c represents the value of y at the point where the line crosses the y-axis. The gradient (or slope) of the graph is the same everywhere, and is equal to m. That is, for any two points (x_1, y_1) and (x_2, y_2) on the graph, we have

$$\frac{y_2 - y_1}{x_2 - x_1} = m.$$

In this course, if no domain is specified for a function, assume it to be $\mathbb{R}$.

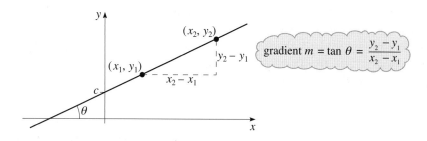

Figure 2.1   The graph of $y = mx + c$

One situation where linear functions arise is when an object is moving in a straight line with constant speed. Let us look at an example.

A boat, suspected of carrying contraband, passed a detector buoy 2 kilometres from port at 11.00 pm, and is moving at a steady 5 metres per second on a straight course directly away from port (along the line AZ in Figure 2.2). A coastguard cutter leaves the port in pursuit at midnight, travelling at 7 metres per second. When will it catch the boat?

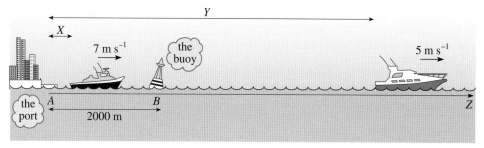

Figure 2.2

Suppose that we choose to measure time in seconds, starting from midnight, and distance in metres, measured from A. Let X metres be the distance of the coastguard cutter from A at time t seconds after midnight, and let Y metres be the distance of the boat from A at the same time. We can readily obtain an expression for X in terms of t, since $X = 0$ when $t = 0$, and the cutter travels at a constant speed of 7 metres per second: we have

The notation $\mathrm{m\,s^{-1}}$ is shorthand for 'metres per second'.

In this course, we shall usually use SI units. The SI units of distance and time are metres and seconds (denoted by m and s, respectively). Commonly used SI units are given in the Handbook.

$$X = 7t.$$

We also want an expression giving Y in terms of t. We know that (at point B) $Y = 2000$ at 11.00 pm, which is 1 hour, or 60^2 seconds, before midnight and so corresponds to $t = -3600$. Also, as the boat is moving at a constant speed of 5 metres per second, Y will be related to t by a linear function of the form

$$Y = 5t + c.$$

*Exercise 2.2
(a) Find the value of c such that $Y = 5t + c$ satisfies the condition $Y = 2000$ at $t = -3600$.

(b) (i) When will the coastguard cutter catch the boat?

(ii) In the direction that the boat is travelling, the limit of territorial waters is 100 kilometres from A. Will the cutter catch the boat within territorial waters?

Simultaneous linear equations

Suppose that we know the paths of two aircraft, each of which is travelling in a straight line, and wish to know where these paths cross. This is one of a wide variety of situations where we need to find the intersection of two straight-line graphs, which is equivalent to the algebraic problem of solving two **simultaneous linear equations**. Consider, for example, the following linear equations (see Figure 2.3):

$$4x + 3y = -1, \tag{2.4}$$
$$3x + y = 3. \tag{2.5}$$

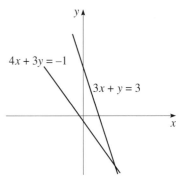

Figure 2.3

These equations are linear, since they can be rewritten in the form $y = mx + c$.

There are many ways of solving these equations: one quick method is **Gaussian elimination**. Let us see how this works for (2.4) and (2.5).

The aim of the method is to subtract a multiple of the first equation from the second in order to eliminate the x terms. First, we multiply (2.4) by $\frac{3}{4}$, to obtain an equation with the same coefficient of x as in (2.5):

$$\tfrac{3}{4} \times 4x + \tfrac{3}{4} \times 3y = \tfrac{3}{4}(-1),$$

which simplifies to

$$3x + \tfrac{9}{4}y = -\tfrac{3}{4}. \tag{2.6}$$

Now we subtract (2.6) from (2.5), to eliminate x, and obtain

$$y - \tfrac{9}{4}y = 3 - (-\tfrac{3}{4}) = 3 + \tfrac{3}{4} = \tfrac{15}{4},$$

that is, $-\tfrac{5}{4}y = \tfrac{15}{4}$, so $y = -3$.

To find x, substitute this value of y into (2.4), to obtain

$$4x + 3(-3) = -1,$$

which gives $4x = -1 + 9 = 8$, and hence $x = 2$.

So the solution of Equations (2.4) and (2.5) is $x = 2$, $y = -3$.

This method was known to Chinese mathematicians in about $100\,\text{BC}$, but not to European ones until it was discovered by the German mathematician Carl Friedrich Gauss (1777–1855). ('Gauss' is pronounced as 'gowce'.)

You may like to check these values, by substitution into (2.4) and (2.5).

*Exercise 2.3

Use Gaussian elimination to solve the equations below for u and v:

$$2u - 5v = 19,$$
$$3u + 4v = -29.$$

2.3 Quadratic functions

Diagnostic test 2.3

Do Exercise 2.4 on page 15, and check your answers with the solutions on page 53. If you are happy with your answers, you may proceed directly to Subsection 2.4.

A **quadratic function** relating y to x is a function of the general form

$$y = ax^2 + bx + c,$$

where a, b and c are constants and $a \neq 0$. The graph of such a quadratic function is a parabola, and may open 'up' or 'down', depending on the sign of a, as illustrated in Figure 2.4.

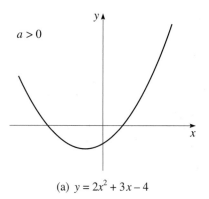

(a) $y = 2x^2 + 3x - 4$

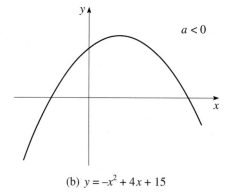

(b) $y = -x^2 + 4x + 15$

Figure 2.4

Where the graph opens 'up' ($a > 0$), values of y may become arbitrarily large, but there is a smallest (minimum) value that y can take. If $a < 0$, then the graph opens 'down', and negative values of y may become arbitrarily large in magnitude, but there is a largest (maximum) value that y can take.

For example, suppose that a ball is thrown directly upwards at time $t = 0$, with velocity $10 \, \text{m s}^{-1}$, and from a height of 2 metres (see Figure 2.5).

The ball moves under the influence of gravity, and the position s after t seconds is given by

$$s = \tfrac{1}{2}(-9.81)t^2 + 10t + 2.$$

Suppose that we want to find when the ball will hit the ground; that is, the value of t when $s = 0$. Then we need to solve the **quadratic equation**

$$\tfrac{1}{2}(-9.81)t^2 + 10t + 2 = 0. \tag{2.7}$$

You will have met before the formula for the solution of a general quadratic equation, given below.

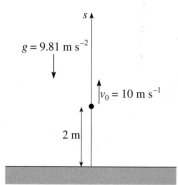

Figure 2.5

This equation will be derived in *Unit 6*.

Solution of a quadratic equation

The quadratic equation

$$ax^2 + bx + c = 0,$$

where a, b and c are constants and $a \neq 0$, can be solved for x using the formula

$$x = \frac{-b \pm \sqrt{b^2 - 4ac}}{2a}. \tag{2.8}$$

The solutions of a quadratic equation are often referred to as its **roots**.

Notice that the **sum of the roots** is $-b/a$, which is a useful check.

The term 'root' is also used for a solution to other sorts of equation, as you will see in Section 4.

Using the formula to solve (2.7) for t gives

$$t = \frac{-10 \pm \sqrt{100 + 39.24}}{-9.81} = 2.22 \text{ or } -0.18 \quad \text{(to two decimal places).}$$

Here the solution $t = -0.18$ refers to a time before the ball is thrown, so can be discarded. The ball hits the ground about 2.2 seconds after it is thrown.

In this example, the quadratic equation has two solutions. Look at the graphs in Figure 2.4, and imagine moving them up and down (which corresponds to varying the value of c). The x-axis may meet a quadratic graph in two places, or not at all, or it may happen just to touch the minimum (or maximum) point of the graph (see Figure 2.6). In formula (2.8), we need to find the square root $\sqrt{b^2 - 4ac}$. If $b^2 - 4ac > 0$, then we find a real value, greater than 0, for this square root, and there are two different solutions to the quadratic equation. If $b^2 - 4ac = 0$, then there is just one solution (though, for reasons given below, this one solution is sometimes considered as two equal solutions). If $b^2 - 4ac < 0$, then there are no (real) solutions. The quantity $b^2 - 4ac$ is often referred to as the **discriminant** of the quadratic equation because it discriminates between the cases shown in Figure 2.6.

Complex numbers, which are discussed in Section 4, enable us to express square roots of negative numbers and hence to produce (complex) solutions to a quadratic equation when $b^2 - 4ac < 0$.

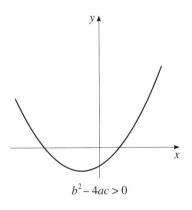

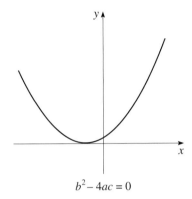

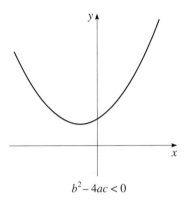

$b^2 - 4ac > 0$ $\qquad\qquad$ $b^2 - 4ac = 0$ $\qquad\qquad$ $b^2 - 4ac < 0$

Figure 2.6

*Exercise 2.4

Solve for x the following equations.

(a) $2x^2 + 7x - 4 = 0$ $\qquad$ (b) $x^2 + x - 6 = 0$

Sometimes, you may find that you need to solve a quadratic equation where the coefficients are letters rather than numbers.

Exercise 2.5

Show that the solutions (for x) of

$$mx^2 + 2kx + mw^2 = 0 \quad (m \neq 0)$$

are $x = -K \pm \sqrt{K^2 - w^2}$, where $K = k/m$.

The solutions of a quadratic equation correspond to a **factorization** of the corresponding quadratic function. For example, $x^2 + x - 6 = 0$ has solutions $x = 2$ and $x = -3$, and we have the factorization

$$x^2 + x - 6 = (x - 2)(x + 3).$$

You may like to check this by multiplying out
$(x - 2) \times (x + 3)$.

With experience, you may find that such factorizations provide a convenient way of solving some quadratic equations, but the formula provides a reliable method that can be used in all cases.

One point of caution: if you want to factorize a quadratic function, you can do this by first solving the equation (e.g. by using formula (2.8)), but you need to be careful to match the coefficient of x^2 in the original quadratic function with that in the factorization. For example, $2x^2 + 7x - 4 = 0$ has solutions $x = \frac{1}{2}$ and $x = -4$, but to factorize $2x^2 + 7x - 4$ we write

$$2x^2 + 7x - 4 = 2(x - \tfrac{1}{2})(x + 4) = (2x - 1)(x + 4),$$

where the 2 is needed to ensure that the coefficients of x^2 are the same on each side.

There are some particular factorizations that it is helpful to recognize. Two useful ones are

$$(x + A)^2 = x^2 + 2Ax + A^2 \quad \text{and} \quad (x - A)^2 = x^2 - 2Ax + A^2.$$

So, for example, $x^2 - 6x + 9 = (x - 3)^2$. We refer to such quadratics as **perfect squares**. Perfect squares correspond to quadratic equations in which the discriminant is $b^2 - 4ac = 0$. (You may like to check this for yourself.) Thus equations in which the discriminant is zero can be written in the form $(x + A)(x + A) = 0$ or $(x - A)(x - A) = 0$, and these factorizations lead us sometimes to consider such equations as having two *equal* roots $x = -A$ and $x = -A$, or $x = A$ and $x = A$, rather just one root.

Another useful factorization is

$$(x + A)(x - A) = x^2 - A^2.$$

So, for example, $x^2 - 16 = (x + 4)(x - 4)$. We refer to such a quadratic as a **difference of two squares**.

One needs to be particularly careful when solving a quadratic equation that involves the *same* letters as appear in the standard formula (2.8), but in a *different* way.

Example 2.1

Solve for x the equation

$$abx^2 - (a + b)x + 1 = 0,$$

where a and b are non-zero constants.

Solution

You need to keep a cool head here, because the letters used in formula (2.8) are used in a different way in the given equation. In (2.8), we need

$$ab \text{ for } a, \qquad -(a + b) \text{ for } b, \qquad 1 \text{ for } c.$$

So we obtain the solutions

$$x = \frac{a + b \pm \sqrt{(a + b)^2 - 4ab}}{2ab}.$$

This expression gives the solutions, but it turns out to be possible to express them in a much simpler form. We have $(a + b)^2 = a^2 + 2ab + b^2$, so the discriminant can be written as

$$(a + b)^2 - 4ab = (a^2 + 2ab + b^2) - 4ab = a^2 - 2ab + b^2 = (a - b)^2.$$

Therefore

$$\frac{a + b \pm \sqrt{(a + b)^2 - 4ab}}{2ab} = \frac{a + b \pm \sqrt{(a - b)^2}}{2ab} = \frac{a + b \pm (a - b)}{2ab}.$$

Now $(a + b) + (a - b) = 2a$ and $(a + b) - (a - b) = 2b$, so the two solutions are $1/a$ and $1/b$. ∎

Note that if we allow A to be positive or negative, then both cases can be written as
$$(x + A)^2 = x^2 + 2Ax + A^2.$$

You will find it advantageous in this course to be able to perform manipulations like this by hand. If you find them difficult, however, you may like to make use of the computer algebra package for the course.

2.4   *Exponential and logarithm functions*

Diagnostic test 2.4

Do Exercises 2.6 and 2.7 below, and check your answers with the solutions starting on page 53. If you are happy with your answers, you may proceed directly to Subsection 2.5.

A function relating y to x of the form $y = ba^x$ (where a and b are constants, with $a > 0$ and $a \neq 1$) is referred to as an **exponential function**. Use of such a function with domain $\mathbb{R}$ requires us to assign a meaning to a^x for non-integer values of x. We start by revising the properties of integer powers.

Powers

You will be familiar with the meaning of a positive integer power of a number, such as $10^5 = 10 \times 10 \times 10 \times 10 \times 10$. In general, a^n means the product of n copies of a (for any real number a and any positive integer n). In particular, $a^1 = a$.

In a^n, a is called the **base**, and n may be referred to as the **power**, the **index** or the **exponent**.

For positive integers m and n, we have the property

$$a^n \times a^m = a^{n+m}, \tag{2.9}$$

since each side is the product of $n + m$ copies of a. For example,

$$10^2 \times 10^5 = 10^7.$$

Consequently, if we multiply m copies of a^n, we obtain

$$\underbrace{a^n \times a^n \times a^n \times \cdots \times a^n}_{m \text{ times}} = a^{\overbrace{n+n+n+\cdots+n}^{m \text{ times}}};$$

that is,

$$(a^n)^m = a^{n \times m}. \tag{2.10}$$

For example, $(10^2)^3 = 10^6$.

The definition of a^n can be extended to cases where n is not a positive integer by assuming that (2.9) and (2.10) hold more generally. For $a \neq 0$, this assumption leads to the definition of a^0 as 1, and a^{-n} as $1/a^n$; and, for $a > 0$, to the definition of $a^{1/n}$ as the nth root of a, and $a^{m/n}$ as the nth root of a^m. So, for example:

Recall that the **nth root** of a number a is a number b such that $b^n = a$, and we write $b = \sqrt[n]{a}$.

$$10^{-4} = 1/10^4 = 0.0001;$$
$$27^{1/3} = \sqrt[3]{27} = 3 \quad (\text{since } 3^3 = 27);$$
$$4^{-3/2} = \frac{1}{4^{3/2}} = \frac{1}{\sqrt[2]{4^3}} = \frac{1}{\sqrt{64}} = \frac{1}{8}.$$

It is conventional to take fractional powers to mean positive roots (where there is a choice). So, for example, $9^{1/2} = \sqrt{9}$ means 3 rather than -3. In general, roots of negative numbers do not necessarily exist (at least, not as real numbers); but where they do, we use the same notation. So, for example, $(-27)^{1/3} = \sqrt[3]{-27} = -3$ (since $(-3)^3 = -27$, and there is no *positive* cube root in this case).

The negative square root of 5, for example, would be written as $-5^{1/2}$ or $-\sqrt{5}$.

We can define a^x for $a > 0$ and for irrational values of x by means of a limiting process that need not concern us here. (The value of a^x for any particular $a > 0$ and x can be found using your calculator.) This definition of a^x leads to the following properties of powers that hold for all real numbers $a > 0$ and all real exponents x and y:

For $a = 0$, 0^x is taken to equal 0. For $a < 0$, the definition of a^x involves complex numbers and need not concern us here.

$$a^x > 0,$$
$$a^{-x} = 1/a^x,$$
$$a^{x+y} = a^x \times a^y,$$
$$(a^x)^y = a^{x \times y},$$
$$a^x/a^y = a^{x-y}.$$

We have not proved these properties, but we shall make use of them as necessary.

Finally, note that for powers of a product or a quotient, we have

$$(ab)^x = a^x b^x \quad \text{and} \quad (a/b)^x = a^x/b^x.$$

For example, $15^7 = 3^7 5^7$ and $(5/3)^4 = 5^4/3^4$.

Exercise 2.6 ———————————————————

Use the properties of indices to simplify each of the following.

(a) $a^3 a^5$ (b) a^3/a^5 (c) $(a^3)^5$ (d) $(2^{-1})^4 \times 4^3$

(e) $8^{-1/3}$ (f) $16^{3/4}$ (g) $\left(\frac{4}{9}\right)^{3/2}$ (h) $(16x^4)^{1/2}$

The exponential and logarithm functions

One function that is particularly important is e^x, where e is the number $2.718\,28\ldots$. This function arises, for example, in the solution of differential equations. This is a consequence of its property that it is unchanged by differentiation. (Indeed, the *only* functions f that are unchanged by differentiation are functions of the form $f(x) = Ae^x$, where A is a constant.) The function e^x is often referred to as *the* **exponential function**, and may also be written $\exp x$. Note that e^x is always positive: $e^x > 0$ for all real x.

Differential equations occur throughout the course, beginning in *Unit 2*.

Differentiation is discussed in Section 5.

The inverse function of e^x is the **natural logarithm function**, written $\ln x$. Now $\ln x$ is defined only for $x > 0$ (since the domain of the inverse function of e^x is the same as the image set of e^x). Since these functions are inverse to each other, we have:

Essentially, the **inverse function** of a function f is one that reverses the effect of f.

$$\ln(\exp x) = x \quad \text{for all real } x;$$
$$\exp(\ln x) = x \quad \text{for all real } x > 0.$$

Another way of looking at this relationship is: if $e^y = x$, then $y = \ln x$. In particular, since $e^0 = 1$, we have $\ln 1 = 0$.

This can be taken as a *definition* of $\ln x$.

The properties of powers given above lead to corresponding results about the logarithm function:

$$\ln(1/u) = -\ln u,$$
$$\ln(u \times v) = \ln u + \ln v,$$
$$\ln(u^v) = v \times \ln u,$$
$$\ln(u/v) = \ln u - \ln v.$$

Another logarithm function that will be used occasionally in the course is $\log_{10}$, where if $10^y = x$, then $y = \log_{10} x$. The results given here for $\ln$ also hold for $\log_{10}$.

Before the advent of calculators and computers, these properties were commonly used in calculating powers, reciprocals and products 'using logarithms'. Such applications are no longer needed, but these properties of logarithms are still important in the manipulation of expressions involving exponentials and logarithms.

Exercise 2.7

Simplify each of the following (where $a > 0$, $b > 0$ and $x > 0$).

(a) $\ln 7 + \ln 4 - \ln 14$ (b) $\ln a + 2 \ln b - \ln(a^2 b)$

(c) $e^x \times (e^y)^2 \div e^{2x}$ (d) $\ln(e^x \times e^y)$ (e) $e^{2 \ln x}$ (f) $e^{-2 \ln x}$

(g) $\exp(2 \ln x + \ln(x + 1))$

Exercise 2.8

By taking logs of both sides of the equation

$$a^x = e^{kx},$$

where $a > 0$, show that we can find a value for k so that this equation holds for all values of x.

In light of the equivalence established in Exercise 2.8, it is common practice to use functions of the form e^{kx}, for suitable values of k, rather than exponential functions of the form a^x for values of a (> 0) other than e. (This is more convenient when doing calculus, for example.) For $k \neq 0$, the graph of this standard exponential function takes one of the forms shown in Figure 2.7. For $k > 0$, the larger the value of k, the faster the value of e^{kx} increases as x increases (and so the graph climbs more steeply). Similarly, for $k < 0$, the larger the magnitude of k, the faster e^{kx} decreases.

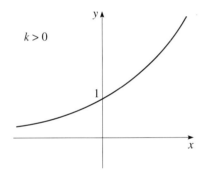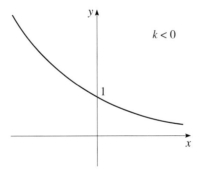

Figure 2.7   Graphs of $y = e^{kx}$

Log plots

Suppose that you have data on some quantity y at various times t, and you believe that y is an exponential function of t. To test such a hypothesis, you can plot $\ln y$ against t. If such a plot gives a straight line, then this confirms that y is of the form Ae^{kt}. For example, suppose that a plot of $\ln y$ against t suggests the linear relationship

Such plots are often referred to as **log–linear plots**.

$$\ln y = 1.47t + 3.82.$$

Then, taking exponentials of each side, we have

$$y = \exp(1.47t + 3.82)$$
$$= \exp(1.47t) \times \exp(3.82)$$
$$= 45.6e^{1.47t}.$$

The next exercise shows how we can test data (on variables x and y) for a different form of relationship by plotting $\ln x$ against $\ln y$.

Exercise 2.9 ─────────────────────────────

(a) Suppose that

$$\ln y = 2.83 \ln x + 0.37.$$

Using the properties of exp and ln, express y as a function of x.

(b) In general, suppose that

$$\ln y = a \ln x + b,$$

where a and b are constants. What form of relationship is there between y and x?

Plots of $\ln y$ against $\ln x$ are called **log–log plots**.

From Exercise 2.9(b), we see that if a plot of $\ln y$ against $\ln x$ is linear, then y is a **power function** of x; that is,

$$y = cx^a,$$

where c and a are constants. Note that this is *not* an exponential function. Power functions of x include

$$x^2, \quad x^3, \quad x^{5/2} \ (= x^2\sqrt{x}).$$

If a is a positive integer, then the power function $f(x) = x^a$ is defined for all real x; but for other values of a, this power function has domain $x > 0$.

In an exponential function, x appears as the exponent, as in for example

$$2^x, \quad 3^x, \quad 2.5^x,$$

each of which can be expressed as e^{kx} for a suitable value of k.

2.5 Combining functions

Diagnostic test 2.5 ─────────────────────────

(a) If $f(x) = \ln x$ and $g(x) = 1/(x-1)^2$, and $x > 1$, find the following.

　(i) $f(g(x))$　　(ii) $g(f(x))$

(b) Express $h(x) = (1 + e^x)^2$ as a composition of basic functions.

Now check your solutions against those given below. If you are happy with the answers, you may proceed directly to Section 3.

Solution

(a) (i) $f(g(x)) = \ln(1/(x-1)^2) = -2\ln(x-1)$

　(ii) $g(f(x)) = 1/(\ln x - 1)^2$ (This has no easy simplification.)

(b) We can obtain $h(x)$ in three steps.

　Step 1　Start with e^x.

　Step 2　Add 1 to the result of Step 1.

　Step 3　Apply the square function to the result of Step 2.

　Then $h(x) = p(q(r(x)))$, where

$$p(x) = x^2, \quad q(x) = x + 1, \quad r(x) = e^x.$$

Consider the motion of a stone that is thrown vertically upwards with a velocity of $10 \, \text{m} \, \text{s}^{-1}$ from a point $2 \, \text{m}$ above the ground (see Figure 2.5 on page 14). We shall see in *Unit 6* that the height s of the stone in terms of time t may be modelled by the equation

$$s = -\tfrac{1}{2}gt^2 + 10t + 2, \tag{2.11}$$

and that its velocity is given by

$$v = 10 - gt, \tag{2.12}$$

where $g = 9.81 \, \mathrm{m\,s^{-2}}$ is the acceleration due to gravity.

Now suppose that we wish to know the velocity as a function of height ($v = v(s)$). By manipulating the two equations above, eliminating t, you can see that

$$v^2 = 4g + 100 - 2gs,$$

of which one solution is

$$v = \sqrt{4g + 100 - 2gs}. \tag{2.13}$$

Here we take the positive square root, which corresponds to the upward motion of the stone. *Unit 6* will deal with both cases.

However, there is now potential for confusion about what is meant by v. In Equation (2.12), $v = v(t)$ is a function of time t; in Equation (2.13), $v = v(s)$ is a function of height s.

Unfortunately, this notation suggests that we are using the same 'name', v, for two *different* functions. (The expressions on the right in (2.12) and (2.13) are different!) In such a context, it may be necessary, for clarity, to introduce different names for these functions. In fact, we could resolve the situation by solving Equation (2.11) for t, giving

$$t = \frac{10 - \sqrt{100 + 4g - 2gs}}{g} = f(s), \text{ say.} \tag{2.14}$$

Again we must be careful about the sign of the square root, so that the equation corresponds to the upward motion of the stone.

Now Equation (2.12) is of the form $v = g(t)$ (where $g(t) = 10 - gt$). Then Equation (2.13), which shows the dependency of v on s, can be written as

$$v = g(f(s)).$$

In general, the function h with the rule

$$h(x) = g(f(x))$$

is called a **composite function**; it is the **composition** of the functions g and f.

When combining functions in this way, it is important to check how the domains affect each other. In the above example, (2.14) is valid only when $100 + 4g - 2gs \geq 0$, and we can see from (2.13) that the same condition must hold in order to find the composite function $v = h(s)$.

You will see later that when doing calculus it is useful to be able to form compositions of functions, and even more useful to be able to recognize a complicated function as the composition of simpler ones.

Example 2.2

If $f(x) = e^x$ ($x \in \mathbb{R}$) and $g(x) = 1 + x^2$ ($x \in \mathbb{R}$), what are the following?

(a) $g(f(x))$ (b) $f(g(x))$

Solution

(a) $g(f(x)) = g(e^x) = 1 + (e^x)^2 = 1 + e^{2x}$

(b) $f(g(x)) = f(1 + x^2) = e^{1+x^2}$ ∎

In this example, both functions f and g are defined for all x in $\mathbb{R}$, so we need not worry about domains.

Notice that $g(f(x))$ and $f(g(x))$ are *different*. The function $g(f(x))$ is 'apply f first, then g', while $f(g(x))$ is 'apply g first, then f'; the order in which f and g are applied matters!

Example 2.3

Express the function

$$h(x) = \frac{1}{\left(\sqrt{1 + 2x^2}\right)^3} \tag{2.15}$$

as a composite of a quadratic function and a power function.

Solution

Note first that $1 + 2x^2$ is a quadratic function and that, writing $y = 1 + 2x^2$, the right-hand side of (2.15) becomes $\dfrac{1}{(\sqrt{y})^3} = y^{-3/2}$ (a power function). So we can obtain $h(x)$ in two steps.

Step 1   Calculate $y = 1 + 2x^2$.

Step 2   Apply $\dfrac{1}{(\sqrt{y})^3} = y^{-3/2}$ to the result of Step 1.

So if $f(x) = 1 + 2x^2$ and $g(x) = x^{-3/2}$, then $h(x) = g(f(x))$.   ∎

Here, the domain of g is $x > 0$, but since $f(x) = 1 + 2x^2$ is always greater than 0, there is no problem.

Exercise 2.10

(a) If $f(x) = e^{-x}$ and $g(x) = 1 - x^3$, find the following.

(i) $f(g(x))$ (ii) $g(f(x))$

(b) Express

$$h(x) = \frac{1}{(4 + 9x^2)^4}$$

as a composite of a quadratic function and a power function.

3 Trigonometric functions

In this section, we add another class of functions to the 'library' developed in Section 2. These are the trigonometric functions. They originate in the geometry of right-angled triangles, but in this course we are equally often concerned with their use in modelling repetitive or oscillatory behaviour. In particular, they arise as solutions of certain differential equations.

3.1 Introducing the trigonometric functions

Diagnostic test 3.1

Do Exercise 3.1 on page 23, and check your answers with the solutions given on page 54. If you are happy with your answers, you may proceed directly to Subsection 3.2.

You will have met $\sin\theta = a/h$, $\cos\theta = b/h$ and $\tan\theta = a/b$ as ratios in a right-angled triangle (see Figure 3.1). However, these definitions of the sine, cosine and tangent functions work only for $0 < \theta < \frac{\pi}{2}$. (Note that we shall almost always express angles in radians in this course.)

The Greek letter θ is read as 'theta'. The Greek alphabet is given in the Handbook.

Recall that $180° = \pi$ radians.

To define the **sine** and **cosine** functions for a general value of θ, we can use Figure 3.2, which shows a circle of radius 1. Imagine that the line OA started along the x-axis, and was then rotated anticlockwise through an angle θ. Then the point A has coordinates $(\cos\theta, \sin\theta)$. Here θ may be *any* value, positive or negative. (A negative value of θ corresponds to a rotation *clockwise*.)

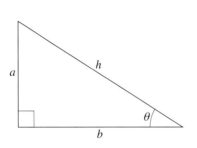

Figure 3.1

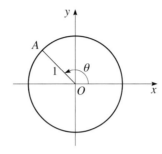

Figure 3.2

If we rotate through 2π radians ($360°$), then we go round a full circle. So rotations of θ and $\theta + 2\pi$ leave A in exactly the same place. This leads to the repetitive nature of the graphs of sin and cos (see Figure 3.3). The word **periodic** is used to refer to the fact that these functions repeat their values every 2π: that is, $\sin(\theta + 2\pi) = \sin\theta$ and $\cos(\theta + 2\pi) = \cos\theta$, for any θ.

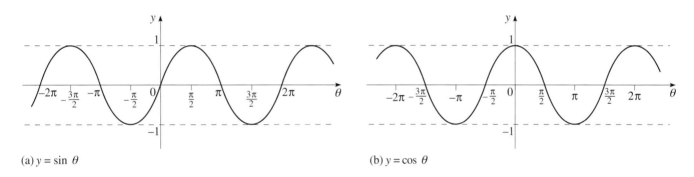

(a) $y = \sin\theta$

(b) $y = \cos\theta$

Figure 3.3

Other trigonometric functions can be defined in terms of sin and cos. You will have met $\tan\theta = \sin\theta/\cos\theta$. This is defined for all real θ except where $\cos\theta = 0$ (i.e. at $\theta = \pm\frac{\pi}{2}, \pm\frac{3\pi}{2}$, and so on). You may also have met

These functions may be referred to as **tangent**, **secant**, **cosecant** and **cotangent**.

$$\sec\theta = \frac{1}{\cos\theta}, \quad \operatorname{cosec}\theta = \frac{1}{\sin\theta} \quad \text{and} \quad \cot\theta = \frac{1}{\tan\theta} = \frac{\cos\theta}{\sin\theta}.$$

We need to restrict the domains of cosec and cot to exclude points where $\sin\theta = 0$, and the domains of sec and tan to exclude points where $\cos\theta = 0$.

Exercise 3.1

(a) Find the values of $\sin\theta$ and $\cos\theta$ for $\theta = 0$ and $\theta = \frac{\pi}{2}$.

(b) Hence find the values of $\tan\theta$, $\sec\theta$, $\operatorname{cosec}\theta$ and $\cot\theta$ for $\theta = 0$ and $\theta = \frac{\pi}{2}$, where they are defined.

(c) Two right-angled triangles are shown in Figure 3.4. Use these to calculate the values of $\sin\theta$, $\cos\theta$, $\tan\theta$, $\operatorname{cosec}\theta$, $\sec\theta$ and $\cot\theta$ for θ equal to each of $\frac{\pi}{6}$, $\frac{\pi}{4}$ and $\frac{\pi}{3}$.

(d) For what values of θ is $\sin\theta = 0$? (Refer to Figure 3.3(a).)

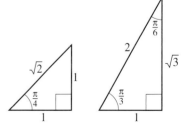

Figure 3.4

The function tan has the graph shown in Figure 3.5. Notice that tan actually repeats its values every π. (This is because $\sin(\theta + \pi) = -\sin\theta$ and $\cos(\theta + \pi) = -\cos\theta$, so that $\tan(\theta + \pi) = \tan\theta$.)

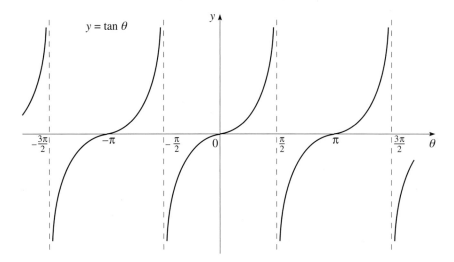

The graphs of sec, cosec and cot are given in the Handbook (as well as those of sin, cos and tan).

Figure 3.5

3.2   Inverse trigonometric functions

Diagnostic test 3.2

(a) Find all the solutions of $\cos\theta = 0.5$ in the range -2π to 4π.

(b) Find all the solutions of $\tan\theta = 1/\sqrt{3}$.

Now check your solutions against those given below. If you are happy with the answers, you may proceed directly to Subsection 3.3.

Solution

(a) In the range $-\pi$ to π, we know that $\cos(\pm\frac{\pi}{3}) = \frac{1}{2} = 0.5$. Further solutions may be found by adding or subtracting multiples of 2π to these values:

$$-\tfrac{5\pi}{3}, \ -\tfrac{\pi}{3}, \ \tfrac{\pi}{3}, \ \tfrac{5\pi}{3}, \ \tfrac{7\pi}{3}, \ \tfrac{11\pi}{3}.$$

(b) In the range 0 to $\frac{\pi}{2}$, we know that $\tan\frac{\pi}{6} = 1/\sqrt{3}$. From the graph in Figure 3.5 we see that the required solutions are obtained by adding or subtracting any multiple of π, so the solutions are

$$\tfrac{\pi}{6} + n\pi \quad (n \in \mathbb{Z}).$$

Suppose that you need to solve for x the equation

$$\cos x = \tfrac{1}{2}.$$

What solutions are there? You have seen (in Exercise 3.1(c)) that $\cos\frac{\pi}{3} = \frac{1}{2}$, so one solution is certainly $x = \frac{\pi}{3}$. There are others, however. For instance, since cos repeats its values every 2π, another solution is $x = \frac{\pi}{3} + 2\pi$. We can find an infinite number of solutions by adding or subtracting multiples of 2π to/from $\frac{\pi}{3}$. There are even more solutions. If you look at the graph of cos in Figure 3.3(b), you can see that a horizontal line at $y = \frac{1}{2}$ would cut it twice between 0 and 2π: we also have $\cos\frac{5\pi}{3} = \frac{1}{2}$. And more solutions can be found by adding or subtracting multiples of 2π to/from $\frac{5\pi}{3}$.

In general, an equation of the form

$$\cos x = y \tag{3.1}$$

is solved for x by finding a value of the **inverse trigonometric function** arccos:

$$x = \arccos y.$$

However, we need to be careful here. Solutions of Equation (3.1) are not unique, as we saw for $y = \frac{1}{2}$. If we reverse the roles of the axes in Figure 3.3(b), we obtain the curve shown in Figure 3.6. However, this is *not* the graph of a *function*: a vertical line may meet the curve in many places, reflecting the fact that, given y, Equation (3.1) may have multiple solutions x. To ensure that, given y, arccos y has a unique value, we need to restrict the range in which values of arccos can fall. This is equivalent to specifying a *codomain* for the function arccos. The codomain of arccos is given in Table 3.1, together with codomains for two other inverse trigonometric functions, arcsin and arctan. In Figure 3.6, when the values taken by arccos are restricted to this codomain, we obtain just the part of the curve shown in bold, which *is* the graph of a function.

The **codomain** of a function is a set within which its values must lie.

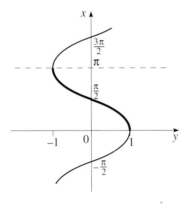

Figure 3.6   The graph of arccos is just the bold part of the curve

The graphs of arcsin and arctan, as well as arccos, are given in the Handbook.

Table 3.1

Function	Inverse	Codomain of inverse function	Domain of inverse function
$y = \sin x$	$x = \arcsin y$	$-\frac{\pi}{2} \le x \le \frac{\pi}{2}$	$-1 \le y \le 1$
$y = \cos x$	$x = \arccos y$	$0 \le x \le \pi$	$-1 \le y \le 1$
$y = \tan x$	$x = \arctan y$	$-\frac{\pi}{2} < x < \frac{\pi}{2}$	$\mathbb{R}$

Some texts use $\sin^{-1}$, $\cos^{-1}$ and $\tan^{-1}$ rather than arcsin, arccos and arctan.

Calculators and computer software can be expected to give values of the inverse trigonometric functions drawn from suitably restricted codomains, such as those in Table 3.1. However, in a particular model this may not give the appropriate value, and in such a situation it is important to be alert to the fact that an equation such as (3.1) actually has infinitely many solutions: there are usually two solutions in the range 0 to 2π, together with infinitely many others obtained by shifting these two by multiples of 2π.

There is another possibility: if $|y| > 1$, then Equation (3.1) has no solutions.

Exercise 3.2

(a) Find all the solutions of $\sin \theta = 0.8$ in the range 0 to 6π.

(b) Find all the solutions of $\tan \theta = 1$.

3.3 Some useful trigonometric identities

Diagnostic test 3.3 _____

Do Exercise 3.3 on page 27, and check your answers with the solutions given on page 55. If you are happy with your answers, you may proceed directly to Section 4.

All the trigonometric identities discussed in this subsection are included in the course Handbook for easy reference.

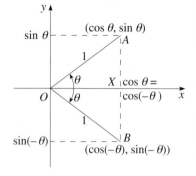

Figure 3.7

Figure 3.7 shows the relation between a clockwise rotation through θ (regarded as a rotation through $-\theta$) and an anticlockwise rotation through θ. Notice that such rotations lead to equal x-coordinates but to y-coordinates of opposite signs. So we have

$$\cos(-\theta) = \cos\theta \quad \text{and} \quad \sin(-\theta) = -\sin\theta.$$

These relations hold for all values of θ, and are examples of **trigonometric identities**. These can be useful in a variety of contexts, such as simplifying expressions involving trigonometric functions.

To derive one particularly useful identity, apply Pythagoras's Theorem to the right-angled triangle OAX in Figure 3.7. This leads to

$$\cos^2\theta + \sin^2\theta = 1. \tag{3.2}$$

Notice that we write $(\sin\theta)^2$ as $\sin^2\theta$.

If we divide each side of (3.2) by $\cos^2\theta$, we obtain the identity

$$1 + \tan^2\theta = \sec^2\theta.$$

Similarly, if we divide each side of (3.2) by $\sin^2\theta$, we obtain

$$\cot^2\theta + 1 = \operatorname{cosec}^2\theta.$$

Strictly speaking, this and the following identities hold only where the functions tan, sec, etc. are defined.

You may also have met previously the identities

$$\sin(\theta + \phi) = \sin\theta\cos\phi + \cos\theta\sin\phi, \tag{3.3}$$
$$\cos(\theta + \phi) = \cos\theta\cos\phi - \sin\theta\sin\phi. \tag{3.4}$$

These identities can be derived using transformation matrices, for example, but we shall not discuss here how this is done.

Replacing ϕ by $-\phi$ in these identities (and using $\cos(-\phi) = \cos\phi$ and $\sin(-\phi) = -\sin\phi$), we obtain

$$\sin(\theta - \phi) = \sin\theta\cos\phi - \cos\theta\sin\phi,$$
$$\cos(\theta - \phi) = \cos\theta\cos\phi + \sin\theta\sin\phi.$$

We can obtain an identity for $\tan(\theta + \phi)$ by dividing those for $\sin(\theta + \phi)$ and $\cos(\theta + \phi)$:

$$\tan(\theta + \phi) = \frac{\sin(\theta + \phi)}{\cos(\theta + \phi)} = \frac{\sin\theta\cos\phi + \cos\theta\sin\phi}{\cos\theta\cos\phi - \sin\theta\sin\phi},$$

and dividing top and bottom by $\cos\theta\cos\phi$ gives

$$\tan(\theta + \phi) = \frac{\tan\theta + \tan\phi}{1 - \tan\theta\tan\phi},$$

All these identities can be useful when manipulating expressions involving trigonometric functions. One situation where such manipulations are needed is when performing certain integrations by hand (as you will see in Section 6), and there expressions for $\sin 2\theta$ and $\cos 2\theta$ can be particularly useful. We ask you to obtain such expressions in the next exercise.

(Note that it is usual to write $\sin 2\theta$ rather than $\sin(2\theta)$ — the spacing makes the meaning clear. However, when using the course computer algebra package you will have to include the brackets. When there is any danger of ambiguity, we shall also use brackets in the text.)

Exercise 3.3 _____

(a) By putting $\phi = \theta$ in the expressions for $\sin(\theta + \phi)$ and $\cos(\theta + \phi)$, establish the following identities.

 (i) $\sin 2\theta = 2 \sin \theta \cos \theta$ (ii) $\cos 2\theta = \cos^2 \theta - \sin^2 \theta$

(b) Using trigonometric identities, and particular values of sin and cos, simplify each of the following.

 (i) $\sin(2\pi - \theta)$ (ii) $\cos(2\pi - \theta)$ (iii) $\sin(\pi - \theta)$

 (iv) $\cos(\pi - \theta)$ (v) $\sin(\frac{\pi}{2} - \theta)$ (vi) $\cos(\frac{\pi}{2} - \theta)$

 (vii) $\cos\left(\frac{3\pi}{2} + x\right)$

_____

The most useful identities to remember are (3.2), (3.3) and (3.4), as most of the others can be derived from these.

4 Complex numbers

Diagnostic test 4.1 _____

Do Exercises 4.1, 4.2, 4.3 and 4.7 below, and check your answers with the solutions starting on page 55. If you are happy with your answers, you may proceed directly to Section 5.

_____

Complex numbers provide a system within which we can solve any quadratic equation (and, indeed, any polynomial equation). They are helpful in some of the mathematical techniques introduced in this course, although the use we shall make of them is quite limited.

There is no *real* number x satisfying the equation

$$x^2 = -1.$$

However, there are circumstances where it is convenient to have a system of 'numbers' in which such an equation can be solved. Such a system is the system of complex numbers. A **complex number** is one of the form

$$z = a + bi \quad \text{(or, equivalently, } z = a + ib),$$

Engineers commonly use j to represent $\sqrt{-1}$.

where $i = \sqrt{-1}$, and a and b are real numbers. We refer to a as the **real part** of z, written $\mathrm{Re}(z)$, and to b as the **imaginary part** of z, written $\mathrm{Im}(z)$. A complex number of the form $a + 0i$ is, in effect, just the real number a; so the real numbers are seen as part of (a subset of) the complex numbers.

Note that $\mathrm{Im}(z)$ is the real number b; $\mathrm{Im}(z)$ is *not* equal to bi.

We denote the set of all complex numbers by $\mathbb{C}$. Within $\mathbb{C}$, we can solve any quadratic equation, since the formula will always give a solution once we can use $\sqrt{-1}$. For example, the equation $x^2 - 2x + 2 = 0$ has the solutions

$$x = \frac{2 \pm \sqrt{2^2 - 4 \times 2}}{2} = \frac{2 \pm \sqrt{-4}}{2} = \frac{2 \pm \sqrt{4} \times \sqrt{-1}}{2} = \frac{2 \pm 2i}{2} = 1 \pm i,$$

and the equation $x^2 = -1$ has the solutions $x = \pm i$.

An **nth-order polynomial** with real coefficients is a function of the form

$$p(x) = a_n x^n + a_{n-1} x^{n-1} + \cdots + a_1 x + a_0,$$

where $a_n \neq 0$ and each coefficient a_k $(k = 0, 1, \ldots, n)$ is a constant in $\mathbb{R}$. Within the complex numbers, any such polynomial can be written as a product of a_n and n factors of the form $x - c_k$ $(k = 1, 2, \ldots, n)$, with each c_k in $\mathbb{C}$. These n factors correspond to the n **roots** (i.e. solutions) $x = c_k$ $(k = 1, 2, \ldots, n)$ of the corresponding polynomial equation $p(x) = 0$; if a factor $x - c$ occurs more than once, then the root $x = c$ is a **repeated root**. In Subsection 2.3 we saw that for second-order (i.e. quadratic) polynomials, repeated roots correspond to perfect squares (i.e. factorizations such as $x^2 - 2cx + c^2 = (x - c)^2$).

> An nth-order polynomial is sometimes referred to as a **polynomial of degree n**.

> In fact, this result also holds if the coefficients a_k are complex.

> Repeated roots are sometimes referred to as **equal roots** or **coincident roots**.

4.1 The arithmetic of complex numbers

We can perform arithmetic (and algebra) with complex numbers, and this follows all the familiar rules for real numbers, such as

$$u(v + w) = uv + uw \quad \text{and} \quad u \times v = v \times u.$$

To add, subtract or multiply complex numbers, just manipulate brackets in the usual way, and remember that $i^2 = -1$. For example,

$$(2 + 3i) + (4 - 7i) = 2 + 4 + 3i - 7i = 6 - 4i$$

and

$$
\begin{aligned}
(2 + 3i) \times (4 - 7i) &= 2 \times (4 - 7i) + 3i \times (4 - 7i) \\
&= 8 - 14i + 12i - 21i^2 \\
&= 8 + 21 - 2i \\
&= 29 - 2i.
\end{aligned}
$$

Division of complex numbers is a little more complicated. The **complex conjugate** of a complex number $z = a + bi$ is $\bar{z} = a - bi$, and the rule for division is best expressed in terms of this. To simplify, for example,

$$\frac{2 + 3i}{4 - 7i},$$

multiply top and bottom by $4 + 7i$, the complex conjugate of the denominator, to obtain

$$
\begin{aligned}
\frac{2 + 3i}{4 - 7i} &= \frac{(2 + 3i) \times (4 + 7i)}{(4 - 7i) \times (4 + 7i)} \\
&= \frac{8 + 14i + 12i - 21}{16 + 28i - 28i + 49} \\
&= \frac{-13 + 26i}{65} \\
&= \frac{-1 + 2i}{5} \\
&= -\tfrac{1}{5} + \tfrac{2}{5}i.
\end{aligned}
$$

This process always reduces the denominator to a real number, since $(a + bi) \times (a - bi) = a^2 + b^2$ is always real. Thus, in general,

$$\frac{c + di}{a + bi} = \frac{(c + di) \times (a - bi)}{a^2 + b^2}.$$

> Note that $a^2 + b^2$ is always positive, unless $a = b = 0$.

The **modulus** of a complex number $z = a + bi$ is $\sqrt{a^2 + b^2}$, written $|z|$, so the rule for division can be written, for complex numbers u and v, as

$$\frac{u}{v} = \frac{u\bar{v}}{|v|^2}.$$

Exercise 4.1

Let $v = 3 - 4i$ and $w = 2 - i$. Evaluate each of the following.

(a) $\bar{v}$ (b) $|v|$ (c) $v - w$ (d) vw

(e) w/v (f) $1/w$ (g) w^2 (h) $2w - 3v$

Exercise 4.2

Solve (for x in $\mathbb{C}$) the quadratic equation $2x^2 + 2x + 1 = 0$.

If a quadratic equation with real coefficients has complex roots (as in Exercise 4.2), then these always form a pair of complex conjugates (of the form $a \pm bi$).

This follows from the formula (2.8) for the solution of a quadratic equation.

4.2 Polar form

Polar coordinates

Polar coordinates provide an alternative way of representing points in the plane. Figure 4.1 shows a point A with Cartesian coordinates (x, y) and polar coordinates $\langle r, \theta \rangle$. The quantity r is the distance from A to the origin, so $r \geq 0$. The angle θ is measured anticlockwise from the x-axis. (Negative angles correspond to measuring clockwise from the x-axis.) It is convenient to allow θ to take any real value, but this has the consequence that the polar representation of a point is not unique. For example, $\langle r, \theta \rangle$ and $\langle r, \theta + 2\pi \rangle$ provide polar coordinates of the same point. We can see from Figure 4.1 that if a point has polar coordinates $\langle r, \theta \rangle$ and Cartesian coordinates (x, y), then

We shall use angle brackets to distinguish polar from Cartesian coordinates. (This is *not* a universal convention.)

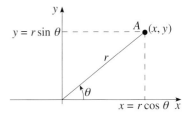

$$x = r \cos \theta \quad \text{and} \quad y = r \sin \theta.$$

These equations allow us to translate from polar to Cartesian coordinates. To translate from Cartesian to polar coordinates, we can use (see Figure 4.1)

Figure 4.1

$$r = \sqrt{x^2 + y^2}, \quad \cos \theta = x/r, \quad \sin \theta = y/r \quad (r \neq 0). \tag{4.1}$$

If $r = 0$, then we can choose any value for θ.

Equations (4.1) do not have a unique solution for θ in $\mathbb{R}$, but they do have a unique solution in the range $-\pi < \theta \leq \pi$.

Exercise 4.3

What are the polar coordinates $\langle r, \theta \rangle$ of each of the following points, for θ in the range $-\pi < \theta \leq \pi$?

(a) $(-2, 0)$ (b) $(1, 1)$ (c) $(-1, -1)$

(d) $(4, 0)$ (e) $(0, 4)$ (f) $(-\sqrt{3}, 1)$

The polar form of a complex number

A complex number $x + yi$ can be represented geometrically on an **Argand diagram** as the point with Cartesian coordinates (x, y). For example, Figure 4.2 shows on an Argand diagram the point $3 + 2i$, with real part 3 and imaginary part 2.

Combining polar coordinates and the Argand diagram leads to the polar form of a complex number. For $z = x + yi$, find the polar coordinates $\langle r, \theta \rangle$ of the point with Cartesian coordinates (x, y). Then, using the relation between polar and Cartesian coordinates, we have

$$z = x + yi = x + iy = r\cos\theta + ir\sin\theta = r(\cos\theta + i\sin\theta).$$

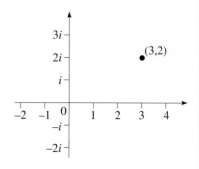

Figure 4.2

This is the **polar form** of z. Here, $r = \sqrt{x^2 + y^2} = |z|$ is the modulus of z. We call θ an **argument** of z. As noted above, θ is not unique, but there *is* a unique value of θ in the range $-\pi < \theta \leq \pi$. This is called the **principal value** of the argument, and we write it as $\text{Arg}(z)$. When there is no possibility of confusion, we often write $\langle r, \theta \rangle$ as shorthand for the polar form $r(\cos\theta + i\sin\theta)$.

Exercise 4.4

If a complex number z has polar form $\langle 2, -\frac{\pi}{4} \rangle$, what is its Cartesian form?

Exercise 4.5

Express each of the following complex numbers in polar form, choosing the principal value of the argument.

(a) -2 (b) $1 + i$ (c) $-1 - i$

(d) 4 (e) $4i$ (f) $-\sqrt{3} + i$

Multiplication of complex numbers in polar form

Multiplication of complex numbers is simpler in polar than in Cartesian form. We have

$$\langle r_1, \theta_1 \rangle \times \langle r_2, \theta_2 \rangle = \langle r_1 r_2, \theta_1 + \theta_2 \rangle. \tag{4.2}$$

That is, to multiply two numbers in polar form, we just multiply their moduli and add their arguments. The equation above can be justified as follows:

Note that although $\theta_1 + \theta_2$ is *an* argument of the product, it may not be the principal value of the argument.

$$r_1(\cos\theta_1 + i\sin\theta_1) \times r_2(\cos\theta_2 + i\sin\theta_2)$$
$$= r_1 r_2(\cos\theta_1 \cos\theta_2 - \sin\theta_1 \sin\theta_2 + i(\sin\theta_1 \cos\theta_2 + \cos\theta_1 \sin\theta_2))$$
$$= r_1 r_2(\cos(\theta_1 + \theta_2) + i\sin(\theta_1 + \theta_2)),$$

using trigonometric identities (3.4) and (3.3) from Section 3.

From (4.2), we can deduce a formula for division of complex numbers in polar form:

The proof of this is not difficult, but we omit it for reasons of space.

$$\langle r_1, \theta_1 \rangle \div \langle r_2, \theta_2 \rangle = \langle r_1/r_2, \theta_1 - \theta_2 \rangle.$$

Also, if we multiply the complex number $\langle r, \theta \rangle$ by itself repeatedly, we obtain a formula for an integer power of a complex number:

$$\langle r, \theta \rangle^n = \langle r^n, n\theta \rangle.$$

With $r = 1$, and written as

$$(\cos\theta + i\sin\theta)^n = \cos n\theta + i\sin n\theta,$$

this result is known as **De Moivre's Theorem**.

Abraham de Moivre (1667–1754) was born in France but spent his adult life living and working in England.

Exercise 4.6

Find $(1-i)^{20}$.

Complex exponentials

For a complex number $z = x + iy$, we can define the **complex exponential** e^z by the formula

$$e^z = e^x(\cos y + i\sin y).$$

We choose this definition because it works! That is, this complex exponential behaves, as we would hope, like the real exponential function. In particular, it retains the property that, for any complex numbers u and v,

$$e^u \times e^v = e^{u+v}.$$

In the case when $x = 0$, the definition of the complex exponential gives

$$e^{iy} = \cos y + i\sin y.$$

This leads us to a third way of expressing a complex number, which is often convenient. If z has polar form $\langle r, \theta \rangle$, then we have

$$z = r(\cos\theta + i\sin\theta) = re^{i\theta},$$

where $re^{i\theta}$ is referred to as the **exponential form** of the complex number z. In this form, r is the modulus of z and θ is the argument of z. As with the polar form, the value of θ is not unique, but there is a unique choice of θ in the range $-\pi < \theta \le \pi$.

This equation is known as **Euler's formula**.

Leonhard Euler (1707–1783) was a prolific mathematician, making many fundamental contributions to diverse areas of mathematics and science.

**Exercise 4.7*

Let $z = \langle r, \theta \rangle$. Use the exponential form of z to find $\mathrm{Re}(ze^{i\omega t})$.

5 Differentiation

The concepts and techniques of calculus are central to many of the mathematical methods discussed in this course. In this section, we consider differentiation.

5.1 Rates of change

Diagnostic test 5.1

Do Exercise 5.3 on page 34, and check your answers with the solutions given on page 56. If you are happy with your answers, you may proceed directly to Subsection 5.2.

Differentiation gives the rate of change of one variable with respect to another. As in Section 2 (see page 10), suppose that a reservoir contains V cubic metres of water at time t minutes after midday on 1 June, where

$$V = 2 \times 10^6 - 15t.$$

For a linear function such as this, the rate at which V is changing as t changes is the same at all times t. (The volume of water is falling by the same amount each minute.) This corresponds to the fact that a linear function has a straight-line graph, whose gradient (or slope) is the same everywhere.

Now consider a non-linear function, such as

$$s = \tfrac{1}{2}(-9.81)t^2 + 10t + 2, \tag{5.1}$$

which was used on page 14 to model the height (s metres at time t seconds) of a ball thrown vertically upwards. The rate of change of height with time, written $\dfrac{ds}{dt}$, is equal to the velocity v of the ball, and this varies with time. This function has a graph that is a parabola, and the gradient (or slope) of a parabola varies from point to point. Using rules discussed below, we can differentiate (5.1) to obtain

$$v = \frac{ds}{dt} = -9.81t + 10.$$

Thus differentiation of the function $s = f(t)$ produces another function, $v = f'(t)$, called the **derivative** or **derived function** of f. At each value of t, $f'(t) = -9.81t + 10$ gives the gradient of the graph of (5.1).

The gradient of a general graph $y = f(x)$ at a particular point $x = x_0$ gives the derivative f' of the function f at that point. The gradient of f at x_0 may be defined as the limiting value of the gradient of the chord AB in Figure 5.1, as B approaches A. The gradient of this chord is $(f(x_0 + h) - f(x_0))/h$. The process 'B approaches A' corresponds to h tending to 0, which we write as $h \to 0$. The definition applies only to suitable functions (called 'smooth'), where this limit exists and is the same whether h approaches 0 through positive or negative values. Thus we may formally define the derivative of f at x_0 by

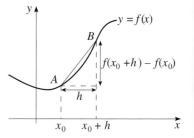

Figure 5.1

$$f'(x_0) = \lim_{h \to 0} \left(\frac{f(x_0 + h) - f(x_0)}{h} \right).$$

Working from this definition, we can obtain the derivatives of the various standard functions discussed in Sections 2 and 3. (The details of this need not concern us here.) These derivatives are tabulated in the Handbook, and we shall use them as required.

Derivatives can also be found using the computer algebra package for the course. However, it is not always convenient to use the computer (and indeed it will not be available to you in an examination), so it is useful to be able to perform differentiation by hand, at least in relatively simple cases. To do this, we combine two elements:

- derivatives of standard functions;
- rules for differentiating combinations of functions of various types, in sums, products, quotients and compositions.

The simplest rules concern constant multiples and sums. In general, the derivative of a combination $af(x) + bg(x)$, where a and b are constants, is $af'(x) + bg'(x)$. This rule enables us to differentiate (5.1) to obtain

The more complicated rules are discussed in Subsection 5.2.

$$\begin{aligned}
\frac{ds}{dt} &= \tfrac{1}{2}(-9.81)\frac{d}{dt}(t^2) + 10\frac{d}{dt}(t) + \frac{d}{dt}(2) \\
&= \tfrac{1}{2}(-9.81)(2t) + 10(1) + 0 \\
&= -9.81t + 10
\end{aligned}$$

(using the derivative of the standard function t^n for $n = 2$ and $n = 1$, and the fact that the derivative of a constant is 0). Similarly, if $V = 2 \times 10^6 - 15t$, we find its derived function to be $V' = -15$. This is constant (not dependent on t), corresponding to the fact that this function has a straight-line graph (with constant gradient).

There are various notations for derivatives, some of which we have used above. We shall use whichever is convenient in a particular context. Notation expressed purely in terms of variables, such as ds/dt, is referred to as *Leibniz* notation (after its inventor, G. W. Leibniz (1646–1717)). This notation is extended to write, for example,

$$\frac{d}{dt}(3t + 5\sin 2t) \quad \text{or} \quad \frac{d}{dx}(ax + bx^2).$$

In text, $\dfrac{ds}{dt}$ may be written as ds/dt, to save space.

Leibniz notation is sometimes a little clumsy, and may be inconvenient in situations where the role of functions is prominent. There the more modern *function* notation of adding a prime (′) to the function name is preferred. We can then write, for example, $f'(3)$ to mean the value of the derived function of f at 3. Sometimes we find it convenient to mix function and variable names, and write, for example, s', rather than introducing a separate name for the function relating the variables s and t. When using Leibniz notation, we may sometimes write $\dfrac{ds}{dt}(t)$ to emphasize that this derivative is a function of t, or $\dfrac{ds}{dt}(4)$ to mean the value of the derivative when $t = 4$. Some of the simpler forms of notation are open to ambiguity if used in inappropriate contexts, and at times we need to be careful about how we express things, for example by using the function notation in a precise manner.

We may sometimes write $s'(t)$ if we want to emphasize that s' is a function of t.

Differentiation of a derivative produces the so-called 'higher' derivatives. If, for example, we have $f(x) = x^3 + 5x$, then differentiation gives $f'(x) = 3x^2 + 5$. This derivative is itself a function of x, and can be differentiated again. This gives the **second derivative** as $f''(x)$. (In the above example, $f''(x) = 6x$.) In Leibniz notation, we write the second derivative, $\dfrac{d}{dx}\left(\dfrac{dy}{dx}\right)$, as $\dfrac{d^2y}{dx^2}$. Differentiating yet again leads to the **third derivative**, written $\dfrac{d^3y}{dx^3}$, or $f'''(x)$, which may also be written $f^{(3)}(x)$. ($f'''(x) = 6$ in this case.)

The derivative dy/dx is sometimes referred to as the *first derivative*.

The process can be continued, and a general **nth derivative** may be written as $\dfrac{d^n y}{dx^n}$ or $f^{(n)}(x)$, where n is referred to as the **order** of the derivative.

There is one final piece of notation to mention. We so often find that time (habitually denoted by t) is the independent variable that there is a separate notational convention for differentiation with respect to time. We use a dot over the variable to indicate a first derivative with respect to t, and two dots to indicate a second derivative. So if $x(t)$ is the position of an object as a function of time t, then $\dot{x}(t)$ means the same as $x'(t)$, and is the *velocity* of the object, while $\ddot{x}(t)$ means the same as $x''(t)$, and is its *acceleration*.

This notation is attributed to Isaac Newton (1642–1727), and so is sometimes referred to as *Newtonian* notation.

The next four exercises offer practice in differentiating standard functions, and constant multiples and sums of these. The Handbook contains a number of standard derivatives, and you can refer to that in answering these exercises. You will, however, find it helpful later in the course if you are able to differentiate polynomials, exponentials and trigonometric functions without reference to the Handbook.

Exercise 5.1

Suppose that an object is moving in a straight line so that its position x (measured from a chosen origin) is related to time t by the equation

$$x = 5 + 7\cos(3t + 2).$$

(a) Find expressions in terms of t for the velocity $\dot{x}(t)$ and acceleration $\ddot{x}(t)$ of the object.

(b) Use the above equation to eliminate t from your expression for $\ddot{x}(t)$, and hence find a relationship between the position and acceleration of the object that holds at all times.

Exercise 5.2

The weekly wage bill of a company, t years in the future, is projected to be £B, where

$$B = 10^5 \exp(0.04t).$$

Find an expression for the rate at which the wage bill will be rising in t years' time. What will this rate of rise be as a percentage of the wage bill at the time?

*Exercise 5.3

Calculate the following derivatives.

(a) $\dfrac{dy}{dx}$, where $y = 1 - 0.9\exp(-0.5x)$.

(b) $F'(2)$, where $F(x) = 3x^4 - 4x + 1$.

(c) $\dfrac{d^2y}{dt^2}$, where $y = \ln t$ $(t > 0)$.

(d) $F'(\frac{\pi}{6})$, where $F(x) = 3\sec(2x) - 4\cos(-3x)$.

(e) $g''(0)$, where $g(t) = a\cos(3t + \phi) + b\sin(3t + \phi)$ (and a, b and ϕ are constants).

Exercise 5.4

Calculate the following derivatives.

(a) $v'(z)$, where $v = 3\tan z + 2\cos z$.

(b) $\dfrac{dy}{dt}$ at $t = \frac{\pi}{12}$, where $y = A\sin 3t + B\cos 3t$ (and A and B are constants).

(c) $f^{(4)}(\frac{\pi}{2})$, where $f(t) = 2\sin 3t$.

(d) $f'(y)$, where $f(y) = \arctan(3y)$.

(e) $\dfrac{dz}{dx}$ when $x = 0$, where $z = \ln(cx + d)$ (and c and d are constants, with $d > 0$).

5.2 *Differentiating combinations of functions*

Diagnostic test 5.2

Do the starred parts of Exercises 5.5, 5.6 and 5.8 below, and check your answers with the solutions starting on page 56. If you are happy with your answers, you may proceed directly to Subsection 5.3.

As we have shown, derivatives of constant multiples and sums are calculated in a natural way. For derivatives of other combinations — products, quotients and composites — the rules are less obvious. These rules are given below and in the Handbook; you will find it advantageous later in the course if you are familiar with these rules and can use them without reference to the Handbook.

Product Rule $(fg)' = f'g + fg'.$

Or, in Leibniz notation,

$$\frac{d}{dx}(uv) = \frac{du}{dx}v + u\frac{dv}{dx}.$$

A useful way of remembering this rule is: derivative of first times second, plus first times derivative of second.

Quotient Rule $\left(\dfrac{f}{g}\right)' = \dfrac{f'g - fg'}{g^2}.$

Or, in Leibniz notation,

$$\frac{d}{dx}\left(\frac{u}{v}\right) = \frac{\dfrac{du}{dx}v - u\dfrac{dv}{dx}}{v^2}.$$

A useful way of remembering this rule is: derivative of top times bottom, minus top times derivative of bottom, all over bottom squared.

Example 5.1

Find $h'(x)$, where $h(x) = x^3 \cos 2x$.

Solution

The function $h(x)$ is a product, $f(x)g(x)$, with $f(x) = x^3$, $g(x) = \cos 2x$. We have

$$f'(x) = 3x^2 \quad \text{and} \quad g'(x) = -2\sin 2x.$$

So, using the Product Rule, we have

$$h'(x) = 3x^2 \cos 2x - 2x^3 \sin 2x. \quad \blacksquare$$

Exercise 5.5

*(a) Find $\dfrac{dy}{dx}$, where $y = \dfrac{\ln x}{x^2 + 1}$.

*(b) Find $f'(t)$, where $f(t) = t^5 \ln(3t + 4)$.

(c) Find $g'(0)$ (in terms of the constants A, B and C), where $g(t) = (At + B)\sin(At + C)$.

*(d) If the position of an object at time t is given by $e^{-3t} \sin 4t$, find its velocity and acceleration.

The rule for composite functions is a little more complicated to use.

Composite Rule   If $h(x) = g(f(x))$, then $h'(x) = g'(f(x))f'(x)$.

Expressed in Leibniz notation, this rule looks rather different: if y is a function of u, and u is a function of x (so $y = g(u)$ and $u = f(x)$), then

$$\frac{dy}{dx} = \frac{dy}{du}\frac{du}{dx}.$$

In this form, the Composite Rule is referred to as the **Chain Rule**.

In Section 2 (page 20) we mentioned an example of a composite function. There we had velocity v related to time t by the function

$$v = g(t) = 10 - gt,$$

and time related to height s by the function

$$t = f(s) = \frac{10 - \sqrt{100 + 4g - 2gs}}{g}.$$

If we wish to calculate the rate of change of v with respect to s, it is natural to use the Composite Rule in its Leibniz form:

$$\frac{dv}{ds} = \frac{dv}{dt}\frac{dt}{ds}.$$

Now

$$\frac{dv}{dt} = -g$$

and

$$\frac{dt}{ds} = \frac{d}{ds}\left(\frac{10 - \sqrt{100 + 4g - 2gs}}{g}\right) = \frac{1}{\sqrt{100 + 4g - 2gs}}.$$

So, using the Composite Rule,

$$\frac{dv}{ds} = -g\left(\frac{1}{\sqrt{100 + 4g - 2gs}}\right) = -\frac{g}{\sqrt{100 + 4g - 2gs}}.$$

(You can check that this is correct by differentiating Equation (2.13) directly.)

Example 5.2

Find $f'(x)$, where $f(x) = \sin^3 x$.

Solution

If we let $u = \sin x$, then we have $f(x) = u^3$.

We then have

$$f'(x) = \frac{df}{du}\frac{du}{dx} = 3u^2 \cos x = 3\sin^2 x \cos x,$$

replacing the variable u by $\sin x$.   ■

The recognition of $\sin^3 x$ as a composite function, and of how to break it down into two parts, each consisting of a standard function, is the key to differentiating it.

Your proficiency with differentiation will depend on your experience and will develop with practice. It will be helpful for your study of MST209 if you are able to differentiate expressions such as that in Example 5.2 without recourse to the computer algebra package for the course — and, ideally, without even needing to refer to the Handbook. But such proficiency may take some time to develop, and while it is developing feel free to check your work using the computer.

Exercise 5.6

Use the Composite Rule to differentiate each of the following.

*(a) $y = \exp(t^2)$
(b) $f(x) = (3x^3 + 4)^6$

*(c) $z = \tan(3v + 4)$
(d) $g(z) = \sqrt{4 - z^2}$

*(e) $f(x) = \dfrac{1}{\left(\sqrt{1 + 2x^2}\right)^3}$

Exercise 5.7

Differentiate the following functions.

(a) $y = \sec\left(\dfrac{x}{x^2 + 1}\right)$
(b) $z = t^2 \exp(t^3 + 1)$

These differentiations involve more than one rule.

Suppose that we want to find the gradient at the point $(2, 1)$ of the tangent to the ellipse with equation

$$x^2 + 4y^2 = 8. \tag{5.2}$$

We want dy/dx at $x = 2$. We could start by expressing y as a function of x, but a more convenient approach is to differentiate the equation as it stands. To differentiate y^2 with respect to x, we use the Composite Rule, and obtain $\dfrac{d(y^2)}{dy}\dfrac{dy}{dx} = 2y\dfrac{dy}{dx}$. So, differentiating both sides of Equation (5.2) with respect to x, we obtain

$$2x + 4(2y)\frac{dy}{dx} = 0.$$

When $x = 2$ and $y = 1$, this gives $4 + 8\,dy/dx = 0$, so $dy/dx = -\frac{1}{2}$. Therefore the gradient of the tangent to this ellipse at $(2, 1)$ is $-\frac{1}{2}$.

Differentiation with respect to x of an expression such as $x^2 + 4y^2$, where y is a function of x, is known as **implicit differentiation**.

Exercise 5.8

(a) Use the Product and Composite Rules to find the following in terms of x, y and dy/dx.

(i) $\dfrac{d}{dx}(x^2 y)$
(ii) $\dfrac{d}{dx}(y^3)$

(b) Find the gradient at the point $(-1, 1)$ of the tangent to the curve

$$x^3 + x^2 y + y^3 = 1.$$

Just occasionally, we need to consider differentiation of a **complex-valued** function, of the form

$$f(t) = g(t) + ih(t),$$

where g and h are real functions. Differentiation of such a function is defined in a natural way, as

$$f'(t) = g'(t) + ih'(t).$$

So, for example, if $f(t) = \cos 3t + i \sin 3t$, then $f'(t) = -3 \sin 3t + 3i \cos 3t$.

Exercise 5.9

Find the second derivative of the function $f(t) = \cos 2t + i \sin 2t$.

5.3 Investigating functions

Diagnostic test 5.3

Do Exercise 5.10 on page 39, and check your answers with the solutions given on page 57. If you are happy with your answers, you may proceed directly to Section 6.

Faced with an expression made up of some combination of standard functions, how might you investigate its behaviour? As an example, consider the function

$$f = \frac{v}{4 + 1.5v + 0.008v^2},$$

where we would like to see how f varies as v varies.

A sketch graph of f against v helps with this, and a computer algebra package or graphics calculator will provide such a graph. However, it is not always obvious for what range of values to plot the graph, so it is helpful to be able to deduce some information about the general behaviour of a function 'by hand', without recourse to a machine. Such information can also be used to cross-check results obtained from a machine, and to flesh out the picture more fully. This example will be continued in Exercise 5.11, but first we shall make some general remarks about sketching graphs.

Questions that you might consider when sketching a graph include the following.

- Are there any points where the function is not defined?
  (This often happens if the expression is a quotient in which the denominator can be 0.)

- Where does the function cross the axes?
  (To find the points where the function crosses the horizontal axis, solve the equation $f(x) = 0$ for x. The function crosses the vertical axis at the point $y = f(0)$.)

- How does the function behave for large and small values of the independent variable (or at the endpoints of the domain if this is an interval)?
  (For a function with domain $\mathbb{R}$, examine the values of the function at large positive and negative values. For a function defined on an interval, simply evaluate the function at the endpoints.)

- On which parts of its domain is the function increasing, and on which is it decreasing?
  (You can look at the sign of the gradient at various points.)

- Are there any local maximum or minimum values?

A function $f(x)$ is **increasing** on an interval if $f(x)$ increases in value as x increases (or equivalently if $f'(x) > 0$). Similarly, $f(x)$ is **decreasing** on an interval if $f(x)$ decreases in value as x increases (or equivalently if $f'(x) < 0$).

The last question can be answered using differentiation. A **stationary point** of a function $f(x)$ is a value of x where $f'(x) = 0$. Local maxima and local minima occur at stationary points, although a stationary point need not necessarily be either. Figure 5.2 illustrates such stationary points.

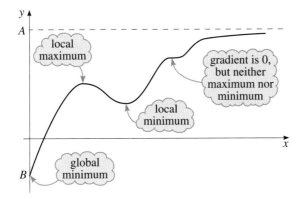

Figure 5.2

In models, we often wish to find the overall maximum or overall minimum of some function, usually referred to as the *global maximum* or *global minimum*, respectively. The global minimum or maximum may well occur at a stationary point; but caution is needed, for they need not necessarily do so. For example, the global minimum of the function with domain $[0, \infty)$ illustrated in Figure 5.2 occurs at an endpoint of its domain ($x = 0$), which for that function is not a stationary point. In fact, a function need not have a global maximum or global minimum. For example, the function $f(x)$ in Figure 5.2 exceeds the local maximum value when x is large, but never reaches a global maximum. However, the value of $f(x)$ in Figure 5.2 does not become arbitrarily large either: it is *bounded above* by (but never actually attains) the value A (but it comes arbitrarily close as x becomes large). We refer to the line $y = A$ as an **asymptote** of the graph of f.

A function $f(x)$ is **bounded above** by a number A if $f(x) \le A$ for all x in the domain of f. Similarly, $f(x)$ is **bounded below** by B if $f(x) \ge B$ for all x in the domain of f. The numbers A and B are referred to as an **upper bound** and a **lower bound** for f, respectively.

Having found a stationary point of a function, we can determine whether it is a local maximum or a local minimum either by looking at the sign of the second derivative at the stationary point, or by looking at the sign of the first derivative to either side of the point. (For example, if b is a stationary point, and $f'(x)$ is positive for x less than b and negative for x greater than b, or if $f''(b)$ is negative, then b is a local maximum. These tests are given in detail in the Handbook.)

Exercise 5.10

Find any stationary points of the function

$$y(x) = 5 - 2(x + 1)e^{-\frac{1}{2}x} \quad (x \ge 0).$$

Classify these as local mimima or local maxima or neither, and evaluate $y(x)$ at these points.

Example 5.3

Suppose that

$$(x^2 - 3)y = x - 2.$$

Sketch a graph of y against x.

Solution

We have $y = \dfrac{x - 2}{x^2 - 3}$, but need to note that this expression for y is not defined if $x^2 - 3 = 0$, i.e. if $x = \pm\sqrt{3}$. We can see that $y = 0$ if (and only if) $x = 2$, so the graph crosses the x-axis at this one point. If x is large (positive or negative), then y will be close to zero.

To look for stationary points, we use the Quotient Rule to calculate

$$\frac{dy}{dx} = \frac{(1)(x^2-3)-(x-2)(2x)}{(x^2-3)^2} = \frac{-x^2+4x-3}{(x^2-3)^2}.$$

This is zero if $x^2-4x+3=0$; i.e. if $x=1$ or 3. The second derivative is a bit complicated to calculate, so it is easier here to look at the sign of the first derivative near $x=1$ and $x=3$ to check whether these stationary points are local maxima or minima. If x is just less than 1, then dy/dx is negative, while if x is just greater than 1, dy/dx is positive, so $x=1$ is a local minimum. For x just below 3, dy/dx is positive, while for x just above 3, it is negative, so $x=3$ is a local maximum. Note that at $x=1$, $y=\frac{1}{2}$, while at $x=3$, $y=\frac{1}{6}$.

Try $x=0.9$ and $x=1.1$.

Try $x=2.9$ and $x=3.1$.

We can incorporate all this information (plus other information, such as the behaviour of y near $x=\pm\sqrt{3}$ and the value of y at certain values of x, e.g. $x=0$) in constructing a sketch graph, as in Figure 5.3.

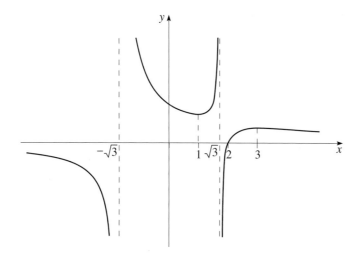

Again we refer to the lines $x=\sqrt{3}$ and $x=-\sqrt{3}$ as asymptotes of this graph.

Figure 5.3   ■

A **continuous** function is one whose graph can be drawn without lifting your pen from the paper. The function $f(x)=(x-2)/(x^2-3)$ is not continuous on any domain containing either $\sqrt{3}$ or $-\sqrt{3}$.

A **smooth** function is continuous and has a continuous derivative. For example, the function

$$f(x) = \begin{cases} 3x, & x \geq 0, \\ -2x, & x < 0, \end{cases}$$

is continuous, but is not smooth (since its derivative is not continuous at $x=0$).

Exercise 5.11

(a) Sketch a graph of the function

$$f(v) = \frac{v}{4+1.5v+0.008v^2} \quad (v \geq 0).$$

In particular, find: any values of v for which $f(v)$ is zero; any values of v for which $f(v)$ is not defined; and any local maxima or minima of $f(v)$. Also, indicate how $f(v)$ behaves as v becomes large.

(b) Find the global maximum and minimum of f.

6 Integration

Subsection 6.1 provides a reminder of the basic idea of integration as 'reversing differentiation'. Subsection 6.2 discusses how we may calculate relatively simple integrals by hand. In Subsection 6.3, we look at two techniques for finding more complicated integrals by hand.

As well as 'reversing differentiation', integrals also arise as the limits of certain sums. In Subsection 6.4, we see how this can lead to integrals arising in models.

6.1 Reversing differentiation

Diagnostic test 6.1 ———————————————

Do Exercises 6.1 and 6.2 below, and check your answers with the solutions starting on page 57. If you are happy with your answers, you may proceed directly to Subsection 6.2.

Throughout this course you will meet a variety of *differential equations*. These are equations involving the derivative of a function, for example

$$\frac{ds}{dt} = 5t + 7. \tag{6.1}$$

The objective is usually to 'solve' the equation by finding an expression for the function itself (rather than its derivative). To do this involves 'reversing' the differentiation, and this process is referred to as **integration**. In the above example we **integrate** both sides of the equation with respect to t, obtaining

$$s = \int (5t + 7)\, dt.$$

To evaluate this integral, you can use the table of standard integrals in the Handbook. These show that $\int t\, dt = \frac{1}{2}t^2$ and $\int 1\, dt = t$, and on integration we obtain

$$s = \tfrac{5}{2}t^2 + 7t + c, \tag{6.2}$$

where c may be any constant. To confirm this, note that with s given by (6.2), we have

The constant c is often referred to as an **arbitrary constant** or a **constant of integration**.

$$\frac{ds}{dt} = \frac{d}{dt}\left(\tfrac{5}{2}t^2 + 7t + c\right) = 5t + 7,$$

as required by (6.1). Since c may be any constant, we see that the differential equation (6.1) does not have a unique solution.

Generalizing, suppose that f is a known function, and

$$F'(x) = f(x).$$

We write the general solution of this differential equation as

$$F(x) = \int f(x)\, dx,$$

where the right-hand side, $\int f(x)\, dx$, is called the **indefinite integral** of $f(x)$, and the function to be integrated, $f(x)$, is called the **integrand**.

Given a differential equation such as

$$F'(x) = \frac{1}{1+x^2},\tag{6.3}$$

finding a function F whose derivative is the function on the right-hand side is a non-trivial task. For (6.3), we are lucky, since the table of standard derivatives in the Handbook gives $\frac{d}{dx}(\arctan x) = \frac{1}{1+x^2}$. Hence we have

$$\int \frac{1}{1+x^2}\,dx = \arctan x + c,$$

where c is an arbitrary constant.

In contrast, consider finding the integral

$$\int \exp(-x^2)\,dx.$$

Any function that differentiates to $1/(1+x^2)$, such as $F(x) = \arctan x + 5$, is referred to as an **integral** (or *antiderivative*) of $1/(1+x^2)$.

At first sight, this might seem no harder a problem to solve than (6.3). In fact, however, it is impossible! To be more precise, there is no simple combination of the standard functions (polynomials, sin, cos, exp and ln) that when differentiated gives $\exp(-x^2)$.

Finding explicit expressions for integrals is a much harder task than finding derivatives. The rules of differentiation ensure that we can, in principle, find an explicit expression for the derivative of any combination of standard functions. The equivalent is not true for integrals. What is more, even where integrals can be found, this may be a messy process. The methods whereby particular functions can be integrated depend on recognizing what happens to work in various particular cases.

Integrals are readily found if they appear in the table of standard integrals in the Handbook (as do $\int e^{2x}\,dx$ and $\int x^7\,dx$, for example). So are the integrals of constant multiples and sums of constant multiples of these, such as $\int (4e^{2x} + 9x^7)\,dx$. There are also integration techniques that enable you to find some more complicated integrals. *Integration by substitution* is based on the rule for differentiating composite functions, while *integration by parts* is based on the rule for differentiating a product. There are brief reminders of these two techniques in Subsection 6.3.

The table of standard integrals in the Handbook contains quite a wide selection of integrals. Some of these integrals are deduced from the table of standard derivatives, others from using integration by parts or substitution. You can regard them all as the fruit of others' experience, and draw on them as needed. The correctness of an integral, obtained either by using the Handbook or from the computer algebra package for the course, can be verified by differentiation.

Exercise 6.1

Use differentiation to verify that the following integrals are correct (where $a \neq 0$ is a constant and c is an arbitrary constant).

(a) $\displaystyle\int x \sin ax\,dx = -\frac{x}{a}\cos ax + \frac{1}{a^2}\sin ax + c$

(b) $\displaystyle\int \tan ax\,dx = -\frac{1}{a}\ln(\cos ax) + c \quad \left(-\frac{\pi}{2} < ax < \frac{\pi}{2}\right)$

Exercise 6.2 ────────────────────────────

(a) Use implicit differentiation (and a trigonometric formula) to show that if $x = \tan y$, then

$$\frac{dy}{dx} = \frac{1}{1 + x^2}.$$

Hence confirm that $\displaystyle\int \frac{1}{1 + x^2}\, dx = \arctan x + c.$

(b) Use implicit differentiation of $x = \sin y$ (and a trigonometric formula) to deduce an expression for the indefinite integral

$$\int \frac{1}{\sqrt{1 - x^2}}\, dx.$$

Here $-1 < x < 1$, $-\frac{\pi}{2} < y < \frac{\pi}{2}$.

Check that your result agrees with the one in the Handbook.

──

6.2 Evaluating integrals

Diagnostic test 6.2 ─────────────────────────

Do Exercises 6.4 and 6.6 below, and check your answers with the solutions starting on page 58. If you are happy with your answers, you may proceed directly to Subsection 6.3.

──

Your first recourse for finding an integral by hand is the table of standard integrals in the Handbook. If the integrals of functions f and g are known, then the integral of $af + bg$, where a and b are constants, is readily found, using the rule

Or, preferably, use your memory!

$$\int (af(x) + bg(x))\, dx = a \int f(x)\, dx + b \int g(x)\, dx.$$

So, for example (referring to the Handbook for $\int e^{2x}\, dx$ and $\int x^7\, dx$),

$$\int (4e^{2x} + 9x^7)\, dx = 4 \int e^{2x}\, dx + 9 \int x^7\, dx$$
$$= 4(\tfrac{1}{2}e^{2x}) + 9(\tfrac{1}{8}x^8) + c$$
$$= 2e^{2x} + \tfrac{9}{8}x^8 + c.$$

Sometimes algebraic manipulation can transform an expression to be integrated into a more amenable form. For example, the manipulation

$$\frac{3x^2 + 2x}{\sqrt{x}} = \frac{3x^2}{\sqrt{x}} + \frac{2x}{\sqrt{x}} = 3x^{3/2} + 2x^{1/2}$$

transforms the expression on the left into a sum of constant multiples of functions in the Handbook table. Less obvious transformations can be achieved using trigonometric formulae. For example, using $\cos 2x = \cos^2 x - \sin^2 x$ (see Exercise 3.3(a)(ii)) and $\sin^2 x + \cos^2 x = 1$ (Identity (3.2)), we obtain $\cos 2x = 2\cos^2 x - 1$. Rearranging this gives

$$\cos^2 x = \tfrac{1}{2}(1 + \cos 2x),$$

which enables us to integrate $\cos^2 x$.

Exercise 6.3

Use the identity

$$\cos^2 ax = \tfrac{1}{2}(1 + \cos 2ax)$$

(where $a \neq 0$ is a constant) to obtain $\int \cos^2 ax\, dx$.

At times, attention needs to be paid to domains, to avoid giving, as integrals, expressions that are not defined. For example, $\ln x$ is defined (as a real number) only for $x > 0$, so $\int \dfrac{1}{x}\, dx = \ln x + c$ holds only for $x > 0$. To integrate $1/x$ for $x < 0$, we use $\int \dfrac{1}{x}\, dx = \ln(-x) + c$. The Handbook gives domain restrictions where necessary. We sometimes write, for convenience, $\int \dfrac{1}{x}\, dx = \ln |x| + c$ $(x \neq 0)$, but do be aware that this covers the two separate cases of $x < 0$ and $x > 0$. Similarly, we sometimes write $\int \dfrac{1}{ax + b}\, dx = \dfrac{1}{a} \ln |ax + b| + c$ $(ax + b \neq 0)$.

For $x < 0$,
$$\frac{d}{dx}(\ln(-x)) = \frac{1}{-x} \times (-1)$$
$$= \frac{1}{x},$$
using the Composite Rule.

*Exercise 6.4

Find the following integrals.

Use the standard integrals given in the Handbook as necessary.

(a) $\displaystyle\int e^{5x}\, dx$ (b) $\displaystyle\int 6\sec^2(3t)\, dt$ (c) $\displaystyle\int \dfrac{1}{36 + 4v^2}\, dv$

(d) $\displaystyle\int \dfrac{1}{3 - 2y}\, dy$ $(y < \tfrac{3}{2})$ (e) $\displaystyle\int \dfrac{1}{3 - 2y}\, dy$ $(y > \tfrac{3}{2})$

Exercise 6.5

Find the following integrals.

Use the standard integrals given in the Handbook as necessary.

(a) $\displaystyle\int (6\cos(-2t) + 8\sin 4t)\, dt$ (b) $\displaystyle\int \dfrac{1}{\sqrt{9 - t^2}}\, dt$ $(-3 < t < 3)$

(c) $\displaystyle\int \dfrac{5t^3 + 7}{t}\, dt$ $(t < 0)$ (d) $\displaystyle\int \left(2\ln(4t) - \dfrac{2}{t}\right) dt$ $(t > 0)$

(e) $\displaystyle\int \dfrac{1}{(x - 1)(x + 1)}\, dx$ $(-1 < x < 1)$

The next example again uses a standard integral from the Handbook, but requires careful matching of parameters and attention to domains.

Example 6.1

For $A > 0$, $x > \dfrac{1}{A}$, find $\displaystyle\int \dfrac{1}{x(1 - Ax)}\, dx$.

Solution

We can match the integrand with that of a standard integral by writing it in the form

$$\frac{1}{x(1 - Ax)} = \frac{-1}{A(x - 0)\left(x - \frac{1}{A}\right)}.$$

The Handbook gives the integral $\int \dfrac{1}{(x-a)(x-b)}\,dx$ for $b < a$. To match that, choose $b = 0$ and $a = \frac{1}{A}$. Since $x > \frac{1}{A}$, we must choose the standard integral for the case $a < x$. So we obtain

$$\int \frac{1}{x(1-Ax)}\,dx = -\frac{1}{A}\int \frac{1}{(x-0)\left(x-\frac{1}{A}\right)}\,dx$$

$$= -\frac{1}{A}\left(\frac{1}{\frac{1}{A}-0}\ln\left(\frac{x-\frac{1}{A}}{x-0}\right)\right) + c$$

$$= -\ln\left(\frac{x-\frac{1}{A}}{x}\right) + c$$

$$= \ln\left(\frac{x}{x-\frac{1}{A}}\right) + c = \ln\left(\frac{Ax}{Ax-1}\right) + c. \quad\blacksquare$$

Exercise 6.6

(a) For $k > 0$, $-k < v < k$, find $\displaystyle\int \frac{1}{v^2 - k^2}\,dv$.

(*Hint*: Remember that $v^2 - k^2 = (v-k)(v+k)$.)

(b) For $a > 0$, $b > 0$, $-\sqrt{\dfrac{a}{b}} < v < \sqrt{\dfrac{a}{b}}$, find $\displaystyle\int \frac{1}{a - bv^2}\,dv$.

6.3   Integration by parts and by substitution

Diagnostic test 6.3

Do Exercises 6.7 and 6.8 below, and check your answers with the solutions starting on page 58. If you are happy with your answers, you may proceed directly to Subsection 6.4.

In this subsection, we look briefly at two methods for evaluating more complicated integrals. You will use these methods later in the course. For now, it is particularly useful to recognize the type of integral illustrated in Equation (6.5).

Integration by substitution

The formula for **integration by substitution** is

$$\int f(g(x))g'(x)\,dx = \int f(u)\,du. \tag{6.4}$$

Or, in Leibniz notation,

$$\int f(u)\frac{du}{dx}\,dx = \int f(u)\,du.$$

We say that we have 'substituted' $u = g(x)$. The following example shows one way of executing integration by substitution.

Example 6.2

Find $\int x\sin(2+3x^2)\,dx$.

Solution

Let $u = 2 + 3x^2$, so $du/dx = 6x$.

We have

$$\int x\sin(2+3x^2)\,dx = \tfrac{1}{6}\int 6x\sin(2+3x^2)\,dx$$

$$= \tfrac{1}{6}\int \sin u\,\frac{du}{dx}\,dx$$

$$= \tfrac{1}{6}\int \sin u\,du$$

$$= -\tfrac{1}{6}\cos u + c$$

$$= -\tfrac{1}{6}\cos(2+3x^2) + c,$$

substituting at the end for u in terms of x. ∎

In (6.4), we are taking $g(x) = 2 + 3x^2$.

Now $g'(x) = 6x$.

Note how, in effect, $\dfrac{du}{dx}\,dx$ is replaced by du.

Notice in this example that the integrand is a composite function, $\sin(2+3x^2)$, multiplied by (in effect) the derivative of the 'inner function' $2 + 3x^2$. We are only 'out' by a constant factor (of $\tfrac{1}{6}$), and this shows up in the final expression. In such a situation it is relatively easy to see that the substitution $u = 2 + 3x^2$ will help to simplify the integral. There are other useful types of substitution that are much less apparent, but we need not discuss those here.

One form of integral comes up sufficiently often to be worth separate mention. We have, for $g(x) \neq 0$,

$$\int \frac{g'(x)}{g(x)}\,dx = \ln|g(x)| + c. \tag{6.5}$$

This follows from treating the cases $g(x) > 0$ and $g(x) < 0$ separately, and using the substitutions $u = g(x)$ and $u = -g(x)$, respectively. When $g(x) > 0$, we have $u = g(x) > 0$, $du/dx = g'(x)$ and

$$\int \frac{g'(x)}{g(x)}\,dx = \int \frac{1}{u}\,du = \ln u + c = \ln(g(x)) + c.$$

When $g(x) < 0$, we have $u = -g(x) > 0$, $du/dx = -g'(x)$ and

$$\int \frac{g'(x)}{g(x)}\,dx = \int \frac{-g'(x)}{-g(x)}\,dx = \int \frac{1}{u}\,du = \ln u + c = \ln(-g(x)) + c.$$

*Exercise 6.7

Find the following integrals.

(a) $\int y^2 \exp(2+4y^3)\,dy$ (b) $\int \cos y \sin^2 y\,dy$

(c) $\int t\sqrt{1-t^2}\,dt$ $(-1 < t < 1)$ (d) $\int \frac{x}{1+x^2}\,dx$

(e) $\int \frac{\sin 2t}{1+\sin^2 t}\,dt$ (f) $\int \frac{y}{1-y^2}\,dy$ $(y \neq \pm 1)$

Part (e) requires use of the trigonometric formula for $\sin 2t$ derived in Exercise 3.3(a)(i).

Integration by parts

The formula for **integration by parts** is

$$\int f(x)g'(x)\, dx = f(x)g(x) - \int f'(x)g(x)\, dx.$$

As with integration by substitution, this formula transforms an integral into a different one, and the key to successful use is to ensure that the 'new' integral is easier to evaluate than the original.

Example 6.3

Find $\int xe^{-2x}\, dx$.

Solution

In the formula, take $f(x) = x$ and $g'(x) = e^{-2x}$. Then $f'(x) = 1$ and $g(x) = -\frac{1}{2}e^{-2x}$, so

Note that an arbitrary constant need not be included in the expression for $g(x)$.

$$\int xe^{-2x}\, dx = x(-\tfrac{1}{2}e^{-2x}) - \int 1(-\tfrac{1}{2}e^{-2x})\, dx$$

$$= -\tfrac{1}{2}xe^{-2x} + \tfrac{1}{2}\int e^{-2x}\, dx$$

$$= -\tfrac{1}{2}xe^{-2x} - \tfrac{1}{4}e^{-2x} + c$$

$$= -\tfrac{1}{4}(2x + 1)e^{-2x} + c. \quad \blacksquare$$

*Exercise 6.8

(a) Use integration by parts to find $\int xe^{-x}\, dx$.

(b) Find $\int x^2 e^{-x}\, dx$. (Use integration by parts, then the result of part (a).)

6.4 Definite integrals

Diagnostic test 6.4

Calculate each of the following integrals.

(a) $\displaystyle\int_0^1 (x^3 - 2)\, dx$ (b) $\displaystyle\int_1^2 (x^3 - 2)\, dx$ (c) $\displaystyle\int_0^2 (x^3 - 2)\, dx$

Now check your solutions against those given below. If you are happy with the answers, you may proceed directly to Section 7.

Solution

(a) We have

$$\int_0^1 (x^3 - 2)\, dx = \left[\tfrac{1}{4}x^4 - 2x\right]_0^1$$

$$= (\tfrac{1}{4} - 2) - (0 - 0) = -\tfrac{7}{4}.$$

(b) Similarly,

$$\int_1^2 (x^3 - 2)\, dx = \left[\tfrac{1}{4}x^4 - 2x\right]_1^2$$

$$= (\tfrac{16}{4} - 4) - (\tfrac{1}{4} - 2) = \tfrac{7}{4}.$$

(c) We can either evaluate the integral directly,

$$\int_0^2 (x^3 - 2)\, dx = \left[\tfrac{1}{4}x^4 - 2x\right]_0^2$$

$$= (\tfrac{16}{4} - 4) - (0 - 0) = 0,$$

or use parts (a) and (b):

$$\int_0^2 (x^3 - 2)\, dx = \int_0^1 (x^3 - 2)\, dx + \int_1^2 (x^3 - 2)\, dx$$

$$= -\tfrac{7}{4} + \tfrac{7}{4} = 0.$$

The indefinite integral is a *function* (or, to be exact, a family of functions containing an arbitrary constant). A different, though closely related, form of integral is the **definite integral**, whose value is a *number*. If we know an integral, say F, of f, then a definite integral of f is readily found, since the value of a definite integral is given by

$$\int_a^b f(x)\, dx = F(b) - F(a).$$

The difference $F(b) - F(a)$ is commonly written as $[F(x)]_a^b$.

So, for example,

$$\int_0^1 \frac{1}{\sqrt{4 - \theta^2}}\, d\theta = \left[\arcsin\left(\tfrac{1}{2}\theta\right)\right]_0^1 = \arcsin\tfrac{1}{2} - \arcsin 0 = \tfrac{\pi}{6} - 0 = \tfrac{\pi}{6}.$$

Any choice of F, an integral of f, leads to the same value for $F(b) - F(a)$.

Exercise 6.9

Evaluate $\displaystyle\int_0^{3/2} \frac{1}{9 + 4z^2}\, dz.$

A rough-and-ready way of thinking of a definite integral $\int_a^b f(x)\, dx$ is as 'the accumulation of the values taken by $f(x)$ as x runs from a to b'. This ties up with a useful way of visualizing definite integrals, as areas. If $f(x) \geq 0$ for $a \leq x \leq b$, then the definite integral $\int_a^b f(x)\, dx$ is equal to the area under the graph of $f(x)$ between $x = a$ and $x = b$ (see Figure 6.1(a)). There is one point to be careful about here. If $f(x) < 0$, corresponding to a region below the x-axis, then we have a *negative* contribution to the integral, whereas area is always a *positive* quantity. Thus for a function f as pictured in Figure 6.1(b), $\int_a^b f(x)\, dx = $ area $A_1 - $ area A_2.

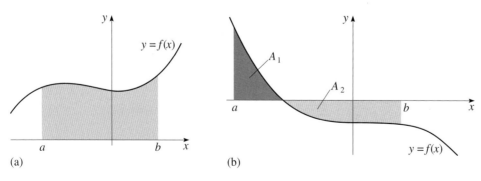

(a)   (b)

Figure 6.1 $\int_a^b f(x)\, dx$ as an area: (a) with $f(x) > 0$; (b) in general.

Whereas indefinite integrals typically arise in solving differential equations ('reversing differentiation'), definite integrals can arise in other circumstances too, such as when an integral is seen as the limit of a sequence of sums. As an example, consider the following model, to estimate the number of seabird nests on an island.

Example 6.4

An island is modelled as a circle of radius 500 metres. The density of nests is greatest on the edge of the island, and least at the centre. (The birds prefer ready access to the sea.) The density is modelled as D, measured in nests per square metre, where

$$D = 0.1 + r/500 = 0.1 + 0.002r,$$

where r is the distance from the centre of the island, measured in metres. Estimate the number of nests on the island.

Solution

Imagine the island divided by concentric circles into narrow 'annular' strips, each of width δr. Figure 6.2 shows a 'typical' strip, between circles of radius r and $r + \delta r$.

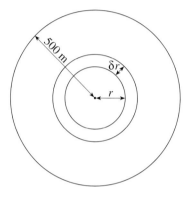

The area of this typical strip is approximately $2\pi r \delta r$ ('length × width'). The number of nests within this strip is (the area) × (the density of nests), and so is approximately

$$2\pi r \delta r D = 2\pi r(0.1 + 0.002r)\delta r.$$

The total number of nests on the island is the sum of the number of nests in all the strips. If we take the limit of this sum as $\delta r \to 0$, then the sum converges to the definite integral of $2\pi r(0.1 + 0.002r)$ between $r = 0$ (the centre of the island) and $r = 500$ (at the edge). That is, an estimate of the number of nests is

Figure 6.2

$$\int_0^{500} 2\pi r(0.1 + 0.002r)\, dr = 6.021 \times 10^5,$$

so there are approximately 600 000 nests.   ■

The equivalence of the two views of integration, as 'reversing differentiation' and as the limit of a sequence of sums, is assured by the Fundamental Theorem of Calculus, but that need not concern us here. Many texts use the limit of a sequence of sums (rather than 'reversing differentiation') as the basis for the definition of integration.

End-of-section Exercise

Exercise 6.10 ────────────────

Find the following integrals (where a is a constant).

(a) $\displaystyle\int_0^{500} 2\pi r(0.1 + 0.002r)\, dr$ (b) $\displaystyle\int \exp(a - 2y)\, dy$

(c) $\displaystyle\int_0^1 \frac{1}{3u + 5}\, du$ (d) $\displaystyle\int_{-3}^{-2} \frac{1}{3u + 5}\, du$ (e) $\displaystyle\int \ln(3t + a)\, dt$

(f) $\displaystyle\int t\cos(3t + a)\, dt$ (g) $\displaystyle\int_0^{\frac{\pi}{4}} \frac{\sin 2x}{3 + \cos 2x}\, dx$

7 Computer activities

This section demonstrates how the computer algebra package for the course can assist in performing various tasks that have been studied in the unit. In particular, we can easily perform algebraic manipulations, such as simplifying expressions and solving quadratic equations. We can also solve equations numerically when an algebraic solution cannot be found, and handle the arithmetic of complex numbers. Turning to calculus, you will see how to produce graphs, and how to differentiate and integrate.

Use your computer to complete the following activities.

Symbolic algebra on the computer

Activity 7.1

(a) Evaluate $\left(\frac{4}{9}\right)^{1/2}$.

(b) Simplify $\left(\frac{4}{9}\right)^{1/2}$.

(c) Simplify each of the following.

    (i) $a^3 a^5$ (ii) $\exp(2\ln x + \ln(x+1))$ (iii) $\sqrt{x^2}$

(d) Try 'simplifying' $x^5 + x^7$.

The solutions to these questions, and further comments, are given in the computer worksheets.

Activity 7.2

Expand each of the following.

(a) $(x+2)^3$ (b) $(2x+3)^{10}$

Activity 7.3

Suppose that $\ln y = 2.83 \ln x + 0.37$. Express y as a function of x.

Activity 7.4

(a) Solve for x the following equations.

    (i) $2x^2 + 7x - 4 = 0$ (ii) $x^2 + x - 6 = 0$ (iii) $x^2 - 2x + 2 = 0$

(b) Solve for x the quadratic equation $abx^2 - (a+b)x + 1 = 0$.

Solving equations numerically on the computer

Activity 7.5

Find the values of x that satisfy the equation $\cos x = 0.2x$.

Complex numbers on the computer

Activity 7.6

Evaluate the following.

(a) $(1+i)(1-2i)$ (b) $|4+i|$

Activity 7.7

(a) Expand $(\cos x + i \sin x)^4$. Find $\operatorname{Re}\!\left((\cos x + i \sin x)^4\right)$, and hence use De Moivre's Theorem to obtain an expression for $\cos 4x$ in terms of $\sin x$ and $\cos x$.

(b) Expand $\cos 4x$. Compare the result with your answer to part (a).

Graphs and differentiation on the computer

Activity 7.8

Consider the function

$$y(x) = 5 - 2(x+1)\exp(-\tfrac{1}{2}x) \quad (x \ge 0).$$

(a) Obtain a graph of $y(x)$ against x.

(b) How does $y(x)$ appear to behave as x becomes large?

(c) Can you find the global maximum and global minimum values taken by $y(x)$?

You may wish to refer back to Exercise 5.10 in answering this.

Activity 7.9

(a) Find $\dfrac{dy}{dx}$, where $y = 1 - 0.9\exp(-0.5x)$.

(b) Find $\dfrac{dy}{dx}$, where $y = \dfrac{x}{x^2+1}$.

(c) Find $\dfrac{d^2y}{dt^2}$, where $y = \ln t$.

The functions in parts (a) and (c) were also considered in Exercise 5.3.

Integration on the computer

Activity 7.10

(a) Find the following integrals.

(i) $\displaystyle\int \exp(5x)\,dx$ (ii) $\displaystyle\int \frac{5t^3 + 7}{t}\,dt$

(b) Try to find the following integrals.

(i) $\displaystyle\int \frac{1}{v^2 - k^2}\,dv$ (ii) $\displaystyle\int \frac{1}{a - bv^2}\,dv$

Activity 7.11

Evaluate the following definite integrals, first numerically and then symbolically.

(a) $\displaystyle\int_1^4 \frac{1}{x}\,dx$ (b) $\displaystyle\int_0^1 \exp(-x^2)\,dx$

Activity 7.12

Evaluate the following.

(a) $\displaystyle\int_a^b \frac{1}{x}\,dx$, symbolically   (b) $\displaystyle\int_{-1}^2 \frac{1}{x}\,dx$, numerically

Outcomes

After studying this unit you should be able to do the following.

- Interpret the following notation: scientific notation, $\mathbb{Z}$, $\mathbb{R}$, $\mathbb{C}$, $[a,b]$, $(a,b]$, $[a,b)$, (a,b), $|x|$, $f(x)$, $\exp(x)$, e^x, $\ln x$, $\sin x$, $\cos x$, $\tan x$, $\sec x$, $\operatorname{cosec} x$, $\cot x$, $\arccos x$, $\arcsin x$, $\arctan x$, $i\,(=\sqrt{-1})$, $\operatorname{Re}(z)$, $\operatorname{Im}(z)$, $\overline{z}$, $|z|$, e^z (for z in $\mathbb{C}$), $\langle r,\theta \rangle$, $\lim\limits_{h\to 0} f(h)$, $f'(x)$, $f''(x)$, $f^{(n)}(x)$, $\dfrac{dy}{dx}$, $\dfrac{d^2y}{dx^2}$, $\dfrac{d^ny}{dx^n}$, $\dot{x}(t)$, $\ddot{x}(t)$, $\int f(x)\,dx$, $\int_a^b f(x)\,dx$, $[F(x)]_a^b$.

- Interpret the following terminology: integer, real number, interval, decimal places, significant figures, rounding; variable, dependent variable, independent variable, parameter; function, domain, image set, codomain; linear function, quadratic function, polynomial function (and root of a polynomial equation); exponential function, logarithm function, power function, trigonometric function; composite function; complex number, complex conjugate, real and imaginary parts (of a complex number), modulus and argument (of a complex number); polar coordinates, polar form and exponential form (of a complex number), De Moivre's Theorem, Euler's formula; differentiation, derivative, Leibniz notation, Chain Rule (for differentiation), implicit differentiation, higher derivative; gradient of a function, stationary point, local maximum, local minimum, global maximum, global minimum, derivative of a complex-valued function; continuous function; integration, integral, integrand, indefinite integral, definite integral, arbitrary constant.

- Use the formulae for: the solution of a quadratic equation; the algebraic properties of indices (and the exponential function); the algebraic properties of logarithm functions; various trigonometric identities; multiplying complex numbers in polar form; finding powers in polar form; derivatives of standard functions; differentiating products, quotients and composite functions; standard integrals; integration by parts and by substitution.

  The formulae are all given in the Handbook.

- Solve two simultaneous linear equations by Gaussian elimination.

- Factorize quadratic functions.

- Sketch the graphs of linear, quadratic, exponential and trigonometric functions.

- Sketch the graphs of more general functions, including identifying stationary points and asymptotes.

- Use log–linear plots to recognize relationships of the form $y = Ae^{kx}$.

- Use log–log plots to recognize relationships of the form $y = Ax^b$.

- Add, subtract, multiply and divide complex numbers, and move between Cartesian, polar and exponential forms of a complex number.

- Find derived functions, using the table of standard derivatives and the rules for differentiating various types of combination of functions.

- Find indefinite integrals, using the table of standard integrals and (in simple cases) the rules for integration by substitution and for integration by parts.

- Find definite integrals (of suitable functions).

- Use the computer to: simplify and expand algebraic expressions, graph a function, solve an equation (numerically or symbolically), find derivatives, find integrals.

Solutions to the exercises

Section 1

1.1 (a) (i) 6.48235×10^4 (Count the number of places the decimal point is moved to the left to find the power of 10.)

(ii) 7.3×10^{-5}

(b) (i) y lies between $127.683 - 0.006 = 127.677$ and $127.683 + 0.006 = 127.689$; that is, in the interval

$$[127.677, 127.689].$$

(ii) We cannot be certain of the fifth significant figure (it could be either 7 or 8), so we can only give y as 127.7 (to four significant figures).

(c) The condition $|x - 2.763| < 5 \times 10^{-4}$ is equivalent to $-5 \times 10^{-4} < x - 2.763 < 5 \times 10^{-4}$.

So $\quad x < 2.763 + 5 \times 10^{-4} = 2.7635$

and $\quad x > 2.763 - 5 \times 10^{-4} = 2.7625$.

So $2.7625 < x < 2.7635$; that is, x lies in the interval

$$(2.7625, 2.7635).$$

Since 2.7635 does not lie in this interval, we can be certain that $x = 2.763$ to three decimal places.

Section 2

2.1 Because the reservoir is initially at 60% capacity, $V_0 = 0.6C$.

The volume V will have reduced to 20% of C when

$$0.2C = 0.6C - 10t, \quad \text{i.e. when } 0.4C = 10t.$$

Thus crisis measures will be needed when $t = 0.04C$.

(Note that, because of the domain conditions, this solution is valid only if $0.04C \leq 72\,000$, i.e. for $C \leq 1\,800\,000$.)

2.2 (a) We need

$$2000 = 5(-3600) + c = -18\,000 + c.$$

Hence $c = 2000 + 18\,000 = 20\,000$.

(b) (i) The cutter catches the boat when $X = Y$, i.e. when

$$7t = 5t + 20\,000.$$

This gives $2t = 20\,000$, so $t = 10\,000$.

10 000 seconds is 2 hours, 46 minutes and 40 seconds. So the cutter catches the boat at around 2.50 am.

(ii) At $t = 10\,000$, both X and Y are equal to 70 000. So the cutter catches the boat 70 km from A, which *is* inside territorial waters.

2.3 Multiplying the first equation by $\frac{3}{2}$ gives

$$3u - \frac{15}{2}v = \frac{57}{2}.$$

Subtracting this from the second equation gives

$$(4 + \tfrac{15}{2})v = -29 - \tfrac{57}{2},$$

i.e. $\frac{23}{2}v = -\frac{115}{2}$, so $v = -\frac{115}{23} = -5$.

Substituting this into the first equation gives

$$2u - 5(-5) = 19,$$

so $u = (19 - 25)/2 = -3$.

Thus the solution is $u = -3$, $v = -5$.

(It is good practice to check solutions where you can, and this is easily done here. With $u = -3$ and $v = -5$, we have

$$2u - 5v = 2(-3) - 5(-5) = -6 + 25 = 19,$$

$$3u + 4v = 3(-3) + 4(-5) = -9 - 20 = -29,$$

so these values of u and v do satisfy the given equations.)

2.4 (a) Using formula (2.8), we obtain

$$\begin{aligned}
x &= \frac{-7 \pm \sqrt{7^2 - 4 \times 2 \times (-4)}}{2 \times 2} \\
&= \frac{-7 \pm \sqrt{49 + 32}}{4} \\
&= \frac{-7 \pm 9}{4} = \tfrac{1}{2} \text{ or } -4.
\end{aligned}$$

(Again, these solutions can be checked by substitution into the equation. For example, with $x = -4$,

$$2x^2 + 7x - 4 = 32 - 28 - 4 = 0,$$

as required.)

(b) We obtain $x = -3$ or 2.

2.5 $\quad \begin{aligned}
x &= \frac{-2k \pm \sqrt{4k^2 - 4m(mw^2)}}{2m} \\
&= \frac{-2k \pm 2\sqrt{k^2 - m^2w^2}}{2m} \\
&= -\frac{k}{m} \pm \frac{\sqrt{k^2 - m^2w^2}}{m} \\
&= -\frac{k}{m} \pm \frac{\sqrt{k^2 - m^2w^2}}{\sqrt{m^2}} \\
&= -\frac{k}{m} \pm \sqrt{\frac{k^2 - m^2w^2}{m^2}} \\
&= -\frac{k}{m} \pm \sqrt{\frac{k^2}{m^2} - w^2}.
\end{aligned}$

Putting $K = k/m$, this gives $x = -K \pm \sqrt{K^2 - w^2}$, as required.

2.6 (a) $a^3 a^5 = a^{3+5} = a^8$

(b) $a^3 / a^5 = a^{3-5} = a^{-2}$ (or $1/a^2$)

(c) $(a^3)^5 = a^{3 \times 5} = a^{15}$

(d) $(2^{-1})^4 \times 4^3 = 2^{-4} \times (2^2)^3 = 2^{-4} \times 2^6 = 2^2 = 4$

(e) $8^{-1/3} = 1/8^{1/3} = 1/\sqrt[3]{8} = \frac{1}{2}$

(f) $16^{3/4} = (16^{1/4})^3 = (\sqrt[4]{16})^3 = 2^3 = 8$

(g) $(\frac{4}{9})^{3/2} = \left(\sqrt{\frac{4}{9}}\right)^3 = (\frac{2}{3})^3 = \frac{8}{27}$

(h) $(16x^4)^{1/2} = 16^{1/2}(x^4)^{1/2} = \sqrt{16}\,x^{4 \times 1/2} = 4x^2$

2.7 (a) $\ln 7 + \ln 4 - \ln 14 = \ln(7 \times 4 \div 14) = \ln 2$

(b) $\ln a + 2 \ln b - \ln(a^2 b) = \ln a + \ln(b^2) - \ln(a^2 b)$
$$= \ln\big(a \times b^2 \div (a^2 b)\big)$$
$$= \ln(b/a) \quad (\text{or } \ln b - \ln a)$$

(c) $e^x \times (e^y)^2 \div e^{2x} = e^x \times e^{2y} \div e^{2x}$
$$= e^{x+2y-2x} = e^{2y-x}$$

(d) $\ln(e^x \times e^y) = \ln(e^{x+y}) = x + y$

(Alternatively, $\ln(e^x \times e^y) = \ln(e^x) + \ln(e^y) = x + y$.)

To simplify the expression in part (d), we first rearranged it in the form $\ln(e^{something})$, which just equals *something*.

In parts (e)–(g), we first rearrange the expression as $e^{\ln(something)}$, which also just equals *something*.

(e) $e^{2 \ln x} = e^{\ln(x^2)} = x^2$

(f) $e^{-2 \ln x} = e^{\ln(x^{-2})} = x^{-2}$ (or $1/x^2$)

(g) $\exp(2 \ln x + \ln(x+1)) = \exp(\ln(x^2 \times (x+1)))$
$$= x^2(x+1)$$

(Alternatively, $\exp(2 \ln x + \ln(x+1))$
$= \exp(\ln(x^2)) \times \exp(\ln(x+1)) = x^2(x+1)$.)

2.8 Taking logs of $a^x = e^{kx}$ gives
$$\ln(a^x) = \ln(e^{kx}), \quad \text{i.e. } x \ln a = kx.$$
This holds for all x so long as
$$k = \ln a.$$

2.9 (a) Taking exponentials of each side of
$$\ln y = 2.83 \ln x + 0.37,$$
we obtain
$$\exp(\ln y) = \exp(2.83 \ln x + 0.37),$$
i.e. $y = \exp(\ln(x^{2.83})) \times \exp(0.37) = 1.4x^{2.83}$.

(b) If $\ln y = a \ln x + b$, then taking exponentials gives
$$\exp(\ln y) = \exp(a \ln x + b),$$
i.e. $y = \exp(\ln(x^a)) \times e^b = e^b x^a = cx^a$, where $c = e^b$ is a positive constant.

2.10 (a) (i) $f(g(x)) = f(1 - x^3)$
$$= e^{-(1-x^3)} = e^{x^3 - 1}$$

(ii) $g(f(x)) = g(e^{-x}) = 1 - (e^{-x})^3 = 1 - e^{-3x}$

(b) We can obtain $h(x)$ in two steps.

Step 1   Calculate $y = 4 + 9x^2$.
Step 2   Apply y^{-4} to the result of Step 1.

Then $h(x) = g(f(x))$, where $g(x) = x^{-4}$ and $f(x) = 4 + 9x^2$. (We need to exclude $x = 0$ from the domain of g, but $f(x)$ is never equal to 0, so this is not a problem.)

Section 3

3.1 (a) The figure shows a circle of radius 1, and radii rotated through 0 (OA) and $\frac{\pi}{2}$ (OB). We see from the figure that A has coordinates $(1, 0) = (\cos 0, \sin 0)$, and B has coordinates $(0, 1) = (\cos \frac{\pi}{2}, \sin \frac{\pi}{2})$. Therefore
$$\sin 0 = 0, \quad \cos 0 = 1, \quad \sin \tfrac{\pi}{2} = 1, \quad \cos \tfrac{\pi}{2} = 0.$$

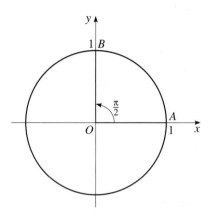

(b) Since $\sin 0 = 0$, $\operatorname{cosec} 0$ and $\cot 0$ are not defined. We have
$$\tan 0 = 0 \quad \text{and} \quad \sec 0 = 1.$$
Since $\cos \frac{\pi}{2} = 0$, $\tan \frac{\pi}{2}$ and $\sec \frac{\pi}{2}$ are not defined. We have
$$\cot \tfrac{\pi}{2} = 0 \quad \text{and} \quad \operatorname{cosec} \tfrac{\pi}{2} = 1.$$

(c) We obtain:
$$\sin \tfrac{\pi}{6} = \tfrac{1}{2}, \quad \cos \tfrac{\pi}{6} = \tfrac{\sqrt{3}}{2}, \quad \tan \tfrac{\pi}{6} = \tfrac{1}{\sqrt{3}},$$
$$\operatorname{cosec} \tfrac{\pi}{6} = 2, \quad \sec \tfrac{\pi}{6} = \tfrac{2}{\sqrt{3}}, \quad \cot \tfrac{\pi}{6} = \sqrt{3};$$
$$\sin \tfrac{\pi}{4} = \tfrac{1}{\sqrt{2}}, \quad \cos \tfrac{\pi}{4} = \tfrac{1}{\sqrt{2}}, \quad \tan \tfrac{\pi}{4} = 1,$$
$$\operatorname{cosec} \tfrac{\pi}{4} = \sqrt{2}, \quad \sec \tfrac{\pi}{4} = \sqrt{2}, \quad \cot \tfrac{\pi}{4} = 1;$$
$$\sin \tfrac{\pi}{3} = \tfrac{\sqrt{3}}{2}, \quad \cos \tfrac{\pi}{3} = \tfrac{1}{2}, \quad \tan \tfrac{\pi}{3} = \sqrt{3},$$
$$\operatorname{cosec} \tfrac{\pi}{3} = \tfrac{2}{\sqrt{3}}, \quad \sec \tfrac{\pi}{3} = 2, \quad \cot \tfrac{\pi}{3} = \tfrac{1}{\sqrt{3}}.$$

(d) $\sin \theta = 0$ if $\theta = 0$, but also if θ differs from 0 by $\pm 2\pi$, $\pm 4\pi$, $\pm 6\pi$, and so on. Also, $\sin \theta = 0$ if $\theta = \pi$, or θ differs from π by a multiple of 2π. In general, $\sin \theta = 0$ if $\theta = n\pi$, where $n \in \mathbb{Z}$.

3.2 (a) One solution is $\arcsin 0.8 = 0.93$ (to two decimal places). Looking at the graph of $y = \sin \theta$ below, we see that it is symmetric about $\theta = \frac{\pi}{2}$. So there is also a solution of $\sin \theta = 0.8$ at $\theta = \pi - 0.93 = 2.21$ (to two decimal places). These are the only solutions with θ between 0 and 2π. (If θ is between π and 2π, $\sin \theta$ is negative.) The other solutions are obtained by adding multiples of 2π to these two. The solutions in the required range are (to two decimal places):
$$0.93, \quad 2.21, \quad 7.21, \quad 8.50, \quad 13.49, \quad 14.78.$$

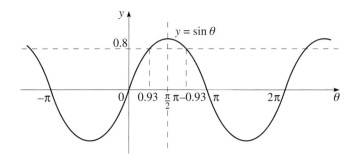

(b) We saw in Exercise 3.1(c) that $\tan \frac{\pi}{4} = 1$, so $\theta = \frac{\pi}{4}$ is one solution. We can see from the graph of tan (Figure 3.5) that there is one solution of this equation in the range $-\frac{\pi}{2}$ to $\frac{\pi}{2}$, and that other solutions are obtained by adding multiples of π to this. We can express the full set of solutions as

$\frac{\pi}{4} + n\pi$,

where $n \in \mathbb{Z}$.

3.3 (a) (i) $\sin 2\theta = \sin(\theta + \theta)$
$$= \sin\theta \cos\theta + \cos\theta \sin\theta$$
$$= 2\sin\theta \cos\theta$$

(ii) $\cos 2\theta = \cos(\theta + \theta) = \cos\theta \cos\theta - \sin\theta \sin\theta$
$$= \cos^2\theta - \sin^2\theta$$

(b) (i) $\sin(2\pi - \theta) = \sin 2\pi \cos\theta - \cos 2\pi \sin\theta$
$$= 0 \times \cos\theta - 1 \times \sin\theta = -\sin\theta$$

(ii) $\cos(2\pi - \theta) = \cos 2\pi \cos\theta + \sin 2\pi \sin\theta$
$$= 1 \times \cos\theta + 0 \times \sin\theta = \cos\theta$$

(iii) $\sin(\pi - \theta) = \sin\pi \cos\theta - \cos\pi \sin\theta$
$$= 0 \times \cos\theta - (-1) \times \sin\theta = \sin\theta$$

(iv) $\cos(\pi - \theta) = \cos\pi \cos\theta + \sin\pi \sin\theta$
$$= (-1) \times \cos\theta + 0 \times \sin\theta = -\cos\theta$$

(v) $\sin(\frac{\pi}{2} - \theta) = \sin\frac{\pi}{2} \cos\theta - \cos\frac{\pi}{2} \sin\theta$
$$= 1 \times \cos\theta - 0 \times \sin\theta = \cos\theta$$

(vi) $\cos(\frac{\pi}{2} - \theta) = \cos\frac{\pi}{2} \cos\theta + \sin\frac{\pi}{2} \sin\theta$
$$= 0 \times \cos\theta + 1 \times \sin\theta = \sin\theta$$

For $0 < \theta < \frac{\pi}{2}$, the results of parts (v) and (vi) can be confirmed by examination of a right-angled triangle.

(vii) $\cos\left(\frac{3\pi}{2} + x\right) = \cos\frac{3\pi}{2} \cos x - \sin\frac{3\pi}{2} \sin x$
$$= 0 \times \cos x - (-1) \times \sin x = \sin x$$

Section 4

4.1 (a) $\bar{v} = 3 + 4i$

(b) $|v| = \sqrt{3^2 + 4^2} = 5$

(c) $v - w = 1 - 3i$

(d) $vw = (3 - 4i)(2 - i) = 6 - 8i - 3i + 4i^2 = 2 - 11i$

(e) $\dfrac{w}{v} = \dfrac{w\bar{v}}{|v|^2} = \dfrac{(2-i)(3+4i)}{25} = \frac{10}{25} + \frac{5}{25}i = \frac{2}{5} + \frac{1}{5}i$

(f) $\dfrac{1}{w} = \dfrac{\bar{w}}{|w|^2} = \dfrac{2+i}{5} = \frac{2}{5} + \frac{1}{5}i$

(g) $w^2 = (2 - i)(2 - i) = 3 - 4i$

(h) $2w - 3v = 4 - 2i - (9 - 12i) = -5 + 10i$

4.2 We obtain
$$x = \frac{-2 \pm \sqrt{4 - 8}}{4} = -\frac{1}{2} \pm \frac{1}{2}i.$$

4.3

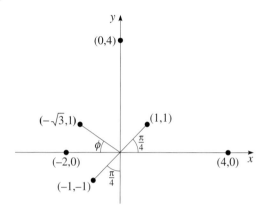

(a) $\langle 2, \pi \rangle$

(b) $\langle \sqrt{2}, \frac{\pi}{4} \rangle$

(c) $\langle \sqrt{2}, -\frac{3\pi}{4} \rangle$

(d) $\langle 4, 0 \rangle$

(e) $\langle 4, \frac{\pi}{2} \rangle$

(f) This is $\langle 2, \pi - \phi \rangle$, where ϕ is as shown in the figure. Now $\tan\phi = \frac{1}{\sqrt{3}}$, so $\phi = \frac{\pi}{6}$ (see Solution 3.1(c)). So $(-\sqrt{3}, 1)$ has polar coordinates $\langle 2, \frac{5\pi}{6} \rangle$.

4.4 $z = 2\left(\cos\left(-\frac{\pi}{4}\right) + i\sin\left(-\frac{\pi}{4}\right)\right) = 2\left(\frac{1}{\sqrt{2}} - \frac{1}{\sqrt{2}}i\right)$
$$= \sqrt{2}(1 - i)$$

4.5 This solution is identical to the solution to Exercise 4.3.

4.6 First express $1 - i$ in polar form, as $\langle \sqrt{2}, -\frac{\pi}{4} \rangle$. Then
$$\langle \sqrt{2}, -\tfrac{\pi}{4} \rangle^{20} = \langle (\sqrt{2})^{20}, -\tfrac{20\pi}{4} \rangle = \langle 2^{10}, -5\pi \rangle$$
$$= \langle 1024, \pi \rangle,$$

adding 6π to the argument to obtain its principal value. Returning to Cartesian form, we obtain
$$(1 - i)^{20} = 1024(\cos\pi + i\sin\pi) = -1024.$$

4.7 $z = re^{i\theta}$, so
$$\text{Re}(ze^{i\omega t}) = \text{Re}(re^{i\theta}e^{i\omega t})$$
$$= \text{Re}(re^{i(\omega t + \theta)})$$
$$= r\cos(\omega t + \theta).$$

Section 5

5.1 (a) $\dot{x}(t) = -21\sin(3t+2)$,
$$\ddot{x}(t) = -63\cos(3t+2).$$

(b) Note that $7\cos(3t+2) = x(t) - 5$, so
$$-63\cos(3t+2) = -9(x(t)-5).$$
Hence we have $\ddot{x}(t) = -9(x(t)-5)$, or equivalently
$$\ddot{x}(t) + 9x(t) = 45.$$

5.2 The rate at which the wage bill will be rising is given by
$$\frac{dB}{dt} = 10^5(0.04)\exp(0.04t) = 4000e^{0.04t}.$$
As a fraction of the future wage bill, B, the rate of rise dB/dt is
$$\frac{1}{B}\frac{dB}{dt} = \frac{10^5(0.04)\exp(0.04t)}{10^5\exp(0.04t)} = 0.04.$$
So the rate of rise is 4% per year.

5.3 (a) $\dfrac{dy}{dx} = (-0.9)(-0.5)\exp(-0.5x)$
$$= 0.45\exp(-0.5x).$$

(b) $F'(x) = 12x^3 - 4$, so putting $x = 2$ gives
$$F'(2) = 12 \times 2^3 - 4 = 92.$$

(c) $\dfrac{dy}{dt} = \dfrac{1}{t}$, and then $\dfrac{d^2y}{dt^2} = -\dfrac{1}{t^2}$.

(d) $F'(x) = 6\sec(2x)\tan(2x) - 12\sin(-3x)$.
Hence
$$F'\left(\tfrac{\pi}{6}\right) = 6\sec\tfrac{\pi}{3}\tan\tfrac{\pi}{3} - 12\sin\left(-\tfrac{\pi}{2}\right) = 12\sqrt{3} + 12.$$

(e) $g'(t) = -3a\sin(3t+\phi) + 3b\cos(3t+\phi)$, and then $g''(t) = -9a\cos(3t+\phi) - 9b\sin(3t+\phi)$, so
$$g''(0) = -9a\cos\phi - 9b\sin\phi.$$

5.4 (a) $v'(z) = 3\sec^2 z - 2\sin z$.

(b) $\dfrac{dy}{dt} = 3A\cos 3t - 3B\sin 3t$.
The value of this at $t = \tfrac{\pi}{12}$ is
$$3A\cos\tfrac{\pi}{4} - 3B\sin\tfrac{\pi}{4} = 3A/\sqrt{2} - 3B/\sqrt{2}$$
$$= \tfrac{3}{\sqrt{2}}(A - B).$$

(c) We need to find the fourth derivative:
$$f'(t) = 6\cos 3t, \quad f''(t) = -18\sin 3t,$$
$$f^{(3)}(t) = -54\cos 3t, \quad f^{(4)}(t) = 162\sin 3t.$$
Since $\sin\tfrac{3\pi}{2} = -1$, we obtain $f^{(4)}\left(\tfrac{\pi}{2}\right) = -162$.

(d) $f'(y) = \dfrac{3}{1 + 9y^2}$.

(e) $\dfrac{dz}{dx} = \dfrac{c}{cx+d}$, so $\dfrac{dz}{dx} = \dfrac{c}{d}$ when $x = 0$.

5.5 (a) This is a quotient. We obtain
$$\frac{dy}{dx} = \frac{(\frac{1}{x})(x^2+1) - (\ln x)(2x)}{(x^2+1)^2} = \frac{x + x^{-1} - 2x\ln x}{(x^2+1)^2}.$$

(b) $f'(t) = 5t^4\ln(3t+4) + \dfrac{3t^5}{3t+4}$.

(c) $g'(t) = A\sin(At+C) + (At+B)A\cos(At+C)$, so
$$g'(0) = A\sin C + AB\cos C.$$

(d) For $x(t) = e^{-3t}\sin 4t$, we want $\dot{x}(t)$ and $\ddot{x}(t)$. Using the Product Rule:
$$\dot{x}(t) = -3e^{-3t}\sin 4t + e^{-3t}(4\cos 4t)$$
$$= e^{-3t}(4\cos 4t - 3\sin 4t).$$
Using the Product Rule again:
$$\ddot{x}(t) = -3e^{-3t}(4\cos 4t - 3\sin 4t)$$
$$+ e^{-3t}(-16\sin 4t - 12\cos 4t)$$
$$= e^{-3t}(-7\sin 4t - 24\cos 4t).$$

5.6 In each case, we suggest an intermediate variable, u, but (except in part (a)) omit details.

(a) Setting $u = t^2$, we obtain $y = e^u$, $dy/du = e^u$ and $du/dt = 2t$, so
$$\frac{dy}{dt} = \frac{dy}{du}\frac{du}{dt} = e^u 2t = 2t\exp(t^2).$$

(b) Setting $u = 3x^3 + 4$, we obtain
$$f'(x) = 6(3x^3+4)^5(9x^2) = 54x^2(3x^3+4)^5.$$

(c) Setting $u = 3v + 4$, we obtain
$$\frac{dz}{dv} = 3\sec^2(3v+4).$$

(d) Setting $u = 4 - z^2$, we obtain
$$g'(z) = \tfrac{1}{2}(4-z^2)^{-1/2}(-2z) = \frac{-z}{\sqrt{4-z^2}}.$$

(e) Setting $u = 1 + 2x^2$, we have
$$f(x) = (1+2x^2)^{-3/2} = u^{-3/2}$$
(see Example 2.3), so
$$f'(x) = -\tfrac{3}{2}(1+2x^2)^{-5/2}(4x) = \frac{-6x}{(\sqrt{1+2x^2})^5}.$$

5.7 (a) This is a composite function, with
$$y = \sec u, \quad u = \frac{x}{x^2+1}.$$
Here u is a quotient, and
$$\frac{du}{dx} = \frac{1(x^2+1) - x(2x)}{(x^2+1)^2} = \frac{1-x^2}{(x^2+1)^2}.$$
Then, using the Chain Rule,
$$\frac{dy}{dx} = \frac{dy}{du}\frac{du}{dx}$$
$$= \sec u\tan u\,\frac{1-x^2}{(x^2+1)^2}$$
$$= \frac{1-x^2}{(x^2+1)^2}\sec\left(\frac{x}{x^2+1}\right)\tan\left(\frac{x}{x^2+1}\right).$$

(b) This is a product, but the second part of the product is a composite function. If $v = \exp(t^3 + 1)$, then

$$\frac{dv}{dt} = 3t^2 \exp(t^3 + 1)$$

(using the intermediate function $u = t^3 + 1$). Then, using the Product Rule,

$$\frac{dz}{dt} = 2t \exp(t^3 + 1) + t^2(3t^2 \exp(t^3 + 1))$$

$$= (3t^4 + 2t) \exp(t^3 + 1).$$

5.8 **(a)** **(i)** The Product Rule gives

$$\frac{d}{dx}(x^2 y) = 2xy + x^2 \frac{dy}{dx}.$$

(ii) The Composite Rule gives

$$\frac{d}{dx}(y^3) = 3y^2 \frac{dy}{dx}.$$

(b) Using implicit differentiation, we obtain

$$3x^2 + 2xy + x^2 \frac{dy}{dx} + 3y^2 \frac{dy}{dx} = 0.$$

When $x = -1$ and $y = 1$, this gives

$$3 - 2 + \frac{dy}{dx} + 3\frac{dy}{dx} = 0.$$

Hence $dy/dx = -\frac{1}{4}$, and the required gradient is $-\frac{1}{4}$.

5.9 We have $f'(t) = -2\sin 2t + 2i\cos 2t.$
Then $f''(t) = -4\cos 2t - 4i\sin 2t.$

5.10 To test for stationary points, use the Product Rule to find

$$y'(x) = -2e^{-\frac{1}{2}x} + \frac{1}{2}(2(x+1))e^{-\frac{1}{2}x} = (x-1)e^{-\frac{1}{2}x}.$$

So $y'(x) = 0$ only at $x = 1$. The derivative is negative if $x < 1$ and positive if $x > 1$, so this is a local minimum. We have $y(1) = 2.574$ (to three decimal places).

5.11 **(a)** $f(v) = 0$ only when $v = 0$.

The denominator $4 + 1.5v + 0.008v^2$ is positive for all $v \geq 0$, so $f(v)$ is defined for all $v \geq 0$.

As $v \to \infty$, $f(v) \to 0$.

To find any stationary points, differentiate $f(v)$ using the Quotient Rule, to obtain

$$f'(v) = \frac{(4 + 1.5v + 0.008v^2) - v(1.5 + 0.016v)}{(4 + 1.5v + 0.008v^2)^2}$$

$$= \frac{4 - 0.008v^2}{(4 + 1.5v + 0.008v^2)^2}.$$

This is 0 when $v = \pm\sqrt{500} = \pm 22.36$ (to two decimal places).

The negative stationary point is outside the domain ($v \geq 0$), so we need consider only $v = 22.36$. For $v < 22.36$, $f'(v) > 0$, while for $v > 22.36$, $f'(v) < 0$. Therefore $v = 22.36$ is a local maximum. We have $f(22.36) = 0.538$ (to three decimal places).

A sketch graph of f is shown below.

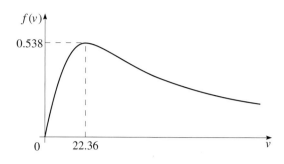

(b) From the graph we see that the global maximum of f occurs at the local maximum, i.e. $v = \sqrt{500}$. The global minimum occurs at the endpoint of the domain, i.e. $v = 0$.

Section 6

In all solutions for this section, c is an arbitrary constant.

6.1 **(a)** Using the Product Rule for derivatives,

$$\frac{d}{dx}\left(-\frac{x}{a}\cos ax + \frac{1}{a^2}\sin ax + c\right)$$

$$= -\frac{1}{a}\cos ax + \left(-\frac{x}{a}\right)(-a\sin ax) + \frac{a}{a^2}\cos ax$$

$$= x\sin ax.$$

Therefore

$$\int x\sin ax\, dx = -\frac{x}{a}\cos ax + \frac{1}{a^2}\sin ax + c,$$

so verifying the given integral.

(b) Using the Composite Rule for derivatives,

$$\frac{d}{dx}\left(-\frac{1}{a}\ln(\cos ax) + c\right)$$

$$= \left(-\frac{1}{a}\right)\frac{1}{\cos ax}\frac{d}{dx}(\cos ax)$$

$$= \left(-\frac{1}{a}\right)\frac{-a\sin ax}{\cos ax}$$

$$= \tan ax,$$

so verifying the given integral.

6.2 **(a)** If $x = \tan y$, then, differentiating with respect to x, we obtain

$$1 = \frac{d}{dx}(\tan y) = \frac{d}{dy}(\tan y)\frac{dy}{dx} = \sec^2 y\frac{dy}{dx}.$$

Then, using the formula $\sec^2 y = 1 + \tan^2 y$, and the fact that $x = \tan y$, we obtain

$$1 = (1 + \tan^2 y)\frac{dy}{dx} = (1 + x^2)\frac{dy}{dx}.$$

Therefore

$$\frac{dy}{dx} = \frac{1}{1 + x^2}.$$

Now, if $x = \tan y$, then $y = \arctan x$, so

$$\int \frac{1}{1 + x^2}\, dx = \arctan x + c.$$

(b) If $x = \sin y$, then, differentiating with respect to x,

$$1 = \cos y \, \frac{dy}{dx}.$$

Using $\sin^2 y + \cos^2 y = 1$, and the fact that $\cos y > 0$ because $-\frac{\pi}{2} < y < \frac{\pi}{2}$, we have

$$\cos y \, \frac{dy}{dx} = \sqrt{1 - \sin^2 y} \, \frac{dy}{dx}$$

$$= \sqrt{1 - x^2} \, \frac{dy}{dx} \quad (\text{since } \sin y = x).$$

Therefore

$$\frac{dy}{dx} = \frac{1}{\sqrt{1 - x^2}}.$$

Now, if $x = \sin y$, then $y = \arcsin x$, so

$$\int \frac{1}{\sqrt{1 - x^2}} \, dx = \arcsin x + c.$$

This corresponds with the Handbook entry for $\int \frac{1}{\sqrt{a^2 - x^2}} \, dx$, with $a = 1$.

6.3 We have

$$\int \cos^2 ax \, dx = \tfrac{1}{2} \int (1 + \cos 2ax) \, dx$$

$$= \tfrac{1}{2} \left(x + \frac{1}{2a} \sin 2ax \right) + c$$

$$= \tfrac{1}{2}x + \frac{1}{4a} \sin 2ax + c.$$

6.4 (a) $\frac{1}{5}e^{5x} + c$

(b) $2 \tan 3t + c$

(c) This does not quite match a Handbook entry as it stands. We have $36 + 4x^2 = 4(9 + x^2)$, so

$$\int \frac{1}{36 + 4v^2} \, dv = \int \frac{1}{4(9 + v^2)} \, dv$$

$$= \tfrac{1}{4} \int \frac{1}{9 + v^2} \, dv$$

$$= \tfrac{1}{4} \left(\tfrac{1}{3} \arctan \left(\frac{v}{3} \right) \right) + c$$

$$= \tfrac{1}{12} \arctan \left(\frac{v}{3} \right) + c.$$

(d) For $y < \frac{3}{2}$, the integrand is positive, and we have

$$\int \frac{1}{3 - 2y} \, dy = -\tfrac{1}{2} \ln(3 - 2y) + c.$$

(e) For $y > \frac{3}{2}$, the integrand is negative, and we have

$$\int \frac{1}{3 - 2y} \, dy = -\tfrac{1}{2} \ln(-3 + 2y) + c$$

$$= -\tfrac{1}{2} \ln(2y - 3) + c.$$

6.5 (a) $-3 \sin(-2t) - 2 \cos 4t + c$.   Note that you can use $\cos \theta = \cos(-\theta)$ to simplify the integrand (or use $\sin \theta = -\sin(-\theta)$ to simplify the result) to obtain $3 \sin 2t - 2 \cos 4t + c$.

(b) $\arcsin(t/3) + c$

(c) $\displaystyle \int \frac{5t^3 + 7}{t} \, dt = \int \left(5t^2 + \frac{7}{t} \right) dt$

$$= \tfrac{5}{3}t^3 + 7 \ln(-t) + c \quad (t < 0).$$

(d) For $t > 0$,

$$\int \left(2 \ln(4t) - \frac{2}{t} \right) dt = 2t(\ln(4t) - 1) - 2 \ln t + c.$$

(e) Choose $a = 1$, $b = -1$ in the standard integral, and note that we are in the case $-1 < x < 1$:

$$\int \frac{1}{(x - 1)(x + 1)} \, dx = \tfrac{1}{2} \ln \left(\frac{1 - x}{x + 1} \right) + c.$$

6.6 (a) Using $v^2 - k^2 = (v - k)(v + k)$, and taking $a = k$ and $b = -k$ in the Handbook entry for $\int \frac{1}{(x - a)(x - b)} \, dx$, we obtain

$$\int \frac{1}{v^2 - k^2} \, dv = \int \frac{1}{(v - k)(v + k)} \, dv$$

$$= \frac{1}{2k} \ln \left(\frac{k - v}{v + k} \right) + c \quad (-k < v < k).$$

(b) Since $a - bv^2 = -b(v^2 - a/b)$, we can use part (a) with $k = \sqrt{a/b}$ to obtain (for $-\sqrt{a/b} < v < \sqrt{a/b}$)

$$\int \frac{1}{a - bv^2} \, dv = \frac{1}{-b} \int \frac{1}{v^2 - a/b} \, dv$$

$$= \frac{1}{-b} \left(\frac{1}{2\sqrt{a/b}} \right) \ln \left(\frac{\sqrt{a/b} - v}{v + \sqrt{a/b}} \right) + c$$

$$= -\frac{1}{2\sqrt{ab}} \ln \left(\frac{\sqrt{a} - v\sqrt{b}}{v\sqrt{b} + \sqrt{a}} \right) + c.$$

6.7 (a) If $u = 2 + 4y^3$, then $du/dy = 12y^2$. So

$$\int y^2 \exp(2 + 4y^3) \, dy = \tfrac{1}{12} \int 12y^2 \exp(2 + 4y^3) \, dy$$

$$= \tfrac{1}{12} \int \exp u \, du$$

$$= \tfrac{1}{12} \exp u + c$$

$$= \tfrac{1}{12} \exp(2 + 4y^3) + c.$$

(b) If $u = \sin y$, then $du/dy = \cos y$. So

$$\int \cos y \sin^2 y \, dy = \int u^2 \, du = \tfrac{1}{3}u^3 + c = \tfrac{1}{3} \sin^3 y + c.$$

(c) If $u = 1 - t^2$, then $du/dt = -2t$. So

$$\int t\sqrt{1 - t^2} \, dt = -\tfrac{1}{2} \int -2t\sqrt{1 - t^2} \, dt$$

$$= -\tfrac{1}{2} \int u^{1/2} \, du$$

$$= -\tfrac{1}{2} (\tfrac{2}{3}u^{3/2}) + c$$

$$= -\tfrac{1}{3} (\sqrt{1 - t^2})^3 + c.$$

(d) If $u = 1 + x^2$, then $du/dx = 2x$. So

$$\int \frac{x}{1 + x^2} \, dx = \tfrac{1}{2} \int \frac{2x}{1 + x^2} \, dx = \tfrac{1}{2} \ln(1 + x^2) + c,$$

since the integrand is of the form $g'(x)/g(x)$ with $g(x) > 0$.

(e) If $u = 1 + \sin^2 t$, then $du/dt = 2\sin t \cos t = \sin 2t$, using the trigonometric formula for $\sin 2t$. So the integrand is of the form $g'(x)/g(x)$ with $g(x) > 0$, and hence

$$\int \frac{\sin 2t}{1 + \sin^2 t}\, dt = \ln(1 + \sin^2 t) + c.$$

(f) Using Equation (6.5) with $g(y) = 1 - y^2$, so that $g'(y) = -2y$, we have (for $y \neq \pm 1$)

$$\int \frac{y}{1 - y^2}\, dy = -\frac{1}{2}\int \frac{-2y}{1 - y^2}\, dy = -\frac{1}{2}\ln|1 - y^2| + c.$$

6.8 (a) Take $f(x) = x$ and $g'(x) = e^{-x}$, so $f'(x) = 1$ and $g(x) = -e^{-x}$. Then

$$\int xe^{-x}\, dx = x(-e^{-x}) - \int (-e^{-x})\, dx$$
$$= -xe^{-x} + \int e^{-x}\, dx$$
$$= -xe^{-x} - e^{-x} + c$$
$$= -(x+1)e^{-x} + c.$$

(b) Take $f(x) = x^2$ and $g'(x) = e^{-x}$, so $f'(x) = 2x$ and $g(x) = -e^{-x}$. Then

$$\int x^2 e^{-x}\, dx = x^2(-e^{-x}) - \int 2x(-e^{-x})\, dx$$
$$= -x^2 e^{-x} + 2\int xe^{-x}\, dx$$
$$= -x^2 e^{-x} + 2(-(x+1)e^{-x} + b)$$

(by part (a), where b is an arbitrary constant)
$$= -(x^2 + 2x + 2)e^{-x} + c$$

(where $c = 2b$ is an arbitrary constant).

6.9 $\displaystyle\int_0^{3/2} \frac{1}{9 + 4z^2}\, dz = \frac{1}{4}\int_0^{3/2} \frac{1}{\frac{9}{4} + z^2}\, dz$

$$= \frac{1}{4}\left[\frac{1}{\frac{3}{2}}\arctan\left(\frac{x}{\frac{3}{2}}\right)\right]_0^{3/2}$$
$$= \frac{1}{6}(\arctan 1 - \arctan 0)$$
$$= \frac{1}{6}\left(\frac{\pi}{4} - 0\right) = \frac{\pi}{24}$$

6.10 (a) $\displaystyle\int_0^{500} 2\pi r(0.1 + 0.002r)\, dr$

$$= \pi\left[0.1r^2 + 0.004\left(\frac{r^3}{3}\right)\right]_0^{500}$$
$$= \pi\left(0.1 \times 500^2 + 0.004 \times \frac{500^3}{3}\right)$$
$$= 6.0 \times 10^5 \quad \text{(to two significant figures)}.$$

(b) Since $\exp(a - 2y) = e^a e^{-2y}$, we have

$$\int \exp(a - 2y)\, dy = e^a \int e^{-2y}\, dy$$
$$= -\frac{1}{2}e^a e^{-2y} + c$$
$$= -\frac{1}{2}\exp(a - 2y) + c.$$

(The same result can be obtained using integration by substitution with $u = a - 2y$.)

(c) For $0 \leq u \leq 1$, we have $3u + 5 > 0$, so

$$\int_0^1 \frac{1}{3u + 5}\, du = \left[\frac{1}{3}\ln(3u + 5)\right]_0^1$$
$$= \frac{1}{3}(\ln 8 - \ln 5) = \frac{1}{3}\ln\frac{8}{5}.$$

(d) For $-3 \leq u \leq -2$, we have $3u + 5 < 0$, so

$$\int_{-3}^{-2} \frac{1}{3u + 5}\, du = \left[\frac{1}{3}\ln(-3u - 5)\right]_{-3}^{-2}$$
$$= \frac{1}{3}(\ln 1 - \ln 4) = -\frac{1}{3}\ln 4.$$

(e) Substitute $u = 3t + a$, so $du/dt = 3$. Then

$$\int \ln(3t + a)\, dt = \frac{1}{3}\int 3\ln(3t + a)\, dt$$
$$= \frac{1}{3}\int \ln u\, du$$
$$= \frac{1}{3}u(\ln|u| - 1) + c$$
$$= \frac{1}{3}(3t + a)(\ln|3t + a| - 1) + c.$$

(f) Use integration by parts with $f(t) = t$ and $g'(t) = \cos(3t + a)$, so $f'(t) = 1$ and $g(t) = \frac{1}{3}\sin(3t + a)$. Then

$$\int t\cos(3t + a)\, dt$$
$$= t(\frac{1}{3}\sin(3t + a)) - \int \frac{1}{3}\sin(3t + a)\, dt$$
$$= \frac{1}{3}t\sin(3t + a) + \frac{1}{9}\cos(3t + a) + c.$$

(g) We have

$$\frac{d}{dx}(3 + \cos 2x) = -2\sin 2x$$

and $3 + \cos 2x > 0$ for all x, so

$$\int_0^{\frac{\pi}{4}} \frac{\sin 2x}{3 + \cos 2x}\, dx = -\frac{1}{2}\int_0^{\frac{\pi}{4}} \frac{-2\sin 2x}{3 + \cos 2x}\, dx$$
$$= -\frac{1}{2}[\ln(3 + \cos 2x)]_0^{\frac{\pi}{4}}$$
$$= -\frac{1}{2}(\ln 3 - \ln 4)$$
$$= -\frac{1}{2}\ln\frac{3}{4} = \frac{1}{2}\ln\frac{4}{3}.$$

UNIT 2   First-order differential equations

Study guide for Unit 2

This unit introduces the topic of differential equations. It is an important field of study, and several subsequent units are also devoted to it. There are many applications of differential equations throughout the course.

The subject is developed without assuming that you have come across it before, but the unit assumes that you have previously had a basic grounding in calculus. In particular, you will need to have a good grasp of the basic rules for differentiation and integration. (These were revised in *Unit 1* of this course.)

From the point of view of later studies, Sections 3 and 4 contain the most important material.

The recommended study pattern is to study one section per study session, and to study the sections in the order in which they appear.

You will need the computer algebra package for the course for Subsection 2.3 and for all of Section 5. The computer work for Subsection 2.3 may be postponed until later (for example until your study of Section 5) without affecting your ability to study the subsequent sections.

Introduction

An important class of the equations that arise in mathematics consists of those that feature the *rates of change* of one or more variables with respect to one or more others. These rates of change are expressed mathematically by *derivatives*, and the corresponding equations are called *differential equations*. Equations of this type crop up in a wide variety of situations. They are found, for example, in models of physical, electronic, economic, demographic and biological phenomena.

First-order differential equations, which are the particular topic of this unit, feature derivatives of order one only; that is, if the rate of change of variable y with respect to variable x is involved, the equations feature dy/dx but not d^2y/dx^2, d^3y/dx^3, etc.

When a differential equation arises, it is usually an important aim to *solve* the equation. For an equation that features the derivative dy/dx, this entails expressing the *dependent variable y* directly in terms of the *independent variable x*. The solution process requires the effect of the derivative to be 'undone'. The reversal of differentiation is achieved by integration, so it is to be expected that integration will feature significantly in the methods of solution for differential equations.

Integration can be attempted either symbolically, to obtain an exact formula for the integral, or numerically, to give approximate numerical values from which the integral can be tabulated or graphed. The same two approaches can therefore be tried to obtain solutions of differential equations, and both are introduced in this unit.

Section 1 considers in detail one example of how a differential equation arises in a mathematical model. This is followed by some basic definitions and terminology associated with differential equations and their solutions. We also note how errors and accuracy are defined.

Section 2 starts by looking at the *direction field* associated with a first-order differential equation. This is a device for visualizing the overall behaviour of the differential equation and of its solutions, and leads to a basic numerical method of solution known as *Euler's method*. Both direction fields and Euler's method are implemented in a computer subsection.

Section 3 turns to *analytic* (that is, symbolic) methods of solution, considering first *direct integration* and then *separation of variables*.

Section 4 describes a further analytic approach to solving differential equations, called the *integrating factor method*. It applies only to equations that are *linear*. Linear first-order differential equations are important in their own right, but also give valuable clues on how to solve linear *second-order* differential equations, which are the subject of *Unit 3*.

In Section 5 you will see how each of the analytic methods from Sections 3 and 4 can be implemented on your computer.

1 Some basics

Subsection 1.1 develops a mathematical model for a specific situation which leads naturally to a first-order differential equation. A key step in deriving this equation is to apply the *input–output principle*, which is a useful device for building relations between variables.

Subsection 1.2 addresses what is meant by the term 'solution' in the context of first-order differential equations, and brings out the distinction between the *general* solution and the various possible *particular* solutions. The specification of a constraint, or *initial condition*, usually permits us to find a unique function that is a particular solution of the differential equation and also satisfies the constraint.

The short Subsection 1.3 provides the definition and description of numerical errors, in anticipation of Euler's method in Section 2.

1.1 Why differential equations?

In the course you will meet many examples of differential equations. Frequently these arise from studying the motion of physical objects, but we shall start with an example drawn from biology and show how this leads naturally to a particular differential equation.

Suppose that we are interested in the size of a particular population, and in how it varies over time. The first point to make is that any population size is measured in integers (whole numbers), so it is not clear how differentiation will be relevant. (Differentiable functions must be continuous, and therefore defined on an interval of real numbers in $\mathbb{R}$.) Nevertheless, if the population is large, say in the hundreds of thousands, a change of one unit will be relatively very small, and in these circumstances we may choose to model the population size as a *continuous* function of time. We shall write this function as $P(t)$, and our task is to show how $P(t)$ may be described by a differential equation.

Let us assume a fixed starting time (which we shall label $t = 0$). If the population is not constant, then there will be 'leavers' and 'joiners'. For example, in a population of humans in a particular country, the former will be those who die or emigrate, whilst the latter represent births and immigrants.

It is usual to express birth rates as a proportion of the current population size. For example, the UK Office for National Statistics quotes birth rates in various age groups as a number per 1000 women. Death rates are specified in a similar way. To emphasize that these rates are expressed as a *proportion* of the current population, we shall use the terms 'proportionate birth rate' and 'proportionate death rate'.

Note that in our model the proportionate birth rate is expressed as a proportion of the whole population, not just the number of women.

For our simple model we shall ignore immigration and emigration, and concentrate solely on births and deaths. Denote the proportionate birth rate by b and the proportionate death rate by c. Then, in a short interval of time δt, we would expect

$$\text{number of births} \simeq bP(t)\delta t, \tag{1.1}$$

$$\text{number of deaths} \simeq cP(t)\delta t, \tag{1.2}$$

where $P(t)$ is the population size at time t.

At this stage, we seek some relationship between the chosen variables. In order to find this, we make use of the **input–output principle**, which can be expressed as

$$\boxed{\text{accumulation}} = \boxed{\text{input}} - \boxed{\text{output}}.$$

This principle applies to any quantity whose change, over a given time interval, is due solely to the specified input and output.

The *accumulation* δP of population over the time interval δt is the population at the end of the interval minus the population at the start of the interval; that is,

$$\delta P = P(t + \delta t) - P(t).$$

The *input* is the number of births (Equation (1.1)), and the *output* is the number of deaths (Equation (1.2)). The input–output principle now enables us to express the accumulation δP of the population over the time interval δt as

$$\delta P \simeq bP(t)\delta t - cP(t)\delta t = (b - c)P(t)\delta t.$$

Dividing through by δt, we obtain

$$\frac{\delta P}{\delta t} \simeq (b - c)P(t).$$

The approximations involved in deriving this equation become progressively more accurate for shorter time intervals. So, finally, by letting δt tend to zero, we obtain

$$\frac{dP}{dt} = (b - c)P(t).$$

This is the step that requires P to be a continuous (rather than discrete) function of t.

(This follows because

$$\frac{dP}{dt} = \lim_{\delta t \to 0} \frac{P(t + \delta t) - P(t)}{\delta t}$$

is the *definition* of the derivative of P.)

This is a *differential* equation because it describes dP/dt rather than the eventual object of our interest (which is P itself). The purpose of this unit is to enable you to solve a wide variety of such equations.

Of course, we can simplify the above equation slightly by using the *proportionate growth rate* r, which is the difference between the proportionate birth and death rates: $r = b - c$. Then our model becomes

$$\frac{dP}{dt} = rP.$$

For very simple population models, r is taken to be a constant. As we shall see, this leads to a prediction of exponential growth (or, if $r < 0$, decay) in population size with time, as illustrated in Figure 1.1. This may be a very good approximation for certain populations, but it cannot be sustained indefinitely if $r > 0$.

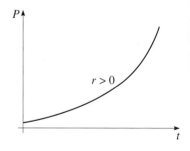

Figure 1.1

In practice, both the proportionate birth rate and the proportionate death rate will vary, and so therefore will the proportionate growth rate. It turns out to be convenient to model these changes as being dependent on the population size, so that the proportionate growth rate r becomes a function of P. The justification for this is as follows. When the population is low, one may assume that there is potential for it to grow (assuming a reasonable environment). The proportionate growth rate should therefore be high. However, as the population grows, there will be competition for resources.

Thus the proportionate growth rate will decline, and in this way unlimited (exponential) growth does not occur.

A particularly useful model arises from taking $r(P)$ to be a decreasing linear function of P. We shall write this as

$$r(P) = k\left(1 - \frac{P}{M}\right), \tag{1.3}$$

where k and M are positive constants. Looking at this formula, you can see that the proportionate growth rate r decreases linearly with P, from the value k (when $P = 0$) to 0 (when $P = M$).

You will see later why this particular form is chosen.

Using this expression for r, the above differential equation satisfied by P becomes

$$\frac{dP}{dt} = kP\left(1 - \frac{P}{M}\right). \tag{1.4}$$

This is well known to biologists as the *logistic equation* — we shall consider it further in Section 2, and see how to solve it in Section 3. For now, we have achieved our objective of showing that differential equations arise naturally in modelling the real world.

Exercise 1.1

Suppose that a population obeys the logistic model (with the proportionate growth rate given by Equation (1.3)), and that you are given the following information. When $P = 10$ the proportionate growth rate is 1, and when $P = 10\,000$ the proportionate growth rate is 0. Find the corresponding values of k and M.

1.2 Differential equations and solutions

This subsection introduces some of the fundamental concepts associated with differential equations. First, however, you are asked to recall some terminology and notation from your previous exposure to calculus.

Some of this terminology and notation was discussed in *Unit 1.*

The *derivative* of a variable y with respect to another variable x is denoted in Leibniz notation by dy/dx. In this derivative expression we refer to y as the *dependent variable* and to x as the *independent variable*.

There are other notations in use for derivatives. If the relation between variables x and y is expressed in terms of a function f, so that $y = f(x)$, then the derivative may be written in function notation as $f'(x)$.

A further notation, attributed to Newton, is restricted to cases in which the independent variable is time, denoted by t. The derivative of $y = f(t)$ could be written in this case as $\dot{y}$, in which the dot over the y stands for the d/dt of Leibniz notation. Thus we may express this derivative in any of the equivalent forms

$$\frac{dy}{dt} = \dot{y} = f'(t).$$

Further derivatives are obtained on differentiating this first derivative. The second derivative of $y = f(t)$ could be represented by any of the forms

$$\frac{d^2y}{dt^2} = \ddot{y} = f''(t).$$

These possible notations have different strengths and weaknesses, and which is most appropriate in any situation depends on the purpose at hand. You will see all of these notations employed at various times during the course.

It is common practice in applied mathematics to reduce the proliferation of symbols as far as possible. One aspect of this practice is that we often avoid allocating separate symbols to variables and to associated functions. Thus, in place of the equation $y = f(t)$ (where y and t denote variables, and f denotes the function that relates them), we could write $y = y(t)$, which is read as 'y is a function of t'. (You have seen examples of this in the previous subsection.)

Strictly speaking, this is an abuse of notation, since there is ambiguity as to exactly what the symbol y represents: it is a variable on the left-hand side of $y = y(t)$ but a function on the right-hand side. However, it is a very convenient abuse.

The following definitions explain just what are meant by a *differential equation*, by the *order* of such an equation, and by a *solution* of it.

Definitions

(a) A **differential equation** for $y = y(x)$ is an equation that relates the independent variable x, the dependent variable y, and one or more derivatives of y.

(b) The **order** of such a differential equation is the order of the highest derivative that appears in the equation. Thus a **first-order** differential equation for $y = y(x)$ features only the first derivative, dy/dx.

(c) A **solution** of such a differential equation is a function $y = y(x)$ that satisfies the equation.

These definitions have been framed in terms of an independent variable x and a dependent variable y. You should be able to translate them to apply to any other independent and dependent variables. Thus Equation (1.4) is a differential equation in which t is the independent variable and P is the dependent variable. It is a first-order equation, since dP/dt appears in it but higher derivatives such as d^2P/dt^2 do not. By contrast, the differential equation

$$3\frac{d^2y}{dx^2} + y^2 \sin x = x^2$$

is of second order, since the second derivative d^2y/dx^2 appears in it but higher derivatives do not.

The topic of this unit is first-order differential equations. Moreover, it concentrates upon first-order equations that can be expressed (possibly after some algebraic manipulation) in the form

Second-order differential equations are the subject of *Unit 3*.

$$\frac{dy}{dx} = f(x, y).$$

The right-hand side here stands for an expression involving both, either or neither of the variables x and y, but no other variables and no derivatives.

Equation (1.4) is of this form, with $f(t, P) = kP\left(1 - \dfrac{P}{M}\right).$

According to the definition above, a function has to *satisfy* a differential equation in order to be regarded as a solution of it. The differential equation is satisfied by the function provided that when the function is substituted into the equation, the left- and right-hand sides of the equation give an identical expression.

This substitution includes the requirement that the function should be *differentiable* (i.e. that it should have a derivative) at all points where it is claimed to be a solution.

You are asked to verify in the next exercise that several functions are solutions of corresponding first-order differential equations. Later in the unit, you will see how all of these differential equations may be solved; but even when a solution has been deduced, it is worth checking in the manner of this exercise (i.e. by substitution) that the supposed solution is indeed correct.

Exercise 1.2 ———————————————————

Verify that each of the functions given below is a solution of the corresponding differential equation.

*(a) $y = 2e^x - (x^2 + 2x + 2)$; $\dfrac{dy}{dx} = y + x^2$.

Remember that an asterisk denotes an exercise (or part of one) that is considered particularly important.

(b) $y = \frac{1}{2}x^2 + \frac{3}{2}$; $\dfrac{dy}{dx} = x$.

*(c) $u = 2e^{x^2/2}$; $u' = xu$.

(d) $y = \sqrt{\dfrac{27 - x^2}{3}}$ $(-3\sqrt{3} < x < 3\sqrt{3})$; $\dfrac{dy}{dx} = -\dfrac{x}{3y}$ $(y \neq 0)$.

Note that the restriction $y \neq 0$ placed on the differential equation in part (d) is necessary to ensure that $-x/3y$ is well defined.

*(e) $y = t + e^{-t}$; $\dot{y} = -y + t + 1$.

*(f) $y = t + Ce^{-t}$; $\dot{y} = -y + t + 1$.   (Here C is an arbitrary constant.)

In the last two parts of Exercise 1.2 you were asked to verify that

$$y = t + e^{-t} \quad \text{and} \quad y = t + Ce^{-t}$$

are solutions of the differential equation $\dot{y} = -y + t + 1$, where in the second case C is an arbitrary constant. In saying that C is *arbitrary*, we mean that it can assume any real value. Whatever number is chosen for C, the corresponding expression for $y(t)$ is always a solution of the differential equation. The particular function $y = t + e^{-t}$ is just one example of such a solution, obtained by choosing $C = 1$.

This demonstrates that solutions of a differential equation can exist in profusion; as a result, we need terms to distinguish between the totality of all these solutions for a given equation and the individual solutions that are completely specified.

Definitions

(a) The **general solution** of a differential equation is the collection of all possible solutions of that equation.

(b) A **particular solution** of a differential equation is a single solution of the equation, and consists of a solution function whose rule contains no arbitrary constant.

In many cases it is possible to describe the general solution of a first-order differential equation by a single formula involving an arbitrary constant. For example, $y = t + Ce^{-t}$ is the general solution of the equation $\dot{y} = -y + t + 1$; this means that not only is $y = t + Ce^{-t}$ a solution whatever the value of C, but also *every* particular solution of the equation may be obtained by giving C a suitable value.

*Exercise 1.3 ————————————————————————

(a) Verify that, for any value of the constant C, the function $y = C - \frac{1}{3}e^{-3x}$ is a solution of the differential equation

$$\frac{dy}{dx} = e^{-3x}.$$

(b) Verify that, for any value of the constant C, the function $u = Ce^t - t - 1$ is a solution of the differential equation

$$\dot{u} = t + u.$$

(c) Verify that, for any value of the constant C, the function

$$P = \frac{CMe^{kt}}{1 + Ce^{kt}}$$

is a solution of Equation (1.4) on page 65.

————————————————————————

As you have seen, there are many solutions of a differential equation. However, a particular solution of the equation, representing a definite relationship between the variables involved, is often what is needed. This is achieved by using a further piece of information in addition to the differential equation. Often the extra information takes the form of a pair of values for the independent and dependent variables.

For example, in the case of a population model, it would be natural to specify the starting population, P_0 say, and to start measuring time from $t = 0$. We could then write

$$P = P_0 \text{ when } t = 0, \quad \text{or, equivalently,} \quad P(0) = P_0.$$

A requirement of this type is called an *initial condition*.

————————————————————————

Definitions

(a) An **initial condition** associated with the differential equation

$$\frac{dy}{dx} = f(x, y)$$

specifies that the dependent variable y takes some value y_0 when the independent variable x takes some value x_0. This is written either as

$$y = y_0 \text{ when } x = x_0$$

or as

$$y(x_0) = y_0.$$

The numbers x_0 and y_0 are referred to as **initial values**.

(b) The combination of a first-order differential equation and an initial condition is called an **initial-value problem**.

————————————————————————

The word 'initial' in these definitions arises from those (frequent) cases in which the independent variable represents time. In such cases, the differential equation describes how the system being modelled behaves once started, while the initial condition specifies the configuration in which the system is started off. In fact, if the initial condition is $y(x_0) = y_0$, then we are often interested in solving the corresponding initial-value problem for $x > x_0$.

If x represents time, then $x > x_0$ is 'the future' after the system has been started off.

We usually require that an initial-value problem should have a *unique* solution, since then the outcome is completely determined by how the system behaves and its configuration at the start. Almost all the differential equations in this course do have unique solutions.

Example 1.1

Using the result given in Exercise 1.3(b), solve the initial-value problem

$$\frac{dy}{dx} = x + y, \quad y(0) = 1.$$

Solution

From Exercise 1.3(b), on replacing the variables t, u by x, y, respectively, the general solution of the differential equation here is

$$y = Ce^x - x - 1.$$

The initial condition says that $y = 1$ when $x = 0$, and on feeding these values into the general solution we find that

$$1 = Ce^0 - 0 - 1 = C - 1.$$

Hence $C = 2$, and the particular solution of the differential equation that solves the initial-value problem is

$$y = 2e^x - x - 1. \quad \blacksquare$$

Exercise 1.4

The size of a population (measured in hundreds of thousands) is modelled by the logistic equation

$$\frac{dP}{dt} = kP\left(1 - \frac{P}{M}\right), \quad P(0) = 1,$$

where $k = 0.15$ and $M = 10$.

*(a) Use your answer to Exercise 1.3(c) to find a solution to this initial-value problem.

(b) Can you predict the long-term behaviour of the population size from your answer?

Finally in this subsection, note that one needs to keep an eye on the *domain* of the function defining the differential equation. 'Gaps' in the domain usually show up as some form of restriction on the nature of a solution curve. For example, consider the differential equation

$$\frac{dy}{dx} = \frac{1}{x}. \tag{1.5}$$

It turns out that there are two distinct families of solutions of this equation, given by $y = \ln x + C$ (if $x > 0$) and $y = \ln(-x) + C$ (if $x < 0$). These two families of solutions are illustrated in Figure 1.2. Notice that the right-hand side of Equation (1.5) is not defined at $x = 0$, and that there is no solution that crosses the y-axis.

This unit deals with numerical and analytic (symbolic) methods of solving differential equations. However, before we can discuss numerical methods, we need to know something about the way that errors and accuracy are described: this is the topic of the next subsection.

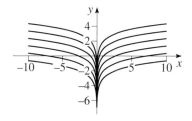

Figure 1.2

Since $|x| = -x$ if $x < 0$, you can see that this agrees with what we know from *Unit 1*, namely that

$$\int \frac{1}{x}\,dx = \ln|x|.$$

1.3 *Approximations in calculations*

We often find that we need to make a calculation based on numerical values that are not exact — for example, there may be limitations on the accuracy to which a measurement can be taken. Finding a numerical solution to a differential equation almost always involves inexact arithmetic: any calculator or computer will have some limit on the accuracy (number of significant figures) to which a decimal can be stored, and rounding errors will occur.

In fact, using a numerical method usually involves repeated calculations, so inaccuracies may build up and have a significant effect on the result. When using a numerical method, one wants (if possible) to know how accurate the result is. With this in mind, we recall a few basic ideas relating to approximation and accuracy.

One simple form of calculation is the evaluation of a function. Suppose that we want the value of $f(\pi)$ for some function f, and use a value of π which is rounded to three decimal places, that is, 3.142. Since this is the value of π to three decimal places, we know that

$$|3.142 - \pi| \leq 0.0005 = 5 \times 10^{-4}$$

(since $3.1415 \leq \pi < 3.1425$). This gives us some idea of how accurate 3.142 is as an estimate of π. In general, we refer to the difference

approximate value − true value

as the **error** in the approximate value, and to the modulus of this difference, that is,

|approximate value − true value|,

as the **absolute error** in the approximate value. So if ε is the absolute error in using 3.142 as an estimate of π, then we know that

$$\varepsilon \leq 0.0005.$$

Notice that, by definition, the absolute error is always greater than or equal to zero, whereas the error can be positive or negative.

In this context, the quantity 0.0005 is referred to as an **absolute error bound**.

If we take π to be 3.142, what is the consequent error in $f(\pi)$? This will depend on the function f.

Exercise 1.5

For each of the functions f given below, use your calculator to find $f(3.142)$. Then estimate $f(\pi)$ more accurately, using $\pi = 3.1415926$ (to seven decimal places). Hence estimate the error in using $f(3.142)$ as an approximation to $f(\pi)$.

You are welcome to use your computer rather than a calculator if you prefer.

(a) $f(x) = x^3$ (b) $f(x) = e^{10x}$

In Exercise 1.5(b), you saw that an absolute error of less than 0.0005 in the value of π results in an absolute error of the order of 1.8×10^{11} in the calculated value of $f(\pi)$, for $f(x) = e^{10x}$. For this function f, errors are severely magnified! However, the situation is not quite so bad as this statement might suggest. The calculated value of $f(\pi)$ is not completely unreliable — it is accurate to two significant figures. The value of $f(\pi)$ is itself very large (4.4×10^{13}), so an error of 1.8×10^{11} is not quite so serious as it sounds. We often want a measure of 'error' that takes into account the size of the error relative to the size of the number being calculated.

We define the **relative error** as

$$\left| \frac{\text{approximate value} - \text{true value}}{\text{true value}} \right|.$$

So the relative error in $f(3.142)$ as an estimate of $f(\pi)$ here is (roughly)

$$\frac{1.8 \times 10^{11}}{4.4 \times 10^{13}} \simeq 0.4 \times 10^{-2}.$$

A relative error of this size corresponds to a value that is accurate to two significant figures, as obtained in Exercise 1.5(b). Relative errors provide a guide to the number of significant figures that can be relied on, while absolute errors relate to the number of decimal places that are accurate.

Usually, a relative error of 0.5×10^{-n} corresponds to a value that is accurate to n significant figures.

End-of-section Exercises

Exercise 1.6 —————————————————————

(a) Verify that, for any value of the constant C, the function

$$y = \arcsin x + C \quad (-1 < x < 1)$$

is a solution of the differential equation

$$\frac{dy}{dx} = \frac{1}{\sqrt{1 - x^2}}.$$

(b) Using the result of part (a), find the solution of the initial-value problem

$$\frac{dy}{dx} = \frac{1}{\sqrt{1 - x^2}}, \quad y(\tfrac{1}{2}) = \tfrac{\pi}{2}.$$

Exercise 1.7 —————————————————————

(a) Verify that, for any value of the constant C, the function

$$x = \tan(t + C) \quad \left(-\tfrac{\pi}{2} < t + C < \tfrac{\pi}{2}\right)$$

is a solution of the differential equation

$$\dot{x} = 1 + x^2.$$

(b) Using the result of part (a), find the solution of the initial-value problem

$$\dot{x} = 1 + x^2, \quad x\left(\tfrac{\pi}{4}\right) = 1.$$

2 Direction fields and Euler's method

Subsection 2.1 shows that qualitative information about the solutions of a first-order differential equation may be gleaned directly from the equation itself, without undertaking any form of integration process. The main concept here is the *direction field*, sketches of which usually give a good idea of how the graphs of solutions behave.

Direction fields can also be regarded as the starting point for a numerical (that is, calculational rather than algebraic) method of solution called *Euler's method*, which is described and applied in Subsection 2.2.

In Subsection 2.3 you will see how both direction fields and Euler's method can be implemented on your computer.

2.1 Direction fields

We start this subsection by considering what can be deduced about solutions of the differential equation

$$\frac{dy}{dx} = f(x, y) \tag{2.1}$$

from direct observation of this equation.

In Section 1 we encountered the logistic equation

$$\frac{dP}{dt} = kP\left(1 - \frac{P}{M}\right), \tag{2.2}$$

Here we have

$$f(t, P) = kP\left(1 - \frac{P}{M}\right).$$

where k and M are positive constants. In certain circumstances this is a useful mathematical model of population changes, in which $P(t)$ denotes the size of the population at time t. The right-hand side of this equation is equal to zero if either $P = 0$ or $P = M$. Hence, since $dP/dt = 0$ in both cases, each of the constant functions $P = 0$ and $P = M$ is a particular solution of Equation (2.2). Within the model, these solutions correspond to a complete absence of the population ($P = 0$), and an equilibrium population level ($P = M$) for which the proportionate birth and death rates are equal.

Such spotting of constant functions that are particular solutions is useful on occasion but of limited applicability. In general, more useful information can be deduced from the observation that, for any given point (x, y) in the plane, the equation

$$\frac{dy}{dx} = f(x, y) \tag{2.1}$$

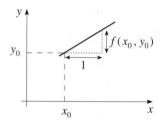

Figure 2.1 A graphical representation of the slope at the point (x_0, y_0)

describes the *direction* in which the graph of the particular solution through that point is heading (see Figure 2.1). This is because if $y = y(x)$ is any solution of the differential equation, then dy/dx is the *gradient* or *slope* of the graph of that function. Equation (2.1) therefore tells us that $f(x, y)$ represents the slope at (x, y) of the graph of the particular solution that passes through (x, y). If the slope $f(x, y)$ at this point is positive, then the corresponding solution graph is increasing (rising) from left to right through the point (x, y); if the slope is negative, then the graph is decreasing (falling); and if the slope is zero, then the graph is horizontal at the point.

For example, if $f(x, y) = x + y$, then the slope at the point $(1, 2)$ is $f(1, 2) = 1 + 2 = 3$, the slope at the point $(2, -7)$ is $f(2, -7) = 2 - 7 = -5$, and the slope at the point $(3, -3)$ is $f(3, -3) = 3 - 3 = 0$.

When looking at $f(x, y)$ in this light, it is referred to as a *direction field*, since it describes a *direction* (slope) for each point (x, y) where $f(x, y)$ is defined.

Definition

A **direction field** associates a unique direction to each point within a specified region of the (x, y)-plane. The direction corresponding to the point (x, y) may be thought of as the slope of a short line segment through the point.

In particular, the direction field for the differential equation

$$\frac{dy}{dx} = f(x, y)$$

associates the direction $f(x, y)$ with the point (x, y).

Direction fields can be visualized by constructing the short line segments referred to above for a finite set of points in an appropriate region of the plane, where typically the points are chosen to form a rectangular grid.

An example is shown in Figure 2.2, which corresponds to the differential equation

$$\frac{dy}{dx} = x + y. \tag{2.3}$$

Here $f(x, y) = x + y$.

In this case the chosen region is the set of points (x, y) such that $-2 \le x \le 2$ and $0 \le y \le 2$, and the rectangular grid consists of the points at intervals of 0.2 in both the x- and y-directions within this region.

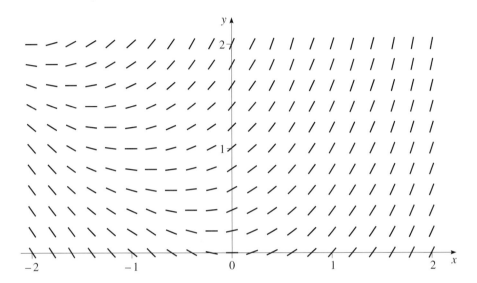

Figure 2.2

From this diagram, we can gain a good qualitative impression of how the graphs of particular solutions of Equation (2.3) behave. The aim is mentally to sketch curves on the diagram in such a way that the tangents to the curves are always parallel to the local slopes of the direction field. For example, starting from the point $(-1, 0.5)$ (that is, taking the initial condition to be $y(-1) = 0.5$), we expect the solution graph initially to fall as we move to the right. The magnitude of the negative slope decreases, however, and eventually reaches zero, after which the slope becomes positive and then increases. On this basis, we could sketch the graph of the corresponding particular solution and obtain something like the curve shown in Figure 2.3.

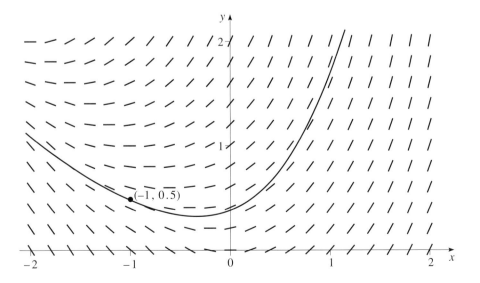

Figure 2.3

Exercise 2.1

(a) Part of the direction field for the logistic equation

$$\frac{dP}{dt} = P\left(1 - \frac{P}{1000}\right)$$

This is Equation (2.2) with $k = 1$ and $M = 1000$.

is sketched in Figure 2.4. Using this diagram, sketch the solution curves that pass through the following points:

$$(0, 1500), \quad (0, 1000), \quad (0, 100), \quad (0, 0), \quad (0, -100).$$

From your results, describe the graphs of particular solutions of the differential equation.

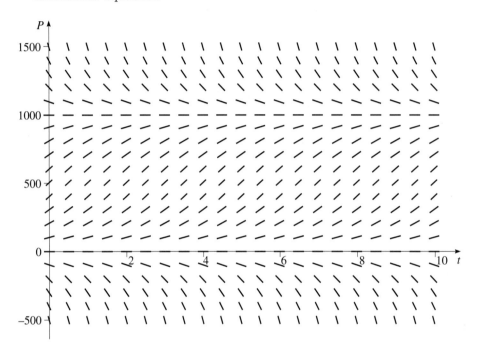

Figure 2.4

(b) What does your answer to part (a) tell you about the predicted behaviour of a population whose size $P(t)$ at time t is modelled by this logistic equation?

Drawing *by hand* precise grids of line segments to represent direction fields is not a good use of your time. However, it is a task that your computer can be programmed to perform, as you will see in Subsection 2.3. Before investigating this, you will see in Subsection 2.2 how the concept of direction fields helps in constructing approximate numerical solutions for first-order differential equations.

2.2 Euler's method

In the previous subsection it was suggested that the graphs of particular solutions of a differential equation

$$\frac{dy}{dx} = f(x, y)$$

could be 'mentally sketched' on a diagram of the direction field given by $f(x, y)$. This was to be done in such a way that the tangent to the solution curve is always 'parallel to the local slope' of the direction field. While this gives a good visual image of the connection between the direction field and the graph of a solution, it is somewhat short on precision. We could not expect, by this approach, to predict with any accuracy the actual solution to an initial-value problem. That task is the subject of the current subsection, which shows how an initial-value problem

$$\frac{dy}{dx} = f(x, y), \quad y(x_0) = y_0, \tag{2.4}$$

may be 'solved' by calculational means. However, the direction field diagram is still of use in explaining how this numerical method arises.

Suppose that instead of trying to sketch a solution curve to fit the direction field, we move in a sequence of straight-line steps whose directions are governed by the direction field. The aim is to produce a sequence of points that provide approximate values of the solution function $y(x)$ for the initial-value problem at a sequence of x-values. The steps are constructed as follows.

Corresponding to the given initial condition $y(x_0) = y_0$, there is a point P_0 in the (x, y)-plane with coordinates (x_0, y_0), and this is our starting point. At P_0, the direction field $f(x, y)$ defines a particular slope, namely $f(x_0, y_0)$. We move off from P_0 along a straight line that has this slope, and continue until we have travelled a horizontal distance h to the right of P_0. The point that has now been reached is labelled P_1, as in Figure 2.5.

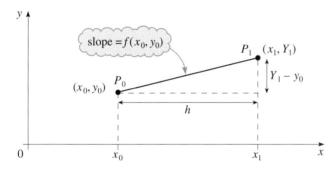

Figure 2.5

The idea is that the point P_1, whose coordinates have been denoted by (x_1, Y_1), provides an approximate value Y_1 of the solution function $y(x)$ at $x = x_1$. Now, unless the solution function follows a straight line as x moves from x_0 to x_1, Y_1 is unlikely to give the exact value of $y(x_1)$. However, the hope is that, because we headed off from x_0 along the correct slope, as given by the direction field, Y_1 will be reasonably close to the exact value. Before worrying about accuracy, let us continue with the construction of the points in our sequence.

The reason for using Y_1 here, rather than y_1, will be explained shortly.

The next thing that we need to do, before proceeding to the second step in the construction process, is determine formulae for x_1 and Y_1 in terms of x_0, y_0, h and $f(x_0, y_0)$. By the construction described, as the point P_1 is reached from P_0 by taking a step to the right of horizontal length h, we have

$$x_1 = x_0 + h. \tag{2.5}$$

We can express Y_1 in terms of other quantities by equating two expressions for the slope of the line segment P_0P_1,

$$\frac{Y_1 - y_0}{h} = f(x_0, y_0),$$

and then rearranging to give

$$Y_1 = y_0 + hf(x_0, y_0). \tag{2.6}$$

This completes the first step, and we now take a second step to the right.

The direction of the second step is along the line with slope defined by the direction field at the point P_1, namely $f(x_1, Y_1)$. The second step moves us from P_1 through a further horizontal distance h to the right, to the point labelled P_2, as illustrated in Figure 2.6. This point provides an approximate value Y_2 of the solution function $y(x)$ at $x = x_2$.

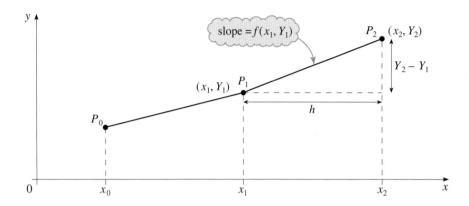

Figure 2.6

As in the first step, we need now to express the coordinates (x_2, Y_2) of P_2 in terms of x_1, Y_1, h and $f(x_1, Y_1)$. We have

$$x_2 = x_1 + h \tag{2.7}$$

and (equating two expressions for the slope of the line segment $P_1 P_2$)

$$\frac{Y_2 - Y_1}{h} = f(x_1, Y_1),$$

which can be rearranged to give

$$Y_2 = Y_1 + h f(x_1, Y_1). \tag{2.8}$$

Having carried out two steps of the process, it is possible to see that the same procedure can be applied to construct any number of further steps, and we next generalize to a description of what happens at the $(i + 1)$th step, where i represents any non-negative integer.

Suppose that after i steps we have reached the point P_i, with coordinates (x_i, Y_i). For the $(i + 1)$th step, we move away from P_i along the line with slope $f(x_i, Y_i)$, as defined by the direction field at P_i. After moving through a horizontal distance h to the right, we reach the point P_{i+1}, whose coordinates are denoted by (x_{i+1}, Y_{i+1}), as illustrated in Figure 2.7. The point P_{i+1} provides an approximate value Y_{i+1} of the solution function $y(x)$ at $x = x_{i+1}$.

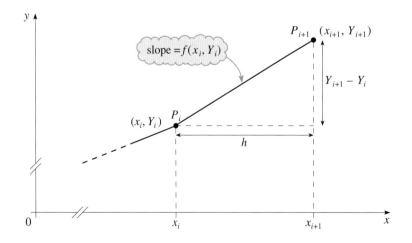

Figure 2.7

Arguing as before, we have

$$x_{i+1} = x_i + h \qquad (2.9)$$

and (equating two expressions for the slope of the line segment $P_i P_{i+1}$)

$$\frac{Y_{i+1} - Y_i}{h} = f(x_i, Y_i),$$

which can be rearranged to give

$$Y_{i+1} = Y_i + hf(x_i, Y_i). \qquad (2.10)$$

Note that Equations (2.5) and (2.7) are the special cases of Equation (2.9) for $i = 0$ and $i = 1$, respectively, and that Equation (2.8) is the special case of Equation (2.10) for $i = 1$. If we also define Y_0 to be equal to the initial value y_0, then Equation (2.6) is the special case of Equation (2.10) for $i = 0$.

To sum up, for the initial-value problem (2.4), we have a procedure for constructing a sequence of points

$$P_i \text{ with coordinates } (x_i, Y_i) \quad (i = 1, 2, \ldots),$$

where the values of x_i and Y_i for each value of i are determined by the respective formulae (2.9) and (2.10). The starting point for the sequence is the point P_0 with coordinates (x_0, Y_0), where $Y_0 = y_0$. Because the procedure is based on the direction field, each Y_i provides an approximation at $x = x_i$ to the value of the solution function $y(x)$ for the initial-value problem. The horizontal distance h by which we move to the right at each stage of the procedure is called the **step size** or **step length**.

Figure 2.8 shows the constructed sequence of points, and for comparison includes a curve representing the graph of the exact solution of the initial-value problem (2.4). This makes clear that the successive points $P_1, P_2, P_3, \ldots$ are only *approximations* to points on the solution curve. In fact, the situation shown in Figure 2.8 is typical of the behaviour of the constructed approximations, in that they gradually move further and further from the exact solution curve. This is because, at each step, the direction of movement is along the slope of the direction field at $P_i = (x_i, Y_i)$ and not along the slope of the direction field at (x_i, y_i), where $y_i = y(x_i)$ denotes the value of the exact solution function at $x = x_i$; that is, for each x_i, the slope for the next step is defined by a point close to the solution curve rather than by the point exactly on that curve.

The common use of $y_i = y(x_i)$ to represent the exact solution at $x = x_i$ explains why we use a different notation, namely Y_i, for the numerical approximation to $y(x_i)$.

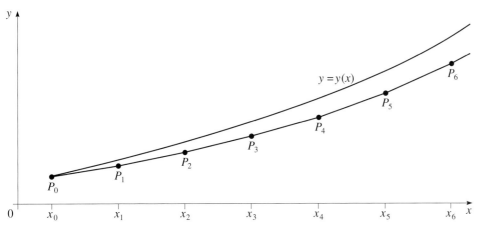

Figure 2.8

Nevertheless, the formulae (2.9) and (2.10) provide a method for finding approximate solutions to the initial-value problem (2.4), in terms of numerical estimates $Y_1, Y_2, Y_3, \ldots$ at the respective domain values $x_1, x_2, x_3, \ldots$. This is called *Euler's method*, and is summarized below.

The accuracy of such approximate solutions, and ways of improving accuracy, will be considered shortly.

Procedure 2.1   Euler's method

To apply Euler's method to the initial-value problem

$$\frac{dy}{dx} = f(x, y), \quad y(x_0) = y_0, \tag{2.4}$$

proceed as follows.

(a) Take x_0 and $Y_0 = y_0$ as starting values, choose a step size h, and set $i = 0$.

(b) Calculate the x-coordinate x_{i+1}, using the formula

$$x_{i+1} = x_i + h. \tag{2.9}$$

(c) Calculate a corresponding approximation Y_{i+1} to $y(x_{i+1})$, using the formula

$$Y_{i+1} = Y_i + hf(x_i, Y_i). \tag{2.10}$$

(d) If further approximate values are required, increase i by 1 and return to Step (b).

Leonhard Euler (1707–1783) was one of the most prolific mathematicians of all time. (His surname is pronounced 'oiler'.) He first devised this method in order to compute the orbit of the moon.

Example 2.1

Consider the initial-value problem

$$\frac{dy}{dx} = x + y, \quad y(0) = 1.$$

Use Euler's method, with step size $h = 0.2$, to obtain an approximation to $y(1)$.

Solution

We have $x_0 = 0$, $Y_0 = y_0 = 1$, and $f(x_i, Y_i) = x_i + Y_i$. The step size is given as $h = 0.2$. Equation (2.9) with $i = 0$ gives

$$x_1 = x_0 + h = 0 + 0.2 = 0.2,$$

and Equation (2.10) with $i = 0$ gives

$$Y_1 = Y_0 + hf(x_0, Y_0) = 1 + 0.2 \times (0 + 1) = 1.2.$$

For the second step, we have (from Equation (2.9) with $i = 1$)

$$x_2 = x_1 + h = 0.2 + 0.2 = 0.4,$$

and (from Equation (2.10) with $i = 1$)

$$Y_2 = Y_1 + hf(x_1, Y_1) = 1.2 + 0.2 \times (0.2 + 1.2) = 1.48.$$

If more than a couple of steps of such a calculation have to be computed by hand, then it is a good idea to lay out the calculation as a table. In this case, by continuing as above and putting i in turn equal to 2, 3 and 4, we obtain Table 2.1.

Table 2.1

i	x_i	Y_i	$f(x_i, Y_i) = x_i + Y_i$	$Y_{i+1} = Y_i + hf(x_i, Y_i)$
0	0	1	1	1.2
1	0.2	1.2	1.4	1.48
2	0.4	1.48	1.88	1.856
3	0.6	1.856	2.456	2.347 2
4	0.8	2.347 2	3.147 2	2.976 64
5	1.0	2.976 64		

After each value of Y_{i+1} has been calculated from the formula and entered in the last column, it is transferred to the Y_i column in the next row.

So, at $x = 1$, Euler's method with step size $h = 0.2$ gives the approximation $y(1) \simeq 2.976\,64$.   ■

Exercise 2.2

Use Euler's method, with step size $h = 0.2$, to obtain an approximation to $y(1)$ for the initial-value problem

$$\frac{dy}{dx} = y, \quad y(0) = 1.$$

The solution of the initial-value problem given in Example 2.1 is in fact known exactly, and is $y = 2e^x - x - 1$. Putting $x = 1$, this gives

This exact solution was found in Example 1.1 (page 69).

$$y(1) = 2e - 1 - 1 = 3.436\,56,$$

correct to five decimal places. This value may be compared with the approximation 2.976 64 for $y(1)$ obtained by Euler's method in Example 2.1, and the comparison indicates that the approximation is not at all accurate. Indeed, the absolute error in this case is

$$|2.976\,64 - 3.436\,56| = 0.459\,92,$$

which is about 13% of the exact value, and indeed not even one decimal place accuracy is achieved.

Similarly, the other values Y_i ($i = 1, 2, 3, 4$) found in Example 2.1 contain significant absolute errors when considered as approximations to the corresponding exact values $y_i = y(x_i)$. This is illustrated in general terms in Figure 2.8, where the absolute error in approximation Y_i is the vertical distance from the point P_i to the point directly above it on the exact solution curve. As shown there, and for reasons given earlier, the absolute error tends to increase as more and more steps are taken.

The realization that Euler's method can produce values that are poor approximations to the exact solution of an initial-value problem invites us to ask whether the accuracy of the approximations can be improved, using this method. In fact, it is not hard to see that improvements in accuracy ought to be achieved by *reducing the step size h*. Our earlier prescription for constructing the sequence of points $P_1, P_2, P_3, \ldots$ from the starting point P_0 and the given direction field amounts loosely to saying 'match the direction of the solution curve at the current point, take a step, then adjust direction so as to try not to move further away from the curve'. It seems natural, therefore, that the approximations will improve if we reduce the size of the steps taken and correspondingly 'adjust direction' more frequently. This is illustrated for a hypothetical case in Figure 2.9.

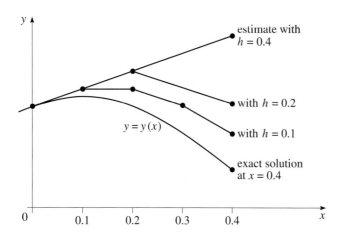

Figure 2.9

In fact, it can be shown that the accuracy of Euler's method does indeed usually improve when we take a smaller step size.

To demonstrate this, consider the initial-value problem from Exercise 2.2. This has the exact solution $y = e^x$ (as you can verify), and its value at $x = 1$ is $y(1) = e = 2.718\,282$, to six decimal places. In Exercise 2.2 you showed that with a step size $h = 0.2$, Euler's method gives the approximation $2.488\,32$ for $y(1)$. Table 2.2 shows the corresponding results (to six decimal places) obtained when we apply Euler's method to this same initial-value problem but with successively smaller step sizes h.

Table 2.2

h	Approximation to $y(1)$	Absolute error	Number of steps
0.1	2.593 742	0.124 539	10
0.01	2.704 814	0.013 468	100
0.001	2.716 924	0.001 358	1000
0.0001	2.718 146	0.000 136	10000

In Exercise 2.2, where $h = 0.2$, the value of $y(1)$ was approximated by Y_5. From the column for 'number of steps' in Table 2.2, you can see that $y(1)$ is approximated by:

Y_{10} when $h = 0.1$;
Y_{100} when $h = 0.01$;
Y_{1000} when $h = 0.001$;
Y_{10000} when $h = 0.0001$.

As expected, the absolute errors in the third column of the table become progressively smaller as h is reduced.

Looking more carefully at these absolute errors, we notice that they seem to tend towards a sequence in which each number is a tenth of the previous one. Since each value of h in the table is a tenth of the previous one, this suggests that:

absolute error is approximately proportional to step size h.

This turns out to be a general property of Euler's method, for sufficiently small values of the step size. So, not only do we know that accuracy can be improved by decreasing the step size h, but this general property also tells us that, by making h small enough, the absolute error in an approximation can

You will see this property stated formally in *Unit 26*, where you will also see how the property can be used to estimate the size of absolute errors.

be made as small as desired. In other words, the absolute error approaches the limit zero as h approaches zero (as you might have expected from the intuitive argument preceding Figure 2.9).

Exercise 2.3 _____

Suppose that when Euler's method is applied to the problem in Exercise 2.2, the absolute error in approximating $y(1)$ is proportional to the step size h, for sufficiently small h.

Use the last row of Table 2.2 to estimate the constant of proportionality, k say, and hence to estimate the step size required to compute $y(1)$ correct to five decimal places (that is, so that the absolute error is less than 5×10^{-6}).

_____

A few words of caution are necessary at this point. Although the absolute error can be made as small as we please by making the step size h sufficiently small, this is valid *only* if the arithmetic is performed using sufficient decimal places. Where a calculator or computer is involved, the number of decimal places that can be used is limited, and as a result *rounding errors* may be introduced into the calculations. After a certain point, any increase in accuracy brought about by reducing the size of h may be swamped by these rounding errors.

Moreover, rounding errors are not the only problem. Before concluding that h should always be chosen to be very small, we must also consider the cost of this additional accuracy. Now, by *cost* is meant the effort involved, which can be measured in a variety of ways; commonly for iterative methods (such as Euler's method) it is measured by the number of steps taken. In general for numerical methods, the greater the accuracy required, the greater the cost. To illustrate this, look back at Table 2.2. The last column of the table shows how the number of steps required for the calculation goes up in inverse proportion to the step size: to move from $x = 0$ to $x = 1$, it takes 10 steps with step size $h = 0.1$, 100 steps with step size $h = 0.01$, and so on. Since, for sufficiently small h, the error in Euler's method is approximately proportional to the step size, it follows that for this method a ten-fold improvement in accuracy is paid for by a ten-fold increase in the number of steps required.

In general, to move from a to b (where $b > a$) with step size h takes $(b - a)/h$ steps.

So, for Euler's method and similar methods, the choice of step size has to be based on a compromise between the two opposing requirements of accuracy and cost. Methods for choosing the step size are discussed in *Unit 26*, which also introduces other numerical methods for solving initial-value problems that are considerably more *efficient* than Euler's method. In fact, Euler's method is not suitable for high-accuracy work. Its virtue lies rather in its simplicity and its clear illustration of the basic principles of how differential equations may be solved numerically.

Greater *efficiency* means that the same or better numerical accuracy is achieved with fewer numerical computations.

In any practical case, calculations of the type described in this subsection are ideally suited to being performed on a computer, as you will see in the next subsection.

2.3   Finding numerical solutions on the computer

In this subsection you will see how the computer can be used to construct direction fields and to implement Euler's method.

Use your computer to complete the following activities.

*Activity 2.1

Plot the direction field for the differential equation

$$\frac{dy}{dx} = x + y$$

in the region

$$-2 \le x \le 2, \quad 0 \le y \le 2.$$

On the basis of the plot of the direction field, what can you say about the graphs of solutions of the differential equation?

This is Equation (2.3) (page 73).

*Activity 2.2

Use Euler's method to obtain approximations to $y(1)$ for the initial-value problem

$$\frac{dy}{dx} = x + y, \quad y(0) = 0,$$

using step sizes $h = 1, 0.5, 0.2, 0.1, 0.01, 0.001, 0.0001$, in turn. In each case, plot the graph of the solution on an appropriate direction field diagram, and observe how each graph compares with the previous one.

*Activity 2.3

Euler's method is to be used to estimate the value of the function $y(x)$ at $x = 0.1, 0.2, \ldots, 1$ for the initial-value problem

$$\frac{dy}{dx} = x + y, \quad y(0) = 0.$$

(a) Use the step sizes $h = 0.1, 0.01, 0.001, 0.0001$, in turn. Compare the results in each case with the exact solution $y = e^x - x - 1$, and comment on how the size of the absolute error varies with h.

(b) Compare your estimates for the step sizes $h = 0.1$ and $h = 0.01$. Then compare your estimates for all four step sizes. What can you conclude?

End-of-section Exercise

Exercise 2.4

(a) Without plotting the direction field, say what you can about the slopes defined by the differential equation

$$\frac{dy}{dx} = f(x, y) = y + x^2.$$

(b) Verify that your conclusions are consistent with the direction field diagram in Figure 2.10.

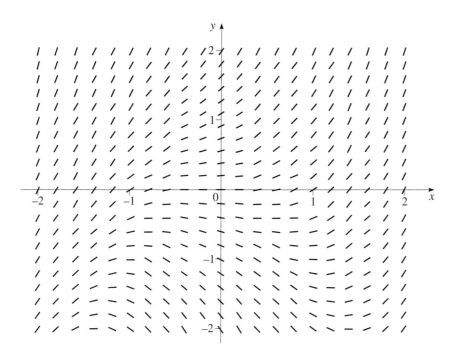

Figure 2.10

(c) On the basis of the direction field, what can be said about the graphs of solutions of the differential equation?

(d) Write down the formulae required in order to apply Euler's method to the initial-value problem

$$\frac{dy}{dx} = y + x^2, \quad y(-1) = -0.2,$$

using a step size $h = 0.1$.

3 Finding analytic solutions

This section and the next look at methods for finding *analytic* solutions of first-order differential equations — that is, solutions expressed in terms of exact formulae. It is not always possible to find analytic solutions, and in these cases numerical methods of approximate solution, such as Euler's method, are applied. Even when a formula for the solution is obtainable, it may be so complicated that a numerical solution is preferred. However, where a simple formula can be found, this is likely to be more informative than use of a numerical method.

This section specializes from the form of differential equation

$$\frac{dy}{dx} = f(x, y)$$

considered earlier. Subsection 3.1 looks at cases in which $f(x, y)$ is taken to be a function of x alone, $f(x)$. You will see that the differential equation can then be solved by *direct integration*, assuming that the necessary integration can be performed. Subsection 3.2 considers cases in which $f(x, y) = g(x)h(y)$ (the product of a function of x and a function of y). These can be solved in principle by the method of *separation of variables*.

3.1 Direct integration

An example of a differential equation that can be solved is

$$\frac{dy}{dx} = x^2. \tag{3.1}$$

In order to do this, we need to find functions $y(x)$ whose derivatives are x^2; one such function is $y = \frac{1}{3}x^3$. There are other functions with this same derivative, for example $y = \frac{1}{3}x^3 + 1$ and $y = \frac{1}{3}x^3 - 2$. In fact, any function of the form

$$y = \tfrac{1}{3}x^3 + C,$$

where C is an arbitrary constant, satisfies the differential equation (3.1). This is an expression for the general solution.

The expression $\frac{1}{3}x^3 + C$ is also *the indefinite integral* of x^2: that is,

$$\int x^2 \, dx = \tfrac{1}{3}x^3 + C.$$

In this case, therefore, the indefinite integral of x^2 is the general solution of Equation (3.1), and a similar connection applies more generally.

Consider the differential equation

$$\frac{dy}{dx} = f(x), \tag{3.2}$$

where the right-hand side, $f(x)$, is a function of x alone. Suppose that we have a particular solution $y = F(x)$ of this differential equation; in other words, $F(x)$ is *an integral* of $f(x)$. In such circumstances, the general solution of Equation (3.2) is given by $y = F(x) + C$, where C is an arbitrary constant; and the indefinite integral of $f(x)$ is given by the same expression,

$$\int f(x) \, dx = F(x) + C.$$

This means that the general solution of Equation (3.2) can be written down directly as an indefinite integral; and, if the integration can be performed, then the equation is solved.

> **Procedure 3.1   Direct integration**
>
> The general solution of the differential equation
>
> $$\frac{dy}{dx} = f(x) \tag{3.2}$$
>
> is
>
> $$y = \int f(x) \, dx = F(x) + C,$$
>
> where $F(x)$ is an integral of $f(x)$ and C is an arbitrary constant.

The values $C = 0$, $C = 1$ and $C = -2$ give the three particular solutions mentioned above.

This is hardly surprising, since integration 'undoes' or reverses the effect of differentiation.

The function $f(x)$ is assumed to be continuous (i.e. its graph has no breaks).

Once the general solution has been found, it is possible to single out a particular solution by specifying a value for the constant C. As before, this value may be found by applying an initial condition.

Example 3.1

(a) Find the general solution of the differential equation

$$\frac{dy}{dx} = e^{-3x}.$$

(b) Find the particular solution of this differential equation that satisfies the initial condition $y(0) = \frac{5}{3}$.

Solution

(a) On applying direct integration, we obtain the general solution

$$y = \int e^{-3x}\, dx = -\tfrac{1}{3}e^{-3x} + C,$$

where C is an arbitrary constant.

(b) In order to satisfy the initial condition $y(0) = \frac{5}{3}$ (that is, $y = \frac{5}{3}$ when $x = 0$), we must have

$$\tfrac{5}{3} = -\tfrac{1}{3}e^{0} + C,$$

so $C = 2$. The required particular solution is therefore

$$y = -\tfrac{1}{3}e^{-3x} + 2. \quad \blacksquare$$

Procedure 3.1 uses x for the independent variable and y for the dependent variable. As usual, you should be prepared to translate this into situations where other symbols are used for the variables. But remember that the method of direct integration applies solely to first-order differential equations for which the derivative is equal to a function of the *independent* variable alone. Thus direct integration can be applied, for example, to the differential equation

$$\frac{dx}{dt} = \cos t,$$

to give the general solution

$$x = \int \cos t\, dt = \sin t + C,$$

where C is an arbitrary constant. (Here t is the independent variable and x is the dependent variable.) On the other hand, the differential equation

$$\frac{dx}{dt} = x^{2}$$

cannot be solved by direct integration, since the right-hand side here is a function of the *dependent* variable, x.

Exercise 3.1

Solve each of the following initial-value problems.

(a) $\dfrac{dy}{dx} = 6x, \quad y(1) = 5.$

(b) $\dfrac{dv}{du} = e^{4u}, \quad v(0) = 2.$

*(c) $\dot{y} = 5\sin 2t, \quad y(0) = 0.$

Remember that $\dot{y}$ stands for dy/dt, where t denotes time.

The method of direct integration succeeds in solving a differential equation of the specified type whenever it is possible to carry out the integration that arises, and this task may require you to apply any of the standard techniques of integration, such as integration by parts and integration by substitution. For more difficult integrals, a computer algebra package can be used.

Integration by parts and integration by substitution are revised in *Unit 1*. Many integrations can be performed by reference to the table of standard integrals in the course Handbook.

Exercise 3.2

Find the general solution of each of the following differential equations.

(a) $\dfrac{dy}{dx} = xe^{-2x}$

*(b) $\dot{p} = \dfrac{t}{1+t^2}$ (*Hint*: For the integral, try the substitution $u = 1 + t^2$.)

The answer to Exercise 3.2(b) can be generalized to any differential equation of the form

$$\frac{dy}{dx} = k\frac{f'(x)}{f(x)} \quad (f(x) \neq 0),$$

where k is a constant, to give the general solution

$$y = k \ln|f(x)| + C,$$

where C is an arbitrary constant.

This is a simple extension of the result from *Unit 1* that

$$\int \frac{f'(x)}{f(x)}\,dx = \ln|f(x)| + C,$$

for $f(x) \neq 0$.

3.2 Separation of variables

Direct integration applies, in an immediate sense, only to the very simplest type of differential equation, as described by Equation (3.2). However, all other analytic methods of solution for first-order equations eventually also boil down to performing integrations. In this subsection, we consider how to solve first-order differential equations of the form

$$\frac{dy}{dx} = f(x, y)$$

where the right-hand side $f(x, y)$ is the *product* of a function of x and a function of y; that is, equations of the form

$$\frac{dy}{dx} = g(x)h(y). \tag{3.3}$$

One example of this type of differential equation is

$$\frac{dy}{dx} = x(1 + y^2). \tag{3.4}$$

Here we have $g(x) = x$ and $h(y) = 1 + y^2$.

We divide both sides of this equation by $1 + y^2$, to obtain

$$\frac{1}{1+y^2}\frac{dy}{dx} = x,$$

Note that $1 + y^2$ is never zero, so it is safe to divide by it.

and then integrate both sides with respect to x, which gives

$$\int \frac{1}{1+y^2}\frac{dy}{dx}\,dx = \int x\,dx. \tag{3.5}$$

Applying the rule for integration by substitution (in Leibniz notation) to the left-hand side, we obtain

See Section 6 of *Unit 1*.

$$\int \frac{1}{1+y^2}\frac{dy}{dx}\,dx = \int \frac{1}{1+y^2}\,dy,$$

so Equation (3.5) becomes

$$\int \frac{1}{1+y^2}\,dy = \int x\,dx.$$

On performing the two integrations, we obtain

$$\arctan y = \tfrac{1}{2}x^2 + C, \tag{3.6}$$

See the table of standard integrals in the Handbook.

where C is an arbitrary constant. Making y the subject of the equation, we obtain the solution expression

$$y = \tan(\tfrac{1}{2}x^2 + C).$$

Note that one arbitrary constant suffices.

The approach just demonstrated applies more widely. In principle, it works for any differential equation of the form

$$\frac{dy}{dx} = g(x)h(y). \tag{3.3}$$

On dividing this equation through by $h(y)$ (for all values of y other than those where $h(y) = 0$), we obtain

$$\frac{1}{h(y)} \frac{dy}{dx} = g(x).$$

Integration with respect to x on both sides gives

$$\int \frac{1}{h(y)} \frac{dy}{dx}\, dx = \int g(x)\, dx,$$

and, on applying the rule for integration by substitution to the left-hand side, this becomes

$$\int \frac{1}{h(y)}\, dy = \int g(x)\, dx. \tag{3.7}$$

This is the form that you need to remember! Note that you can obtain it 'informally' by dividing Equation (3.3) by $h(y)$, 'multiplying through by dx', and then adding the two integral signs.

If the two integrals can be evaluated at this stage, then we reach an equation that relates x and y and features an arbitrary constant. This equation is the general solution of the differential equation (for values of y other than those where $h(y) = 0$); but usually y will not be the subject of this equation. It is a form of the general solution called an **implicit** (general) solution of the differential equation. (An example of an implicit solution is provided by Equation (3.6).) Usually, the final aim is to make y the subject of the equation, if possible — that is, to manipulate the equation into the form

$$y = \text{function of } x.$$

This is called the **explicit** (general) solution of the differential equation.

In either case (implicit or explicit), a particular solution may be obtained from the general solution as before, by applying an initial condition.

The method just described for solving differential equations of the form (3.3) is called the method of *separation of variables* since, in Equation (3.7), we have separated the variables to either side of the equation, with only the dependent variable appearing on the left and only the independent variable on the right. The method is summarized below.

Procedure 3.2   Separation of variables

This method applies to separable differential equations, which are of the form

$$\frac{dy}{dx} = g(x)h(y). \tag{3.3}$$

(a) Divide both sides by $h(y)$ (where $h(y) \neq 0$), and integrate both sides with respect to x, to obtain

$$\int \frac{1}{h(y)}\, dy = \int g(x)\, dx. \tag{3.7}$$

(b) If possible, perform the integrations, to obtain an implicit form of the general solution.

(c) If possible, rearrange the formula found in Step (b) to give y in terms of x. This is the explicit (general) solution.

It is a good idea to check, by substitution into the original differential equation, that the function obtained is indeed a solution.

The separation of variables method is useful, but there are some difficulties with it. First, it may not be possible to perform the necessary integrations. Second, the general solution obtained is restricted to those values of y such that $h(y) \neq 0$. Third, it may not be possible to perform the necessary manipulations to obtain an explicit solution.

Of these difficulties, the first can be overcome by use of a numerical method, such as Euler's method. The second will be discussed shortly. The third will usually also need numerical techniques.

It is necessary to be careful about the domain or image set of the solution obtained, as the following example illustrates.

Example 3.2

(a) Find the general solution of the differential equation

$$\frac{dy}{dx} = -\frac{x}{3y} \quad (y > 0).$$

(b) Find the particular solution that satisfies the initial condition $y(0) = 3$.

Solution

(a) The equation is of the form

$$\frac{dy}{dx} = g(x)h(y),$$

where the obvious choices for g and h are

$$g(x) = -x \quad \text{and} \quad h(y) = 1/(3y).$$

Notice that since $y > 0$, $h(y)$ is never zero.

We now apply Procedure 3.2. On dividing through by $h(y) = 1/(3y)$ (that is, multiplying through by $3y$) and integrating with respect to x, the differential equation becomes

$$\int 3y \, dy = \int -x \, dx.$$

With practice, you will be able to move directly to this stage, as shown in Procedure 3.2.

Evaluating the integrals gives

$$\tfrac{3}{2}y^2 = -\tfrac{1}{2}x^2 + B,$$

where B is an arbitrary constant. This is an implicit form of the general solution.

On solving for y (and noting the condition $y > 0$ given above, which determines the sign of the square root), we obtain the explicit general solution

$$y = \sqrt{\tfrac{1}{3}(2B - x^2)}.$$

This can be simplified slightly by writing C in place of $2B$, where C is another arbitrary constant. However, we need to recognize that the formula for y represents a real quantity greater than zero only when the argument of the square root is positive, so we must have $C - x^2 > 0$. This in turn means that C cannot be completely arbitrary, since it must at least be positive. The general solution in this case is therefore

$$y = \sqrt{\tfrac{1}{3}(C - x^2)} \quad (-\sqrt{C} < x < \sqrt{C}),$$

where C is a positive but otherwise arbitrary constant.

Since $x^2 \geq 0$ for all x, $C - x^2 > 0$ implies that $C > x^2 \geq 0$, so C must be positive.

(b) The initial condition is $y(0) = 3$, so we substitute $x = 0$ and $y = 3$ into the general solution above. This gives $3 = \sqrt{\frac{1}{3}C}$, so $C = 27$, and the required particular solution is

$$y = \sqrt{\frac{1}{3}(27 - x^2)} \quad (-3\sqrt{3} < x < 3\sqrt{3}). \quad \blacksquare$$

You verified in Exercise 1.2(d) that this function is a solution of the differential equation.

Exercise 3.3

A mass $m(t)$ of a uranium isotope, which is present in an object at time t, declines over time due to radioactive decay. Its behaviour is modelled by the differential equation

$$\frac{dm}{dt} = -\lambda m \quad (m > 0),$$

where the *decay constant* λ is a positive constant characteristic of the uranium isotope.

This model can be applied to other radioactive substances by selecting the appropriate value of the parameter λ.

(a) Find the general solution of this differential equation.

(b) Find the particular solution for which the initial amount of uranium present (at time $t = 0$) is m_0.

The condition $m > 0$ in Exercise 3.3 arose from the modelling context. This condition enabled us to find the general solution without needing to worry about dividing by zero at Step (a) of the separation of variables method (and hence without needing to restrict the image set further). Suppose we were to forget the modelling context — that is, suppose we were to remove the restriction $m > 0$. How does this affect the solution process? And how do we cope with the case where $m = 0$? These questions are answered in the following example where, to emphasize the absence of the previous modelling context, the variables used are x and y.

Example 3.3

Find the general solution of the differential equation

$$\frac{dy}{dx} = -\lambda y,$$

where λ is a non-zero constant.

Solution

To apply the separation of variables method, we need to exclude the cases where $y = 0$. So, for $y \neq 0$, on dividing through by y, integrating with respect to x, and using the rule for integration by substitution on the left-hand side, we obtain

$$\int \frac{1}{y}\, dy = \int (-\lambda)\, dx. \tag{3.8}$$

Integrating, we obtain

$$\ln |y| = -\lambda x + B,$$

where B is an arbitrary constant. Taking exponentials gives

$$|y| = e^{-\lambda x + B}$$

or, removing the modulus sign,

$$y = \pm e^{-\lambda x + B} = \pm e^{B} e^{-\lambda x} = C e^{-\lambda x},$$

where $C = \pm e^{B}$ is a non-zero but otherwise arbitrary constant.

You saw in *Unit 1* that

$$\int \frac{1}{y}\, dy = \ln |y| \quad (y \neq 0).$$

This is not quite the general solution, as we have to consider what happens when $y = 0$. Now, looking at the above solution, it is natural to ask what happens when $C = 0$. This gives the zero function, $y = 0$ for all x, and inspection of the differential equation shows that this is a particular solution. So we now have the general solution

$$y = Ce^{-\lambda x},$$

where C is an arbitrary constant. (Positive C corresponds to $y > 0$, negative C to $y < 0$, and $C = 0$ to the particular solution $y = 0$.)   ■

The above example illustrates that:

- the separation of variables method requires that $h(y) \neq 0$ and gives a family of solutions containing an arbitrary constant;

- the case when $h(y) = 0$ is exceptional and can give extra solutions that may or may not have the same form as the family of general solutions.

The following exercises provide you with some practice at applying the separation of variables method and at completing the general solution for values of y such that $h(y) = 0$.

Exercise 3.4

Find the general solution of each of the following differential equations.

*(a) $\dfrac{dy}{dx} = \dfrac{y-1}{x}$ $(x > 0)$ (b) $\dfrac{dy}{dx} = \dfrac{2y}{x^2+1}$

*Exercise 3.5

Solve the initial-value problem

$$\frac{dv}{du} = e^{u+v}, \quad v(0) = 0.$$

End-of-section Exercises

Exercise 3.6

Find the general solution of each of the following differential equations, where a is a non-zero constant.

(a) $\dfrac{dy}{du} = \dfrac{1}{u-a}$ $(u \neq a)$

(b) $\dfrac{dy}{dx} = \dfrac{1}{x(1-ax)}$ $(x \neq 0,\ x \neq 1/a)$

Exercise 3.7

Find the general solution of each of the following differential equations.

(a) $u' = xu$ (b) $\dot{x} = 1 + x^2$

Exercise 3.8

(a) Solve the initial-value problem

$$\frac{dP}{dt} = kP\left(1 - \frac{P}{M}\right), \quad P(0) = P_0 \text{ (where } P_0 > 0\text{)},$$

where k and M are positive constants.

(*Hint*: For the integral involving P, the solution for Exercise 3.6(b) should be of use.)

(b) Describe what happens to the solution $P(t)$ as t becomes large.

The differential equation here is the logistic equation (Equation (2.2)) which, as was pointed out earlier, may be used as a model for the size $P(t)$ of a population at time t. The direction field of this equation in a specific case was examined in Exercise 2.1 (page 74).

4 Solving linear differential equations

This section presents one final method of analytic solution for first-order differential equations. The details of this *integrating factor* method appear in Subsection 4.2. It applies only to a particular form of equation known as a *linear* differential equation. The definition and some properties of this type of equation are introduced in Subsection 4.1.

4.1 Linear differential equations

This subsection introduces the concept of *linearity* as applied to differential equations. Here the concept is introduced in the context of first-order differential equations, but you should be aware that the idea generalizes to higher-order differential equations and is important from a theoretical point of view.

Linear second-order differential equations are considered in *Unit 3*.

Definitions

(a) A first-order differential equation for $y = y(x)$ is **linear** if it can be expressed in the form

$$\frac{dy}{dx} + g(x)y = h(x), \tag{4.1}$$

where $g(x)$ and $h(x)$ are given functions.

(b) A linear first-order differential equation is said to be **homogeneous** if $h(x) = 0$ for all x, and **inhomogeneous** or **non-homogeneous** otherwise.

This differential equation can be written in the general form

$$\frac{dy}{dx} = f(x, y)$$

that we have been using by putting

$$f(x, y) = -g(x)y + h(x).$$

For example, the differential equation

$$\frac{dy}{dx} - x^2 y = x^3$$

is linear, with $g(x) = -x^2$ and $h(x) = x^3$, whereas the equation

$$\frac{dy}{dx} = xy^2$$

is not, due to the presence of the non-linear term y^2.

---

*Exercise 4.1 ――――――――――――――――――――――――――

Decide whether or not each of the following first-order differential equations is linear.

(a) $\dfrac{dy}{dx} + x^3 y = x^5$ (b) $\dfrac{dy}{dx} = x \sin x$ (c) $\dfrac{dz}{dt} = -3z^{1/2}$

(d) $\dot{y} + y^2 = t$ (e) $x\dfrac{dy}{dx} + y = y^2$ (f) $(1 + x^2)\dfrac{dy}{dx} + 2xy = 3x^2$

An important theorem guarantees that an initial-value problem based on a linear first-order differential equation has a unique solution.

Theorem 4.1

If the functions $g(x)$ and $h(x)$ are continuous throughout an interval (a, b) and x_0 belongs to this interval, then the initial-value problem

$$\frac{dy}{dx} + g(x)y = h(x), \quad y(x_0) = y_0,$$

has a unique solution throughout the interval.

This includes the possibility that either $a = -\infty$ or $b = \infty$, so the interval might be all of the real line.

This is a very powerful result, since it means that once you have found a solution in a particular interval, that solution will be the *only* one.

There is a particularly useful technique for solving linear differential equations, to which we turn next.

4.2 The integrating factor method

As you have seen, the method of separation of variables relies upon an application of the rule for integration by substitution, which is equivalent to the Composite Rule (or Chain Rule) for derivatives. It is natural to enquire whether there might similarly be a method for solving first-order differential equations that derives from the rule for integration by parts or, equivalently, from the Product Rule for derivatives. There is indeed such a method, and it is the subject of this subsection.

To introduce the topic, consider the differential equation

$$(1 + x^2)\frac{dy}{dx} + 2xy = 3x^2. \tag{4.2}$$

Note first that $2x$ (the coefficient of y) is the derivative of $1 + x^2$ (the coefficient of dy/dx). It follows from the Product Rule that

As you saw in Exercise 4.1(f), this differential equation is linear; but it is not soluble by direct integration or by separation of variables.

$$\frac{d}{dx}\left((1 + x^2)y\right) = (1 + x^2)\frac{dy}{dx} + 2xy.$$

The right-hand side of this equation is the same as the left-hand side of Equation (4.2), so we can rewrite the latter as

$$\frac{d}{dx}\left((1 + x^2)y\right) = 3x^2. \tag{4.3}$$

Now the left-hand side here is just the derivative of $(1 + x^2)y$, so we can apply direct integration to Equation (4.3) to obtain

$$(1 + x^2)y = \int 3x^2 \, dx = x^3 + C,$$

where C is an arbitrary constant. Division by $1 + x^2$ then gives the general solution of Equation (4.2) explicitly, as

$$y = \frac{x^3 + C}{1 + x^2}.$$

This solution was arrived at by noting that the left-hand side of Equation (4.2) is of the form

$$p\frac{dy}{dx} + \frac{dp}{dx}y, \tag{4.4}$$

where $p = 1 + x^2$, and that this form can be re-expressed, using the Product Rule, as

$$\frac{d}{dx}(py).$$

Linear differential equations need not come in this convenient form. For example, the left-hand side of the equation

$$\frac{dy}{dx} + \left(\frac{2x}{1+x^2}\right)y = \frac{3x^2}{1+x^2} \tag{4.5}$$

is not of the form (4.4). However, Equation (4.2) can be obtained from Equation (4.5) on multiplying through by $p = 1 + x^2$. For this reason, $p = 1 + x^2$ may be called an *integrating factor* for Equation (4.5): it is the factor by which Equation (4.5) needs to be multiplied in order that the resulting differential equation has a left-hand side of the form (4.4), enabling direct integration to be performed.

This leaves the question of how such an integrating factor can be found, starting from Equation (4.5). The answer comes from writing down the two properties that such a function $p = p(x)$ must satisfy, as follows.

- Multiplying Equation (4.5) by p gives, on the left-hand side,

$$p\frac{dy}{dx} + p\left(\frac{2x}{1+x^2}\right)y.$$

- The left-hand side must be of the form

$$p\frac{dy}{dx} + \frac{dp}{dx}y. \tag{4.4}$$

Comparison of these two expressions shows that p must itself be a particular solution of the differential equation

$$\frac{dp}{dx} = \left(\frac{2x}{1+x^2}\right)p. \tag{4.6}$$

This is a homogeneous linear first-order differential equation, and we can solve it by separation of variables. Indeed, following Procedure 3.2, the equation becomes (for $p \neq 0$)

$$\int \frac{dp}{p} = \int \frac{2x}{1+x^2}\,dx.$$

Performing the left-hand integral gives

$$\ln|p| = \int \frac{2x}{1+x^2}\,dx,$$

so

$$|p| = \exp\left(\int \frac{2x}{1+x^2}\,dx\right). \tag{4.7}$$

Now, performing the integral on the right,

$$|p| = \exp\left(\ln(|1+x^2|) + A\right)$$
$$= \exp(A)|1+x^2|$$
$$= D(1+x^2),$$

Note that $1+x^2 > 0$, so $|1+x^2| = 1+x^2$.

where D ($= \exp(A)$) is a positive but otherwise arbitrary constant. Hence

$$p = \pm D(1+x^2),$$

The case $D = 0$ corresponds to the solution $p = 0$ of Equation (4.6), but this solution is not of interest.

which, by redefining D, can be written as

$$p = D(1+x^2),$$

where D is now a non-zero but otherwise arbitrary constant.

Thus an integrating factor for Equation (4.5) is $p(x) = D(1+x^2)$. Multiplying through the equation by this factor yields

$$D(1+x^2)\frac{dy}{dx} + 2Dxy = 3Dx^2,$$

and now you can see that (since $D \neq 0$) the arbitrary constant D can be chosen without affecting the applicability of the form (4.4). Therefore we *choose* the integrating factor to have the simplest possible form — in this case we obtain $p(x) = 1+x^2$.

As you have seen, this leads to the solution of Equation (4.5) by direct integration, and the formula for this integrating factor is given by Equation (4.7) as

$$p = \exp\left(\int \frac{2x}{1+x^2}\,dx\right). \tag{4.8}$$

This approach generalizes to any linear first-order differential equation, provided that the integrals involved can be evaluated. For an equation written in the form

$$\frac{dy}{dx} + g(x)y = h(x), \tag{4.1}$$

the function $g(x)$ takes the place of $2x/(1+x^2)$ in Equation (4.5). To find an integrating factor $p = p(x)$ for Equation (4.1), the argument proceeds as above, with $2x/(1+x^2)$ replaced by $g(x)$ at each step. This leads to the generalized form of Equation (4.8), namely

$$p = \exp\left(\int g(x)\,dx\right), \tag{4.9}$$

which defines the **integrating factor** for Equation (4.1).

Remember that calculation of the integrating factor does not require the inclusion of a constant of integration.

When Equation (4.1) is multiplied through by the integrating factor, the resulting differential equation is

$$p(x)\frac{dy}{dx} + p(x)g(x)y = p(x)h(x), \tag{4.10}$$

the left-hand side of which, by the definition of p, is of the form (4.4); so Equation (4.10) can be re-expressed, using the Product Rule, as

$$\frac{d}{dx}(p(x)y) = p(x)h(x). \tag{4.11}$$

The definition of p ensures that the left-hand side of Equation (4.10) is of the form (4.4) since

$$\frac{dp}{dx} = \frac{d}{dx}\left(\exp\left(\int g(x)\,dx\right)\right)$$
$$= \exp\left(\int g(x)\,dx\right)g(x)$$
$$= p(x)g(x).$$

Direct integration can then be used on Equation (4.11) to try to find the general solution.

This integrating factor method is summarized below.

Procedure 4.1   Integrating factor method

This method applies to differential equations of the form

$$\frac{dy}{dx} + g(x)y = h(x). \tag{4.1}$$

(a) Determine the integrating factor

$$p = \exp\left(\int g(x)\,dx\right). \tag{4.9}$$

The constant of integration is not needed here.

(b) Multiply Equation (4.1) by $p(x)$ to recast the differential equation as

$$p(x)\frac{dy}{dx} + p(x)g(x)y = p(x)h(x).$$

(c) Rewrite the differential equation as

$$\frac{d}{dx}\left(p(x)y\right) = p(x)h(x).$$

(d) Integrate this last equation, to obtain

$$p(x)y = \int p(x)h(x)\,dx.$$

(e) Divide through by $p(x)$, to obtain the general solution in explicit form.

You can, if you wish, check that you have found p correctly by checking that

$$p(x)\frac{dy}{dx} + p(x)g(x)y$$
$$= \frac{d}{dx}\left(p(x)y\right),$$

i.e. by checking that $dp/dx = p(x)g(x)$.

It is a good idea to check, by substitution into the original equation, that the function obtained is indeed a solution.

As with the separation of variables method, it may not be possible to perform the necessary final integration. However, in the remainder of this subsection we give examples and exercises for which this method can be used.

Example 4.1

Use the integrating factor method to find the general solution of each of the following differential equations.

(a) $\dfrac{dy}{dx} = x - \dfrac{2xy}{x^2+1}$ (b) $\dfrac{dy}{dx} = \dfrac{y-1}{x}\ (x>0)$ (c) $\dfrac{dy}{dx} = \dfrac{2y}{1+x^2}$

The first example cannot be solved by separation of variables. The latter two can, as you saw in Exercise 3.4. You can compare these answers with those obtained earlier.

Solution

(a) On rearranging the differential equation as

$$\frac{dy}{dx} + \frac{2xy}{x^2+1} = x,$$

we see that it is in the form of Equation (4.1) with

$$g(x) = \frac{2x}{x^2+1} \quad \text{and} \quad h(x) = x.$$

The integrating factor (from Equation (4.9)) is therefore

$$p = \exp\left(\int \frac{2x}{x^2+1}\,dx\right)$$
$$= \exp(\ln|x^2+1|)$$
$$= \exp(\ln(x^2+1)) \quad \text{(since } 1+x^2>0\text{)}$$
$$= x^2+1.$$

Checking, we see that

$$\frac{dp}{dx} = 2x = g(x)p(x).$$

Multiplying both sides of the differential equation by this factor yields

$$(x^2 + 1)\frac{dy}{dx} + 2xy = x(x^2 + 1),$$

and the differential equation thus becomes

$$\frac{d}{dx}\left((x^2 + 1)y\right) = x(x^2 + 1).$$

Integrating both sides gives

$$\begin{aligned}
(x^2 + 1)y &= \int x(x^2 + 1)\, dx \\
&= \int (x^3 + x)\, dx \\
&= \tfrac{1}{4}x^4 + \tfrac{1}{2}x^2 + C,
\end{aligned}$$

where C is an arbitrary constant. Finally, to obtain an explicit solution we divide by $x^2 + 1$ to obtain

$$y = \frac{x^4 + 2x^2 + 4C}{4(x^2 + 1)}.$$

(b) On rearranging the differential equation as

$$\frac{dy}{dx} - \frac{1}{x}y = -\frac{1}{x},$$

we see that it is in the form of Equation (4.1) with $g(x) = h(x) = -1/x$. The integrating factor (from Equation (4.9)) is therefore

$$\begin{aligned}
p &= \exp\left(\int \left(-\frac{1}{x}\right) dx\right) \\
&= \exp(-\ln x) \quad \text{(since } x > 0\text{)} \\
&= \exp\left(\ln\left(\frac{1}{x}\right)\right) \\
&= \frac{1}{x}.
\end{aligned}$$

Recall that $a \ln x = \ln(x^a)$ and hence, in particular,
$$-\ln x = \ln(x^{-1}) = \ln(1/x).$$

Checking, we see that
$$\frac{dp}{dx} = -\frac{1}{x^2} = g(x)p(x).$$

Multiplying through the equation by $p(x) = 1/x$ gives

$$\frac{1}{x}\frac{dy}{dx} - \frac{1}{x^2}y = -\frac{1}{x^2},$$

and the differential equation becomes

$$\frac{d}{dx}\left(\frac{1}{x}y\right) = -\frac{1}{x^2}.$$

Integration then gives

$$\begin{aligned}
\frac{y}{x} &= \int \left(-\frac{1}{x^2}\right) dx \\
&= \frac{1}{x} + C,
\end{aligned}$$

where C is an arbitrary constant. The general solution is therefore

$$y = 1 + Cx,$$

where C is an arbitrary constant.

(c) In order to put the given differential equation into the form (4.1), we need to bring the term in y to the left-hand side to obtain

$$\frac{dy}{dx} - \frac{2}{1 + x^2} y = 0. \tag{4.12}$$

Hence, in this case, we have $g(x) = -2/(1 + x^2)$ and $h(x) = 0$. The integrating factor is

> The equation is homogeneous.

$$p = \exp\left(\int \left(-\frac{2}{1 + x^2}\right) dx\right) = \exp(-2\arctan x) = e^{-2\arctan x}.$$

Multiplying through by the integrating factor gives

$$e^{-2\arctan x} \frac{dy}{dx} - \frac{2y}{1 + x^2} e^{-2\arctan x} = 0.$$

Thus the differential equation can be rewritten as

$$\frac{d}{dx}\left(e^{-2\arctan x} y\right) = 0.$$

It follows, on integrating, that

$$e^{-2\arctan x} y = C, \quad \text{or, equivalently,} \quad y = Ce^{2\arctan x},$$

where C is an arbitrary constant. This is the general solution. ∎

> Checking, we see that
> $$\frac{dp}{dx} = \frac{-2e^{-2\arctan x}}{1 + x^2}$$
> $$= e^{-2\arctan x}\left(-\frac{2}{1 + x^2}\right)$$
> $$= p(x)g(x).$$

Exercise 4.2

Find the general solution of each of the following differential equations.

(a) $\dfrac{dy}{dx} - y = e^x \sin x$ (b) $\dfrac{dy}{dx} = y + x$

> For part (b), see Examples 1.1 and 2.1. A direction field diagram is shown in Figure 2.2.

Exercise 4.3

Use the integrating factor method to solve each of the following initial-value problems.

(a) $u' = xu, \quad u(0) = 2.$

(b) $t\dot{y} + 2y = t^2, \quad y(1) = 1.$

> You saw the differential equation in part (a) in Exercise 3.7(a), where you solved it using separation of variables.

End-of-section Exercises

Exercise 4.4

Which method would you use to try to solve each of the following linear first-order differential equations?

(a) $\dfrac{dy}{dx} + x^3 y = x^5$ (b) $\dfrac{dy}{dx} = x \sin x$

(c) $\dfrac{dv}{du} + 5v = 0$ (d) $(1 + x^2)\dfrac{dy}{dx} + 2xy = 1 + x^2$

Exercise 4.5

Solve each of the following initial-value problems.

(a) $\dot{y} + y = t + 1, \quad y(1) = 0.$

(b) $e^{3t}\dot{y} = 1 - e^{3t}y, \quad y(0) = 3.$

> The differential equation in part (a) is equivalent to that considered in parts (e) and (f) of Exercise 1.2.

Exercise 4.6

Find the general solution of each of the following differential equations.

(a) $x\dfrac{dy}{dx} - 3y = x \quad (x > 0)$

(b) $\dfrac{dv}{dt} + 4v = 3\cos 2t$

> (*Hint*: If a and b are non-zero constants, then
>
> $$\int e^{at}\cos bt\, dt = \frac{e^{at}}{a^2 + b^2}(a\cos bt + b\sin bt) + C,$$
>
> where C is an arbitrary constant.)

5   Finding analytic solutions on the computer

In this section you will see how direct integration, the method of separation of variables and the integrating factor method can be used on the computer to solve first-order differential equations.

Use your computer to complete the following activities.

PC

*Activity 5.1

Use direct integration to solve the initial-value problem

$$\frac{dy}{dx} = e^{-3x}, \quad y(0) = \tfrac{5}{3}.$$

Compare your solution with that obtained in Example 3.1.

*Activity 5.2

Use separation of variables to find the general solution of each of the following differential equations.

(a) $\dfrac{dy}{dx} = -\lambda y$ (b) $\dfrac{dy}{dx} = \dfrac{2y}{x^2 + 1}$ (c) $\dfrac{dy}{dx} = 1 + y^2$

Compare your solutions with those obtained in Example 3.3 and Exercises 3.4(b) and 3.7(b), respectively.

*Activity 5.3

Use the integrating factor method to solve the following initial-value problems.

(a) $\dfrac{dy}{dx} = x + y, \quad y(0) = 0.$

(b) $x\dfrac{dy}{dx} + 2y = x^2, \quad y(1) = 1.$

Compare your solutions with those obtained in Exercises 4.2(b) and 4.3(b), respectively.

*Activity 5.4

Use the integrating factor method to find the general solution of each of the following differential equations.

(a) $x\dfrac{dy}{dx} - 3y = x$ (b) $\dfrac{dy}{dx} + 4y = 3\cos 2x$

Compare your solutions with those obtained in Exercises 4.6(a) and 4.6(b), respectively.

Outcomes

After studying this unit you should be able to:

- understand and use the basic terminology relating to differential equations and their solutions;
- check by substitution whether a given function is a solution of a given first-order differential equation or initial-value problem;
- find from the general solution of a first-order differential equation the particular solution that satisfies a given initial condition;
- appreciate the difficulties with domains and image sets for the solution of some differential equations;
- deduce the qualitative behaviour of solutions from consideration of a first-order differential equation itself, as visualized from its direction field;
- set up the formulae required by Euler's method for solving an initial-value problem, carry out a few steps of the method by hand, and use the computer to deal with large numbers of steps;
- recognize when a first-order differential equation is soluble by direct integration, and carry out that integration when appropriate, by hand in simple cases and otherwise on the computer;
- recognize when a first-order differential equation is separable, and apply the method of separation of variables by hand in simple cases and otherwise on the computer;
- recognize when a first-order differential equation is linear, and solve such an equation by the integrating factor method, by hand in simple cases and otherwise on the computer.

Solutions to the exercises

Section 1

1.1 We have $r(P) = k\left(1 - \dfrac{P}{M}\right)$, so we simply need to solve the following pair of simultaneous equations:

$$k\left(1 - \frac{10}{M}\right) = 1,$$

$$k\left(1 - \frac{10\,000}{M}\right) = 0.$$

From the second equation, since $k > 0$, we see immediately that $M = 10\,000$. Substituting in the first equation leads to

$$k\frac{999}{1000} = 1, \quad \text{so} \quad k = \frac{1000}{999}.$$

1.2 In each case, differences in notation notwithstanding, the differential equation has the form

$$\frac{dy}{dx} = f(x, y),$$

and we need to show that the given function $y = y(x)$ satisfies this equation, i.e. gives the same expression for either side of the equation.

(a) If $y = 2e^x - (x^2 + 2x + 2)$, then differentiating y gives

$$\frac{dy}{dx} = 2e^x - 2x - 2,$$

and substituting the expression for y into the expression for f gives

$$f(x, y) = y + x^2 = 2e^x - (x^2 + 2x + 2) + x^2$$
$$= 2e^x - 2x - 2,$$

as required.

(b) If $y = \frac{1}{2}x^2 + \frac{3}{2}$, then

$$\frac{dy}{dx} = x \quad \text{and} \quad f(x, y) = x.$$

(c) If $u = 2e^{x^2/2}$, then

$$u' = \frac{du}{dx} = 2xe^{x^2/2}$$

and

$$f(x, u) = xu = 2xe^{x^2/2}.$$

(d) If $y = \sqrt{(27 - x^2)/3} \; (-3\sqrt{3} < x < 3\sqrt{3})$, then

$$\frac{dy}{dx} = -\frac{x}{3}\left(\frac{27 - x^2}{3}\right)^{-1/2}$$

and

$$f(x, y) = -\frac{x}{3y} = -\frac{x}{3}\left(\frac{27 - x^2}{3}\right)^{-1/2}.$$

(e) If $y = t + e^{-t}$, then

$$\dot{y} = \frac{dy}{dt} = 1 - e^{-t}$$

and

$$f(t, y) = -y + t + 1 = -(t + e^{-t}) + t + 1 = 1 - e^{-t}.$$

(f) If $y = t + Ce^{-t}$, then

$$\dot{y} = \frac{dy}{dt} = 1 - Ce^{-t}$$

and

$$f(t, y) = -y + t + 1 = -(t + Ce^{-t}) + t + 1$$
$$= 1 - Ce^{-t}.$$

1.3 In each case, differences in notation notwithstanding, the differential equation has the form

$$\frac{dy}{dx} = f(x, y),$$

and we need to show that the given function $y = y(x)$ satisfies this equation, i.e. gives the same expression for either side of the equation.

(a) If $y = C - \frac{1}{3}e^{-3x}$, then

$$\frac{dy}{dx} = e^{-3x} \quad \text{and} \quad f(x, y) = e^{-3x}.$$

(b) If $u = Ce^t - t - 1$, then

$$\dot{u} = \frac{du}{dt} = Ce^t - 1$$

and

$$f(t, u) = t + u = Ce^t - 1.$$

(c) If

$$P = \frac{CMe^{kt}}{1 + Ce^{kt}},$$

then, using the Quotient Rule for differentiation,

$$\frac{dP}{dt} = \frac{(1 + Ce^{kt})(CMke^{kt}) - (CMe^{kt})(Cke^{kt})}{(1 + Ce^{kt})^2}$$

$$= k\left(\frac{CMe^{kt}}{1 + Ce^{kt}}\right)\left(\frac{1 + Ce^{kt} - Ce^{kt}}{1 + Ce^{kt}}\right)$$

$$= k\left(\frac{CMe^{kt}}{1 + Ce^{kt}}\right)\left(1 - \frac{Ce^{kt}}{1 + Ce^{kt}}\right)$$

$$= kP\left(1 - \frac{P}{M}\right).$$

1.4 (a) From Exercise 1.3(c) we know that

$$P(t) = \frac{CMe^{kt}}{1 + Ce^{kt}} = \frac{10Ce^{0.15t}}{1 + Ce^{0.15t}}$$

is a solution of the differential equation. The initial condition $P(0) = 1$ then implies (since $e^0 = 1$)

$$1 = \frac{10C}{1 + C}, \quad \text{so} \quad C = \frac{1}{9}.$$

A particular solution is therefore

$$P = \frac{\frac{10}{9}e^{0.15t}}{1 + \frac{1}{9}e^{0.15t}} = \frac{10e^{0.15t}}{9 + e^{0.15t}}.$$

(b) Dividing top and bottom by $e^{0.15t}$, we see that

$$P = \frac{10}{9e^{-0.15t} + 1}.$$

For large values of t, the exponential term on the bottom will be very small. The result is that P will approach the value 10 in the long term.

1.5 Calculator results are given to eight significant figures. (Different calculators may give slightly different results.)

(a) $f(3.142) = 31.018\,339,$

$f(3.141\,592\,6) = 31.006\,275.$

So we have

error $= f(3.142) - f(\pi)$

$\simeq f(3.142) - f(3.141\,592\,6)$

$\simeq 0.012.$

(b) $f(3.142) = 4.421\,123\,2 \times 10^{13},$

$f(3.141\,592\,6) = 4.403\,148\,2 \times 10^{13}.$

So we have

error $= f(3.142) - f(\pi)$

$\simeq f(3.142) - f(3.141\,592\,6)$

$\simeq 1.8 \times 10^{11}.$

1.6 (a) If $y = \arcsin x + C$ $(-1 < x < 1)$, then differentiating gives

$$\frac{dy}{dx} = \frac{1}{\sqrt{1 - x^2}},$$

so y satisfies the given differential equation.

(b) The initial condition is $y(\frac{1}{2}) = \frac{\pi}{2}$, i.e. $y = \frac{\pi}{2}$ when $x = \frac{1}{2}$. On substituting these values into the solution from part (a), we have

$\frac{\pi}{2} = \arcsin \frac{1}{2} + C = \frac{\pi}{6} + C.$

This gives $C = \frac{\pi}{3}$, so the solution of the initial-value problem is

$y = \arcsin x + \frac{\pi}{3}$ $(-1 < x < 1).$

1.7 (a) If $x = \tan(t + C)$ $(-\frac{\pi}{2} < t + C < \frac{\pi}{2})$, then differentiating gives

$$\dot{x} = \frac{dx}{dt} = \sec^2(t + C) = 1 + \tan^2(t + C) = 1 + x^2,$$

so x satisfies the given differential equation.

(b) The initial condition is $x(\frac{\pi}{4}) = 1$, i.e. $x = 1$ when $t = \frac{\pi}{4}$. On substituting these values into the solution from part (a), we have

$1 = \tan(\frac{\pi}{4} + C).$

This gives $C = \arctan 1 - \frac{\pi}{4} = 0$, so the solution of the initial-value problem is

$x = \tan t$ $(-\frac{\pi}{2} < t < \frac{\pi}{2}).$

Section 2

2.1 (a) The slope is shown to be zero at all points on the horizontal lines $P = 0$ and $P = 1000$, so these correspond to constant solutions of the differential equation. (As pointed out earlier in the text, these two solutions can also be spotted directly from the form of the differential equation.)

The graphs of solutions through a starting point above the line $P = 1000$ appear to decrease, but at a slower and slower rate, tending from above towards the limit $P = 1000$ as t increases.

The graphs of solutions through starting points in the region $0 < P < 1000$ are increasing, with slope growing before the level $P = 500$ is reached and declining thereafter. For large values of t, these graphs tend from below towards the limit $P = 1000$.

For a starting point in the region $P < 0$, the graphs decrease without limit and with steeper and steeper slope.

These various cases are illustrated by typical graphs in the figure below.

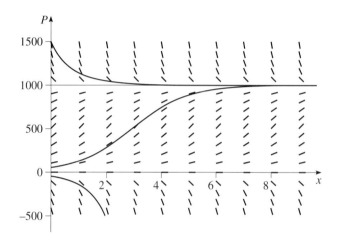

(b) If the differential equation is considered as a model of population behaviour, then the region $P < 0$ must be excluded. The analysis above leads to the following predictions for the population.

- If the population is zero at the start, then it remains zero.

- If the population size starts at 1000, then it remains fixed at this level.

- If the population starts at a level higher than 1000, then it declines (more and more gradually) towards 1000.

- If the population starts at a level below 1000 (but above 0), then it increases and eventually tends gradually towards 1000.

2.2 For the initial-value problem

$$\frac{dy}{dx} = y, \quad y(0) = 1,$$

we have $x_0 = 0$, $Y_0 = y_0 = 1$ and $f(x_i, Y_i) = Y_i$. The step size is given as $h = 0.2$. Equation (2.9) with $i = 0$ gives

$x_1 = x_0 + h = 0 + 0.2 = 0.2,$

and Equation (2.10) with $i = 0$ gives

$Y_1 = Y_0 + hf(x_0, Y_0) = 1 + 0.2 \times 1 = 1.2.$

Applying Equations (2.9) and (2.10) in turn for $i = 1, 2, 3, 4$, we obtain the following table.

i	x_i	Y_i	$f(x_i, Y_i) = Y_i$	$Y_{i+1} = Y_i + hf(x_i, Y_i)$
0	0	1	1	1.2
1	0.2	1.2	1.2	1.44
2	0.4	1.44	1.44	1.728
3	0.6	1.728	1.728	2.0736
4	0.8	2.0736	2.0736	2.48832
5	1.0	2.48832		

The approximation to $y(1)$ is 2.48832.

2.3 Since we are told that, for sufficiently small h, the absolute error is proportional to the step size h, we can deduce from the last row of Table 2.2 that there exists a constant k such that

$$0.000\,136 = 0.0001k,$$

so $k = 1.36$. In order to determine $y(1)$ correct to five decimal places, h must be such that

$$1.36h < 5 \times 10^{-6}$$

or

$$h < \frac{5 \times 10^{-6}}{1.36} \simeq 3.7 \times 10^{-6}.$$

So a suitable choice of h would be $10^{-6} = 0.000\,001$.

(In fact, using this value of h gives an approximation to $y(1)$ of 2.718 280, which *is* correct to 5 decimal places.)

2.4 (a) The slope defined by the direction field $f(x, y) = y + x^2$ is zero when $y = -x^2$, which is a parabola in the lower half-plane with vertex at the origin. Below this parabola we have $y < -x^2$ and $f(x, y) < 0$, while above the parabola we have $y > -x^2$ and $f(x, y) > 0$. Thus all slopes for points of the plane below the parabola $y = -x^2$ are negative, and all slopes for points above it are positive.

Also, if x is fixed, then $f(x, y) = y + x^2$ is an increasing function as y increases. If instead y is fixed, then for $x > 0$, $f(x, y)$ increases as x increases, and for $x < 0$, $f(x, y)$ increases as x becomes more negative. These observations indicate that the slope given by the direction field increases as we move from bottom to top along any vertical line, whereas on moving along any horizontal line, the slope increases with distance from the y-axis.

(b) The features described in the solution to part (a) are all apparent on the direction field diagram. This direction field diagram is repeated below, with the parabola $y = -x^2$ superimposed upon it. (Note that this parabola does not represent a solution of the differential equation.)

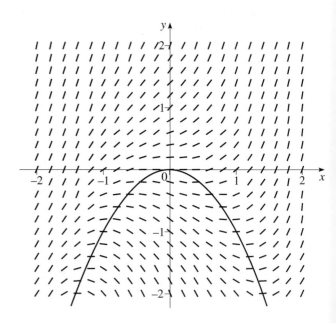

(c) It appears from the direction field that there are several types of solution. Any solution whose graph cuts the y-axis above the origin has positive slope at all points. The solution graph that passes through the origin has zero slope there, but positive slope everywhere else. Any solution graph that cuts the y-axis below the origin has a maximum (where it meets $y = -x^2$ for $x < 0$). Some of these graphs also have a minimum (where they meet $y = -x^2$ for $x > 0$). Others have no minimum (though this is not clear from the diagram given). A solution graph of each type is sketched below.

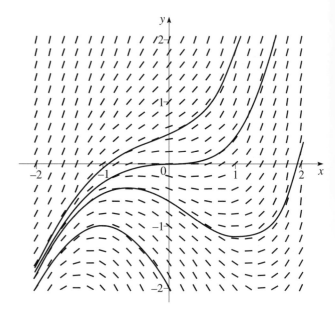

(d) The initial-value problem is

$$\frac{dy}{dx} = y + x^2, \quad y(-1) = -0.2.$$

From Equations (2.9) and (2.10), the necessary formulae are

$$x_{i+1} = x_i + h,$$
$$Y_{i+1} = Y_i + hf(x_i, Y_i).$$

For the current problem, $x_0 = -1$, $Y_0 = y_0 = -0.2$, $f(x_i, Y_i) = Y_i + x_i^2$ and $h = 0.1$. The particular formulae needed here are therefore:

$$x_{i+1} = x_i + 0.1, \quad \text{where } x_0 = -1;$$
$$Y_{i+1} = Y_i + 0.1(Y_i + x_i^2), \quad \text{where } Y_0 = -0.2.$$

The second of these formulae can also be written as

$$Y_{i+1} = 1.1Y_i + 0.1x_i^2, \quad \text{where } Y_0 = -0.2.$$

Section 3

3.1 We apply direct integration to find the general solution. In each case, C is an arbitrary constant.

(a) The differential equation $dy/dx = 6x$ has general solution

$$y = \int 6x\, dx = 3x^2 + C.$$

From the initial condition $y(1) = 5$, we have $5 = 3 + C$, so $C = 2$. The solution of the initial-value problem is therefore

$$y = 3x^2 + 2.$$

(b) The differential equation $dv/du = e^{4u}$ has general solution

$$v = \int e^{4u}\, du = \tfrac{1}{4}e^{4u} + C.$$

From the initial condition $v(0) = 2$, we have $2 = \tfrac{1}{4} + C$, so $C = \tfrac{7}{4}$. The solution of the initial-value problem is therefore

$$v = \tfrac{1}{4}e^{4u} + \tfrac{7}{4}.$$

(c) The differential equation $\dot{y} = 5\sin 2t$ has general solution

$$y = \int 5\sin 2t\, dt = -\tfrac{5}{2}\cos 2t + C.$$

From the initial condition $y(0) = 0$, we have $0 = -\tfrac{5}{2} + C$, so $C = \tfrac{5}{2}$. The solution of the initial-value problem is therefore

$$y = \tfrac{5}{2}(1 - \cos 2t).$$

3.2 (a) The differential equation $dy/dx = xe^{-2x}$ has general solution

$$y = \int xe^{-2x}\, dx.$$

The integral may be found using integration by parts. Taking $f(x) = x$ and $g'(x) = e^{-2x}$, and using the formula

$$\int f(x)g'(x)\, dx = f(x)g(x) - \int f'(x)g(x)\, dx,$$

we have

$$\int xe^{-2x}\, dx = -\tfrac{1}{2}xe^{-2x} + \int \tfrac{1}{2}e^{-2x}\, dx$$
$$= -\tfrac{1}{2}xe^{-2x} - \tfrac{1}{4}e^{-2x} + C,$$

where C is an arbitrary constant. The general solution of the differential equation is therefore

$$y = -\tfrac{1}{4}(2x + 1)e^{-2x} + C.$$

(b) The differential equation $\dot{p} = t/(1 + t^2)$ has general solution

$$p = \int \frac{t}{1 + t^2}\, dt.$$

Using the hint provided, we make the substitution $u = 1 + t^2$, for which $du/dt = 2t$. This gives

$$\int \frac{t}{1 + t^2}\, dt = \tfrac{1}{2}\int \frac{1}{1 + t^2}(2t)\, dt$$
$$= \tfrac{1}{2}\int \frac{1}{u}\, du$$
$$= \tfrac{1}{2}\ln u + C \quad (\text{since } u = 1 + t^2 > 0)$$
$$= \tfrac{1}{2}\ln(1 + t^2) + C,$$

where C is an arbitrary constant. The general solution of the differential equation is therefore

$$p = \tfrac{1}{2}\ln(1 + t^2) + C.$$

3.3 (a) The differential equation is $dm/dt = -\lambda m$, where $m > 0$. Following Procedure 3.2, we obtain

$$\int \frac{1}{m}\, dm = \int (-\lambda)\, dt$$

and, since $m > 0$, integration produces

$$\ln m = -\lambda t + B,$$

where B is an arbitrary constant. On solving this equation for m, by taking the exponential of both sides, we obtain

$$m = e^{-\lambda t + B} = e^B e^{-\lambda t} = Ce^{-\lambda t},$$

where $C = e^B$ is a positive (since $e^B > 0$ for all B), but otherwise arbitrary, constant. The general solution is therefore

$$m = Ce^{-\lambda t},$$

where C is a positive but otherwise arbitrary constant.

(b) The initial condition is $m(0) = m_0$, from which we have $m_0 = Ce^0$, so $C = m_0$. The required particular solution is therefore

$$m = m_0 e^{-\lambda t}.$$

3.4 (a) The differential equation is

$$\frac{dy}{dx} = \frac{y - 1}{x}, \quad \text{where } x > 0.$$

In order to apply the separation of variables method, we need to exclude the cases where $y = 1$. So, for $y \neq 1$, on applying Procedure 3.2 we have

$$\int \frac{1}{y - 1}\, dy = \int \frac{1}{x}\, dx.$$

Since $x > 0$, for $y \neq 1$ (so that $y - 1 \neq 0$), integration produces

$$\ln|y - 1| = \ln x + B,$$

where B is an arbitrary constant. On solving this equation for y, by first taking the exponential of both sides, we obtain

$$y = 1 \pm e^{\ln x + B} = 1 \pm e^B e^{\ln x} = 1 + Cx,$$

where $C = \pm e^B$ is a non-zero but otherwise arbitrary constant.

Examination of the differential equation shows that $C = 0$ also gives a solution (the constant function $y = 1$). The general solution is therefore

$$y = 1 + Cx,$$

where C is an arbitrary constant.

(If you cannot convince yourself that this is the general solution for all y, including $y = 1$, then you will see it proved in Example 4.1.)

(b) The differential equation is $dy/dx = 2y/(x^2 + 1)$. In order to apply the separation of variables method, we need to exclude the cases where $y = 0$. So, for $y \neq 0$, on applying Procedure 3.2 we have

$$\int \frac{1}{y}\, dy = \int \frac{2}{x^2 + 1}\, dx.$$

Since $y \neq 0$, integration produces

$$\ln|y| = 2(\arctan x + B),$$

where B is an arbitrary constant. On solving this equation for y, we obtain

$$y = \pm e^{2\arctan x + 2B} = \pm e^{2B} e^{2\arctan x} = C e^{2\arctan x},$$

where $C = \pm e^{2B}$ is a non-zero but otherwise arbitrary constant. Examination of the differential equation shows that $C = 0$ also gives a solution (the zero function $y = 0$). The general solution is therefore

$$y = C e^{2\arctan x},$$

where C is an arbitrary constant.

(If you cannot convince yourself that this is the general solution for all y, including $y = 0$, then you will see it proved in Example 4.1.)

3.5 The differential equation is $dv/du = e^{u+v} = e^u e^v$. Dividing through by e^v and integrating with respect to u, we obtain

$$\int e^{-v}\, dv = \int e^u\, du.$$

Integration produces

$$-e^{-v} = e^u + B,$$

where B is an arbitrary constant. On solving this equation for v, we obtain

$$v = -\ln(-e^u - B) = -\ln(C - e^u),$$

where $C = -B$. We need $C > 0$ and $u < \ln C$ in order for the argument of ln here to be positive. Hence the general solution is

$$v = -\ln(C - e^u) \quad (u < \ln C),$$

where C is a positive but otherwise arbitrary constant. The initial condition $v(0) = 0$ gives $0 = -\ln(C - e^0)$, so $C - e^0 = 1$ and hence $C = 2$. The solution of the initial-value problem is therefore

$$v = -\ln(2 - e^u) \quad (u < \ln 2).$$

3.6 Each of the differential equations is soluble by direct integration.

(a) The general solution of $dy/du = 1/(u - a)$, where $u \neq a$, is given by

$$y = \int \frac{1}{u - a}\, du.$$

Integration produces the general solution

$$y = \ln|u - a| + C,$$

where C is an arbitrary constant.

(b) The general solution of $dy/dx = 1/(x(1 - ax))$, where $x \neq 0$, $x \neq 1/a$, is given by

$$y = \int \frac{1}{x(1 - ax)}\, dx.$$

This can be solved by using the substitution $u = 1/x$. Alternatively, if the integral is rearranged as

$$y = -\frac{1}{a} \int \frac{1}{(x - 0)(x - 1/a)}\, dx,$$

then we can use the table of standard integrals in the Handbook. Either method of integration gives the general solution

$$y = C - \ln\left|\frac{1}{x} - a\right|,$$

where C is an arbitrary constant.

3.7 Each of the differential equations can be solved by separation of variables.

(a) The differential equation is $u' = du/dx = xu$. For the cases where $u \neq 0$, we divide through by u and integrate with respect to x. This gives

$$\int \frac{1}{u}\, du = \int x\, dx.$$

Integration produces

$$\ln|u| = \tfrac{1}{2}x^2 + B,$$

where B is an arbitrary constant. On solving this equation for u, we obtain

$$u = \pm e^{x^2/2 + B} = \pm e^B e^{x^2/2} = C e^{x^2/2},$$

where $C = \pm e^B$ is a non-zero but otherwise arbitrary constant. However, the case $C = 0$ can be added, since it can be seen by inspection of the differential equation that the zero function $u = 0$ is a solution. Hence the general solution is

$$u = C e^{x^2/2},$$

where C is an arbitrary constant.

(You verified that $u = 2e^{x^2/2}$ is a particular solution of this differential equation in Exercise 1.2(c).)

(b) The differential equation is $\dot{x} = dx/dt = 1 + x^2$. We divide through by $1 + x^2$ and integrate with respect to t. This gives

$$\int \frac{1}{1 + x^2}\, dx = \int 1\, dt.$$

Integration produces

$$\arctan x = t + C,$$

where C is an arbitrary constant. On solving for x, we have

$$x = \tan(t + C).$$

A suitable domain for the solution is $-\frac{\pi}{2} < t + C < \frac{\pi}{2}$, since the image set of arctan is the interval $\left(-\frac{\pi}{2}, \frac{\pi}{2}\right)$.

Thus the general solution is

$$x = \tan(t + C) \quad \left(-\tfrac{\pi}{2} < t + C < \tfrac{\pi}{2}\right),$$

where C is an arbitrary constant.

(You verified that this is a solution of the given differential equation in Exercise 1.7.)

3.8 (a) The given equation is $dP/dt = kP(1 - P/M)$. First, note that (as remarked upon in Section 2) the constant functions $P = 0$ and $P = M$ are both solutions. Assuming that we are considering neither of these possibilities (we are certainly not interested in $P = 0$ since we know that $P_0 > 0$), we can use the separation of variables method to obtain

$$\frac{1}{k} \int \frac{1}{P(1 - P/M)}\, dP = \int 1 \, dt.$$

The integral on the left-hand side is of the form evaluated in Exercise 3.6(b), with $1/M$ in place of a. Hence we have

$$-\frac{1}{k} \ln \left| \frac{1}{P} - \frac{1}{M} \right| = t + B,$$

where B is an arbitrary constant. On solving for P, we find first that

$$\frac{1}{P} - \frac{1}{M} = \pm e^{-k(t+B)}$$
$$= \pm e^{-kB} e^{-kt}$$
$$= C e^{-kt},$$

where $C = \pm e^{-kB}$ is a non-zero but otherwise arbitrary constant. However, note that $C = 0$ corresponds to the constant solution $P = M$ already noted, so the restriction $C \neq 0$ may be dropped. Hence we obtain

$$P = \left(\frac{1}{M} + C e^{-kt} \right)^{-1} \quad (e^{kt} \neq -MC),$$

where C is an arbitrary constant.

From the initial condition $P(0) = P_0$, we have

$$P_0 = \left(\frac{1}{M} + C e^0 \right)^{-1}, \quad \text{so} \quad C = \frac{1}{P_0} - \frac{1}{M}.$$

The solution of the initial-value problem is therefore

$$P = \left(\frac{1}{M} + \left(\frac{1}{P_0} - \frac{1}{M} \right) e^{-kt} \right)^{-1},$$

which yields

$$P = \frac{M}{1 + (M/P_0 - 1)e^{-kt}}.$$

Finally, we rewrite this in the more familiar form

$$P = \frac{M e^{kt}}{e^{kt} + (M/P_0 - 1)}.$$

(b) As $t \to \infty$ we have $e^{-kt} \to 0$, and consequently the value of $P(t)$ approaches M.

(Note that this is true whether the starting value P_0 is greater than or less than M. This result is consistent with the specific direction field shown in Figure 2.4.)

Section 4

4.1 (a) The equation $dy/dx + x^3 y = x^5$ is linear, with $g(x) = x^3$ and $h(x) = x^5$.

(b) The equation $dy/dx = x \sin x$ is linear, with $g(x) = 0$ (for all x) and $h(x) = x \sin x$.

(c) The equation $dz/dt = -3z^{1/2}$ is not linear (because of the $z^{1/2}$ term).

(d) The equation $\dot{y} + y^2 = t$ is not linear (because of the y^2 term).

(e) The equation $x(dy/dx) + y = y^2$ is not linear (because of the y^2 term).

(f) The equation $(1 + x^2)(dy/dx) + 2xy = 3x^2$ is linear, since we can divide through by $1 + x^2$ to obtain $dy/dx + 2xy/(1 + x^2) = 3x^2/(1 + x^2)$, which is of the defined form with $g(x) = 2x/(1 + x^2)$ and $h(x) = 3x^2/(1 + x^2)$.

4.2 (a) The given equation is $dy/dx - y = e^x \sin x$. Comparison with Equations (4.1) and (4.9) shows that the integrating factor is

$$p = \exp\left(\int (-1)\, dx \right) = \exp(-x) = e^{-x}.$$

Multiplying through by $p(x)$ gives

$$e^{-x}\frac{dy}{dx} - e^{-x}y = \sin x.$$

Thus the differential equation can be rewritten as

$$\frac{d}{dx}(e^{-x}y) = \sin x.$$

On integrating, we find the general solution

$$e^{-x}y = -\cos x + C,$$

or, equivalently,

$$y = e^x(C - \cos x),$$

where C is an arbitrary constant.

(b) The given equation, when rearranged into form (4.1), is $dy/dx - y = x$. This has the same left-hand side as the differential equation in part (a), and hence the same integrating factor, $p = e^{-x}$. Multiplying through by $p(x)$ gives

$$e^{-x}\frac{dy}{dx} - e^{-x}y = xe^{-x}.$$

Thus the differential equation can be rewritten as

$$\frac{d}{dx}(e^{-x}y) = xe^{-x}.$$

On integrating (by parts on the right-hand side), we find

$$e^{-x}y = \int xe^{-x}\, dx$$
$$= -xe^{-x} + \int e^{-x}\, dx$$
$$= -xe^{-x} - e^{-x} + C$$
$$= C - (x + 1)e^{-x},$$

where C is an arbitrary constant. After multiplying through by e^x, the general solution in explicit form is

$$y = Ce^x - (x + 1).$$

4.3 **(a)** The given equation, when rearranged into form (4.1), is $du/dx - xu = 0$. The integrating factor is

$$p = \exp\left(\int(-x)\,dx\right)$$
$$= \exp(-x^2/2)$$
$$= e^{-x^2/2}.$$

Multiplying through by $p(x)$ gives

$$e^{-x^2/2}\frac{du}{dx} - xe^{-x^2/2}u = 0.$$

Thus the differential equation can be rewritten as

$$\frac{d}{dx}(e^{-x^2/2}u) = 0.$$

On integrating, we find the general solution

$$e^{-x^2/2}u = C, \quad \text{or, equivalently,} \quad u = Ce^{x^2/2},$$

where C is an arbitrary constant.

From the initial condition $u(0) = 2$, we have $2 = Ce^0$, so $C = 2$. Hence the solution of the initial-value problem is

$$u = 2e^{x^2/2}.$$

(b) After division by t, the given equation can be written as $dy/dt + (2/t)y = t$. (To avoid division by zero, we take $t > 0$, say, which is consistent with the initial condition.) The integrating factor is

$$p = \exp\left(\int\frac{2}{t}\,dt\right)$$
$$= \exp(2\ln t)$$
$$= \exp(\ln(t^2))$$
$$= t^2.$$

Multiplying through by $p(t)$ gives

$$t^2\frac{dy}{dt} + 2ty = t^3.$$

Thus the differential equation can be rewritten as

$$\frac{d}{dt}(t^2 y) = t^3.$$

On integrating, we find the general solution

$$t^2 y = \tfrac{1}{4}t^4 + C, \quad \text{or, equivalently,} \quad y = \tfrac{1}{4}t^2 + Ct^{-2},$$

where C is an arbitrary constant.

From the initial condition $y(1) = 1$, we have $1 = \tfrac{1}{4} + C$, so $C = \tfrac{3}{4}$. Hence the solution of the initial-value problem is

$$y = \tfrac{1}{4}(t^2 + 3t^{-2}).$$

4.4 **(a)** and **(d)** require the integrating factor method. **(b)** is best solved by direct integration. **(c)** can be solved by separation of variables or the integrating factor method.

4.5 **(a)** The given equation is $dy/dt + y = t + 1$. Comparison with Equations (4.1) and (4.9) shows that the integrating factor is

$$p = \exp\left(\int 1\,dt\right)$$
$$= \exp(t)$$
$$= e^t.$$

Multiplying through by $p(t)$ gives

$$e^t\frac{dy}{dt} + e^t y = (t+1)e^t.$$

Thus the differential equation can be rewritten as

$$\frac{d}{dt}(e^t y) = (t+1)e^t.$$

On integrating (by parts on the right-hand side), we find

$$e^t y = \int(t+1)e^t\,dt$$
$$= (t+1)e^t - \int e^t\,dt$$
$$= (t+1)e^t - e^t + C$$
$$= te^t + C,$$

where C is an arbitrary constant. After multiplying through by e^{-t}, the general solution in explicit form is

$$y = Ce^{-t} + t.$$

From the initial condition $y(1) = 0$, we have $0 = Ce^{-1} + 1$, so $C = -e$. Hence the solution of the initial-value problem is

$$y = t - e^{1-t}.$$

(b) After division by e^{3t} and rearrangement, the given equation becomes $dy/dt + y = e^{-3t}$. This has the same left-hand side as the differential equation in part (a), and hence the same integrating factor, $p = e^t$. Multiplying through by $p(t)$ gives

$$e^t\frac{dy}{dt} + e^t y = e^{-2t}.$$

Thus the differential equation can be rewritten as

$$\frac{d}{dt}(e^t y) = e^{-2t}.$$

On integrating, we find the general solution

$$e^t y = -\tfrac{1}{2}e^{-2t} + C,$$

or, equivalently,

$$y = Ce^{-t} - \tfrac{1}{2}e^{-3t},$$

where C is an arbitrary constant.

From the initial condition $y(0) = 3$, we have $3 = Ce^0 - \tfrac{1}{2}e^0$, so $C = \tfrac{7}{2}$. Hence the solution of the initial-value problem is

$$y = \tfrac{1}{2}(7e^{-t} - e^{-3t}).$$

4.6 (a) After division by x (where $x > 0$), the given equation becomes $dy/dx - (3/x)y = 1$. The integrating factor is

$$p = \exp\left(\int \left(-\frac{3}{x}\right) dx\right)$$
$$= \exp(-3\ln x)$$
$$= \exp(\ln(x^{-3}))$$
$$= x^{-3}.$$

Multiplying through by $p(x)$ gives

$$x^{-3}\frac{dy}{dx} - 3x^{-4}y = x^{-3}.$$

Thus the differential equation can be rewritten as

$$\frac{d}{dx}(x^{-3}y) = x^{-3}.$$

On integrating, we find the general solution

$$x^{-3}y = -\tfrac{1}{2}x^{-2} + C,$$

or, equivalently,

$$y = Cx^3 - \tfrac{1}{2}x,$$

where C is an arbitrary constant.

(b) The given equation is $dv/dt + 4v = 3\cos 2t$. The integrating factor is

$$p = \exp\left(\int 4\,dt\right)$$
$$= \exp(4t)$$
$$= e^{4t}.$$

Multiplying through by $p(t)$ gives

$$e^{4t}\frac{dv}{dt} + 4e^{4t}v = 3e^{4t}\cos 2t.$$

Thus the differential equation can be rewritten as

$$\frac{d}{dt}(e^{4t}v) = 3e^{4t}\cos 2t.$$

On integrating (using the hint for the right-hand side, with $a = 4$ and $b = 2$), we find

$$e^{4t}v = \tfrac{3}{20}e^{4t}(4\cos 2t + 2\sin 2t) + C,$$

where C is an arbitrary constant. After multiplying through by e^{-4t}, the general solution in explicit form is

$$v = \tfrac{3}{20}(4\cos 2t + 2\sin 2t) + Ce^{-4t}.$$

UNIT 3 Second-order differential equations

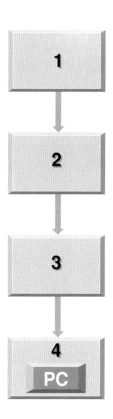

Study guide for Unit 3

This unit extends the ideas of *Unit 2* from first-order differential equations to a particular type of second-order differential equation. This type of second-order differential equation has a variety of applications, some of which are considered later in the course.

This unit requires no previous knowledge beyond that required for *Unit 2*, apart from some familiarity with complex numbers. The relevant material on complex numbers was revised in *Unit 1* of this course.

Sections 1 and 2 contain the most important material.

The recommended study pattern is to study one section per study session and to study the sections in the order in which they appear. However, you may find that Sections 1 and 2 take you rather longer than Sections 3 and 4, and you may wish to spread your study of Sections 1 and 2 over three sessions.

Section 4 uses the computer algebra package for the course and is designed to help you to understand the nature of the solutions obtained in Sections 1–3.

Introduction

Unit 2 introduced you to differential equations, and in particular to first-order differential equations that can be written in the form

$$\frac{dy}{dx} = f(x, y).$$

Such an equation is said to be of first order because it involves only the first derivative dy/dx of the function $y = y(x)$.

This unit considers *second-order* differential equations, that is, differential equations that involve a second (but no higher) derivative. Examples of second-order differential equations are

The *order* of a differential equation was defined in Subsection 1.2 of *Unit 2*.

$$\frac{d^2y}{dx^2} - 3\frac{dy}{dx} + 2y = 4e^x \quad \text{and} \quad 3\frac{d^2y}{dx^2} + y^2 \sin x = x^2.$$

A second-order differential equation may or may not include a first derivative.

As in the case of first-order differential equations, second-order differential equations, and in particular the derivatives in such equations, can be written in a variety of notations. For example, the second derivative of a dependent variable y with respect to an independent variable t (representing time) may be written as d^2y/dt^2, $\ddot{y}$, y'', and so on. Also, as in the case of first-order equations, the dependent variable and sometimes the independent variable can be considered as functions, and the same symbol is frequently used for both the variable and the corresponding function.

Of course, the dependent variable is not always y!

One particularly simple example of a second-order differential equation, with dependent variable s and independent variable t, is

$$\frac{d^2s}{dt^2} = a, \tag{0.1}$$

where a is a given constant. This equation can be solved by applying direct integration twice. One application gives

See Subsection 3.1 of *Unit 2*.

$$\frac{ds}{dt} = \int a\, dt = at + C,$$

where C is an arbitrary constant. Integrating a second time gives

$$s = \int (at + C)\, dt = \tfrac{1}{2}at^2 + Ct + D, \tag{0.2}$$

where D is another arbitrary constant. Equation (0.2) is the *general solution* of the second-order differential equation (0.1).

Recall, from *Unit 2*, that the *general solution* of a differential equation is the collection of all possible solutions of that equation.

Now, in *Unit 2* you saw that the general solution of a first-order differential equation usually involves just one arbitrary constant. But here, even for such a simple second-order differential equation, the general solution involves two arbitrary constants (namely C and D). It is a property of second-order differential equations that the general solution usually involves *two* arbitrary constants.

The remainder of the unit proceeds as follows. Section 1 concentrates on *homogeneous* linear constant-coefficient second-order differential equations, leaving inhomogeneous equations to Section 2. Section 3 considers the types of condition needed to move from a general to a particular solution. Finally, Section 4 uses the computer to examine the nature of solutions.

1 Homogeneous differential equations

After a short introduction in Subsection 1.1, Subsection 1.2 shows how homogeneous second-order differential equations can be solved. Subsection 1.3 explains why the solutions thus obtained are indeed the required general solutions.

1.1 First thoughts

You will recall that a *particular solution* of a first-order differential equation is obtained by applying a *single* condition (known as an *initial condition*) to the general solution in order to find a particular value of the single arbitrary constant. In the case of a second-order differential equation, a particular solution is obtained by applying *two* conditions to the general solution in order to find particular values of the *two* arbitrary constants. The following example illustrates this.

Example 1.1

Suppose that a car is travelling with constant acceleration a along a straight road. If, at time t, its distance from a fixed point is s, then its velocity is given by ds/dt, its acceleration is given by d^2s/dt^2, and its motion is modelled by

$$\frac{d^2 s}{dt^2} = a. \tag{0.1}$$

If the car is initially stationary at position $s = 0$ and thereafter has a constant acceleration of $2\,\mathrm{m\,s}^{-2}$, how long does it take for the car to attain a velocity of $30\,\mathrm{m\,s}^{-1}$, and what distance has it travelled in that time?

Solution

You saw in the Introduction that integrating Equation (0.1) leads to

$$\frac{ds}{dt} = at + C \quad \text{and} \quad s = \tfrac{1}{2}at^2 + Ct + D,$$

where C and D are arbitrary constants. To find these constants (and hence answer the questions asked), we need to make use of the conditions given. These are that the car is initially stationary (i.e. $ds/dt = 0$ when $t = 0$) at position $s = 0$ (i.e. $s = 0$ when $t = 0$). The first of these conditions, together with the equation $ds/dt = at + C$, tells us that $C = 0$. With $C = 0$, the second equation becomes $s = \tfrac{1}{2}at^2 + D$, and this together with the second condition tells us that $D = 0$.

Therefore, when $a = 2$, we have

$$\frac{d^2 s}{dt^2} = 2, \quad \frac{ds}{dt} = 2t, \quad s = t^2.$$

So the velocity is $ds/dt = 30$ when $2t = 30$, i.e. after 15 seconds, and in this time the car has travelled $s = 15^2 = 225$ metres. ∎

The solution of second-order differential equations is rarely as easy as the solution of Equation (0.1) above. In fact, the approach of repeated direct integration works for only some equations of the form

$$\frac{d^2 y}{dx^2} = f(x).$$

Most second-order differential equations cannot be solved by analytic methods at all, and numerical methods have to be employed instead. However, there is one important class of second-order differential equations that can be solved by analytic means: this is the topic of this unit, and we introduce it next.

Such numerical methods are discussed in *Unit 26*.

Linear constant-coefficient differential equations

This unit considers *linear constant-coefficient* second-order differential equations. But what exactly do the terms 'linear' and 'constant-coefficient' mean in this context?

You met the idea of a linear first-order differential equation in *Unit 2*.

The answer lies in the following definitions.

Definitions

(a) A second-order differential equation for $y = y(x)$ is **linear** if it can be expressed in the form

$$a(x)\frac{d^2y}{dx^2} + b(x)\frac{dy}{dx} + c(x)y = f(x),$$

where $a(x)$, $b(x)$, $c(x)$ and $f(x)$ are given continuous functions.

(b) A linear second-order differential equation is **constant-coefficient** if the functions $a(x)$, $b(x)$ and $c(x)$ are all constant, so that the equation is of the form

$$a\frac{d^2y}{dx^2} + b\frac{dy}{dx} + cy = f(x), \tag{1.1}$$

where $a \neq 0$.

(c) A linear constant-coefficient second-order differential equation is said to be **homogeneous** if $f(x) = 0$ for all x, and **inhomogeneous** (or **non-homogeneous**) otherwise.

Compare the definitions for first-order equations in Subsection 4.1 of *Unit 2*. The important feature is the *linear* combination of y and its derivatives on the left-hand side.

If $a = 0$, then the equation is first-order.

Linear constant-coefficient second-order differential equations can be written in other ways. For example, we can divide Equation (1.1) through by a to obtain an equation of the form

$$\frac{d^2y}{dx^2} + \beta\frac{dy}{dx} + \gamma y = \phi(x),$$

and this more closely resembles the definition of linear first-order differential equations from *Unit 2*.

*Exercise 1.1 _____

Consider the following second-order differential equations.

(i) $\dfrac{d^2y}{dx^2} = x^2$ (ii) $3\dfrac{d^2y}{dx^2} + 4\dfrac{dy}{dx} + y = x^2$ (iii) $3\dfrac{d^2y}{dx^2} + 4\dfrac{dy}{dx} + y = 0$

(iv) $xy'' + x^2y = 0$ (v) $2y\dfrac{d^2y}{dx^2} + xy = 3\dfrac{dy}{dx}$ (vi) $2y\dfrac{d^2y}{dx^2} + 4y = 3\dfrac{dy}{dx}$

(vii) $2\dfrac{d^2t}{d\theta^2} + 3\dfrac{dt}{d\theta} + 4t = \sin\theta$ (viii) $\ddot{x} = -4t$ (ix) $\ddot{x} = -4x$

(a) Which of the equations are linear and constant-coefficient?

(b) Which of the linear constant-coefficient equations are homogeneous?

(c) For each equation, identify the dependent and independent variables.

_____

One of the main reasons for concentrating on linear constant-coefficient differential equations is that there is a large body of theory upon which we can call in order to solve them. The next subsection illustrates this.

The principle of superposition

A key theoretical result will turn out to be extremely useful throughout this unit. This is known as the principle of superposition, and is the fundamental property of linear differential equations.

Suppose that we have a solution $y_1(x)$ of

$$a\frac{d^2y}{dx^2} + b\frac{dy}{dx} + cy = f_1(x),$$

Here a, b and c can be functions of x.

and a solution $y_2(x)$ of

$$a\frac{d^2y}{dx^2} + b\frac{dy}{dx} + cy = f_2(x).$$

Then we claim that the linear combination $k_1y_1 + k_2y_2$, where k_1 and k_2 are constants, is a solution of

$$a\frac{d^2y}{dx^2} + b\frac{dy}{dx} + cy = k_1f_1(x) + k_2f_2(x). \tag{1.2}$$

In fact, this is easy to see, for if we substitute $k_1y_1 + k_2y_2$ directly into Equation (1.2), we obtain

$$a\frac{d^2}{dx^2}(k_1y_1 + k_2y_2) + b\frac{d}{dx}(k_1y_1 + k_2y_2) + c(k_1y_1 + k_2y_2)$$

$$= a\left(k_1\frac{d^2y_1}{dx^2} + k_2\frac{d^2y_2}{dx^2}\right) + b\left(k_1\frac{dy_1}{dx} + k_2\frac{dy_2}{dx}\right) + c(k_1y_1 + k_2y_2)$$

$$= k_1\left(a\frac{d^2y_1}{dx^2} + b\frac{dy_1}{dx} + cy_1\right) + k_2\left(a\frac{d^2y_2}{dx^2} + b\frac{dy_2}{dx} + cy_2\right)$$

$$= k_1f_1(x) + k_2f_2(x),$$

as required.

We summarize this important result as a theorem.

Theorem 1.1   Principle of superposition

If $y_1(x)$ is a solution of the linear second-order differential equation

$$a\frac{d^2y}{dx^2} + b\frac{dy}{dx} + cy = f_1(x),$$

and $y_2(x)$ is a solution of the linear second-order differential equation

$$a\frac{d^2y}{dx^2} + b\frac{dy}{dx} + cy = f_2(x)$$

(with the same left-hand side), then the function

$$y(x) = k_1y_1(x) + k_2y_2(x),$$

where k_1 and k_2 are constants, is a solution of the differential equation

$$a\frac{d^2y}{dx^2} + b\frac{dy}{dx} + cy = k_1f_1(x) + k_2f_2(x).$$

1.2 *Method of solution*

This subsection develops a method for solving homogeneous linear constant-coefficient second-order differential equations, i.e. equations of the form

$$a\frac{d^2y}{dx^2} + b\frac{dy}{dx} + cy = 0, \tag{1.3}$$

where a, b, c are constants and $a \neq 0$.

To see how this method arises, consider the *first*-order differential equation

$$b\frac{dy}{dx} + cy = 0, \tag{1.4}$$

where b and c are constants and $b \neq 0$. This is a homogeneous linear equation; as can be shown using the integrating factor method from *Unit 2*, this has a general solution of the form $y = Ae^{\lambda x}$, where A is an arbitrary constant and λ is some fixed constant. To find λ, we could solve the equation as in *Unit 2*; alternatively, we can substitute $y = Ae^{\lambda x}$ into Equation (1.4). Then we have $dy/dx = \lambda Ae^{\lambda x}$, and so

$$b\frac{dy}{dx} + cy = b\lambda Ae^{\lambda x} + cAe^{\lambda x} = (b\lambda + c)Ae^{\lambda x}.$$

Therefore, for $y = Ae^{\lambda x}$ to be a solution, $(b\lambda + c)Ae^{\lambda x}$ must be zero, for all x. Since A is arbitrary and $e^{\lambda x} > 0$, for all x, we must have $b\lambda + c = 0$, i.e. $\lambda = -c/b$.

This useful idea of substituting $y = Ae^{\lambda x}$ as a trial solution can be applied to Equation (1.3) as well. Let us suppose that Equation (1.3) has a solution of the form $y = Ae^{\lambda x}$, for some value of λ. If so, then $dy/dx = \lambda Ae^{\lambda x}$ and $d^2y/dx^2 = \lambda^2 Ae^{\lambda x}$, and substituting into the left-hand side of Equation (1.3) gives

$$a\frac{d^2y}{dx^2} + b\frac{dy}{dx} + cy = a\lambda^2 Ae^{\lambda x} + b\lambda Ae^{\lambda x} + cAe^{\lambda x}$$

$$= (a\lambda^2 + b\lambda + c)Ae^{\lambda x}.$$

Hence $y = Ae^{\lambda x}$ is indeed a solution of Equation (1.3), for any value of A, provided that λ satisfies

$$a\lambda^2 + b\lambda + c = 0. \tag{1.5}$$

Note that the discussion here applies irrespective of whether λ is real or complex. The consequences of λ being complex are explained later.

Equation (1.5) plays such an important role in solving linear constant-coefficient second-order differential equations that it is given a special name.

Definition

The **auxiliary equation** of the homogeneous linear constant-coefficient second-order differential equation

$$a\frac{d^2y}{dx^2} + b\frac{dy}{dx} + cy = 0$$

is the quadratic equation

$$a\lambda^2 + b\lambda + c = 0. \tag{1.5}$$

The auxiliary equation is sometimes called the *characteristic equation*.

The auxiliary equation is obtained from the differential equation by replacing y by 1, $\dfrac{dy}{dx}$ by λ, and $\dfrac{d^2y}{dx^2}$ by λ^2.

Example 1.2

Write down the auxiliary equation of the differential equation

$$3\frac{d^2y}{dx^2} - 2\frac{dy}{dx} + 4y = 0.$$

Solution

The auxiliary equation is

$$3\lambda^2 - 2\lambda + 4 = 0. \quad \blacksquare$$

Exercise 1.2

Write down the auxiliary equation of each of the following differential equations.

(a) $\dfrac{d^2y}{dx^2} - 5\dfrac{dy}{dx} + 6y = 0$ (b) $y'' - 9y = 0$ (c) $\ddot{x} + 2\dot{x} = 0$

Now, so far, we know that $y = Ae^{\lambda x}$ is a solution of Equation (1.3) provided that λ satisfies its auxiliary equation. But the auxiliary equation is a quadratic equation with real coefficients, and so has two roots (which in general are distinct). These two roots, λ_1 and λ_2 say, give two solutions $y_1 = Ce^{\lambda_1 x}$ and $y_2 = De^{\lambda_2 x}$ of Equation (1.3), where C and D are arbitrary constants.

The roots of a quadratic equation were discussed in *Unit 1*.

If $\lambda_1 = \lambda_2$, then we obtain only one solution. This case is dealt with separately below.

Example 1.3

(a) Write down the auxiliary equation of the differential equation

$$\frac{d^2y}{dx^2} - 3\frac{dy}{dx} + 2y = 0,$$

and find its roots λ_1 and λ_2.

(b) Deduce that $y_1 = Ce^x$ and $y_2 = De^{2x}$ are both solutions of the differential equation, for any values of the two constants C and D.

(c) Show that $y = Ce^x + De^{2x}$ is also a solution of the differential equation, for any values of the two constants C and D.

Solution

(a) The auxiliary equation is

$$\lambda^2 - 3\lambda + 2 = 0.$$

This equation may be solved, for example, by factorizing in the form $(\lambda - 1)(\lambda - 2) = 0$, to give the two roots $\lambda_1 = 1$ and $\lambda_2 = 2$.

(b) Since $\lambda_1 = 1$ and $\lambda_2 = 2$ are the roots of the auxiliary equation, $y_1 = Ce^x$ and $y_2 = De^{2x}$ are solutions of the differential equation, for any values of C and D.

(c) To show that $y = Ce^x + De^{2x}$ is a solution of the differential equation, we differentiate and substitute into the differential equation. Differentiating to obtain the first and second derivatives of y gives

$$\frac{dy}{dx} = Ce^x + 2De^{2x}$$

and

$$\frac{d^2y}{dx^2} = Ce^x + 4De^{2x}.$$

Using the formula

$$\lambda_1, \lambda_2 = \frac{-b \pm \sqrt{b^2 - 4ac}}{2a}$$

produces the same answer. It does not matter which of the roots is called λ_1 and which is called λ_2.

Substituting these into the left-hand side of the differential equation gives

$$\frac{d^2y}{dx^2} - 3\frac{dy}{dx} + 2y$$
$$= \left(Ce^x + 4De^{2x}\right) - 3\left(Ce^x + 2De^{2x}\right) + 2\left(Ce^x + De^{2x}\right)$$
$$= C(1 - 3 + 2)e^x + D(4 - 6 + 2)e^{2x}$$
$$= 0.$$

Hence $y = Ce^x + De^{2x}$ is a solution of the differential equation, for any values of C and D. ∎

In Subsection 1.3 we shall prove that if λ_1 and λ_2 are *distinct* roots of the auxiliary equation of a homogeneous linear constant-coefficient second-order differential equation, then any solution is of the form

$$y = Ce^{\lambda_1 x} + De^{\lambda_2 x}, \tag{1.6}$$

for some choice of constants C and D.

Exercise 1.3

Use the auxiliary equation to find the general solution of each of the following differential equations.

(a) $\dfrac{d^2y}{dx^2} + 5\dfrac{dy}{dx} + 6y = 0$ (b) $2\dfrac{d^2y}{dx^2} + 3\dfrac{dy}{dx} = 0$ (c) $\dfrac{d^2z}{du^2} - 4z = 0$

We now consider an example where the two roots of the auxiliary equation are *equal*, in which case the above recipe does not work! Indeed, in light of the earlier discussion, you might expect the solution always to be of the form $y = Ae^{\lambda_1 x} + Be^{\lambda_2 x}$, where A and B are arbitrary constants. But if $\lambda_1 = \lambda_2$, this reduces to $y = (A + B)e^{\lambda_1 x} = Ce^{\lambda_1 x}$, where $C = A + B$ is a *single* arbitrary constant, so this cannot be the general solution of a *second-order* differential equation.

Example 1.4

(a) Write down the auxiliary equation of the differential equation

$$\frac{d^2y}{dx^2} + 6\frac{dy}{dx} + 9y = 0,$$

and find its roots λ_1 and λ_2.

(b) Deduce that $y_1 = Ce^{-3x}$ is a solution of the differential equation, for any value of the constant C.

(c) Show that $y_2 = Dxe^{-3x}$ is also a solution, for any value of the constant D.

(d) Deduce that $y = (C + Dx)e^{-3x}$ is also a solution of the differential equation, for any values of the two constants C and D.

Solution

(a) The auxiliary equation is

$$\lambda^2 + 6\lambda + 9 = 0.$$

The left-hand side is the perfect square $(\lambda + 3)^2$, so the auxiliary equation has equal roots $\lambda_1 = \lambda_2 = -3$.

(b) Since $\lambda_1 = -3$ is a root of the auxiliary equation, $y_1 = Ce^{-3x}$ is a solution of the differential equation, for any value of C.

Note that the 'other' root $\lambda_2 = -3$ gives the same solution.

(c) To show that $y_2 = Dxe^{-3x}$ is a solution of the differential equation, we differentiate and substitute into the differential equation. Differentiating to obtain the first and second derivatives of y_2 gives

$$\frac{dy_2}{dx} = De^{-3x} + Dx\left(-3e^{-3x}\right) = D(1 - 3x)e^{-3x},$$

Here we are using the Product Rule for differentiation.

$$\frac{d^2y_2}{dx^2} = -3De^{-3x} + D(1 - 3x)(-3e^{-3x}) = D(-6 + 9x)e^{-3x}.$$

Substituting these into the left-hand side of the differential equation gives

$$\frac{d^2y_2}{dx^2} + 6\frac{dy_2}{dx} + 9y_2 = D(-6 + 9x)e^{-3x} + 6D(1 - 3x)e^{-3x} + 9Dxe^{-3x}$$
$$= D(-6 + 6)e^{-3x} + D(9 - 18 + 9)xe^{-3x}$$
$$= 0.$$

Hence $y_2 = Dxe^{-3x}$ is a solution of the differential equation, for any value of D.

(d) Since $y_1 = Ce^{-3x}$ and $y_2 = Dxe^{-3x}$ are both solutions of the differential equation, the principle of superposition (Theorem 1.1) tells us that so is $y = Ce^{-3x} + Dxe^{-3x} = (C + Dx)e^{-3x}$, for any values of C and D. ∎

The solution in Example 1.4 is of the form $y = Ce^{\lambda_1 x} + Dxe^{\lambda_1 x}$. The extra x in the second term, $Dxe^{\lambda_1 x}$, is needed, in this special case, to incorporate the second arbitrary constant required by the general solution of a second-order differential equation.

In general, when $\lambda_1 = \lambda_2$, $y = xe^{\lambda_1 x}$ is a solution of Equation (1.3) (page 114). To see this, differentiate twice to obtain

$$\frac{dy}{dx} = e^{\lambda_1 x} + \lambda_1 xe^{\lambda_1 x} = (1 + \lambda_1 x)e^{\lambda_1 x},$$

$$\frac{d^2y}{dx^2} = \lambda_1 e^{\lambda_1 x} + \lambda_1(1 + \lambda_1 x)e^{\lambda_1 x} = (2\lambda_1 + \lambda_1^2 x)e^{\lambda_1 x},$$

and substitute into the left-hand side of Equation (1.3) to obtain

$$a\frac{d^2y}{dx^2} + b\frac{dy}{dx} + cy$$
$$= a\left((2\lambda_1 + \lambda_1^2 x)e^{\lambda_1 x}\right) + b\left((1 + \lambda_1 x)e^{\lambda_1 x}\right) + c\left(xe^{\lambda_1 x}\right)$$
$$= e^{\lambda_1 x}\left(a(2\lambda_1 + \lambda_1^2 x) + b(1 + \lambda_1 x) + cx\right)$$
$$= e^{\lambda_1 x}\left((2a\lambda_1 + b) + (a\lambda_1^2 + b\lambda_1 + c)x\right). \tag{1.7}$$

Since λ_1 is the solution of the auxiliary equation, we have $a\lambda_1^2 + b\lambda_1 + c = 0$. Also, the formula method for solving the auxiliary equation $a\lambda^2 + b\lambda + c = 0$ gives

$$\lambda = \frac{-b \pm \sqrt{b^2 - 4ac}}{2a};$$

since in this case we have equal roots, we must have $b^2 - 4ac = 0$, so $\lambda_1 = -b/2a$, and therefore $2a\lambda_1 + b = 0$. Thus the right-hand side of Equation (1.7) is zero, and $y = xe^{\lambda_1 x}$ is indeed a solution of Equation (1.3). Therefore, when $\lambda_1 = \lambda_2$, by the principle of superposition,

$$y = Ce^{\lambda_1 x} + Dxe^{\lambda_1 x} = (C + Dx)e^{\lambda_1 x}, \tag{1.8}$$

where C and D are arbitrary constants, is always a solution of Equation (1.3). In fact, as you will see in Subsection 1.3, Equation (1.8) gives the *general* solution.

Exercise 1.4 _____

Use the auxiliary equation to find the general solution of the following differential equations.

(a) $\dfrac{d^2y}{dx^2} + 2\dfrac{dy}{dx} + y = 0$ (b) $\ddot{s} - 4\dot{s} + 4s = 0$

Equations (1.6) and (1.8) give us the general solution of Equation (1.3) for the cases where the roots λ_1 and λ_2 of the auxiliary equation are distinct and equal, respectively. However, the distinct roots of a quadratic equation may not be real — they could consist of a pair of complex conjugate roots $\lambda_1 = \alpha + \beta i$ and $\lambda_2 = \alpha - \beta i$. If the auxiliary equation has such a pair of roots, we can still write the general solution in the form

> Recall that the complex conjugate of the complex number $\alpha + \beta i$ is $\alpha - \beta i$.

$$y = Ae^{\lambda_1 x} + Be^{\lambda_2 x} = Ae^{(\alpha+\beta i)x} + Be^{(\alpha-\beta i)x},$$

but we now have a complex-valued solution.

> You will soon see why we use A and B for the arbitrary constants (rather than our usual choice of C and D).

Since Equation (1.3) has real coefficients, we would like a real-valued solution. In order to achieve this, we shall need to allow A and B to be complex. Then we can use Euler's formula, which tells us that

> Euler's formula was discussed in *Unit 1*.

$$e^{i\beta x} = \cos\beta x + i\sin\beta x \quad\text{and}\quad e^{-i\beta x} = \cos\beta x - i\sin\beta x.$$

Now

$$\begin{aligned}
y &= Ae^{\lambda_1 x} + Be^{\lambda_2 x}\\
&= Ae^{(\alpha+\beta i)x} + Be^{(\alpha-\beta i)x}\\
&= Ae^{\alpha x}e^{i\beta x} + Be^{\alpha x}e^{-i\beta x}\\
&= Ae^{\alpha x}(\cos\beta x + i\sin\beta x) + Be^{\alpha x}(\cos\beta x - i\sin\beta x)\\
&= e^{\alpha x}((A+B)\cos\beta x + (Ai - Bi)\sin\beta x)\\
&= e^{\alpha x}(C\cos\beta x + D\sin\beta x),
\end{aligned}$$

where $C = A + B$ and $D = (A - B)i$. Provided that any initial conditions are real-valued, C and D are real, and this is the required real-valued solution containing two arbitrary constants.

> The constants in the final expression are now C and D, in keeping with our previous solutions.

Example 1.5

(a) Write down the auxiliary equation of the differential equation

$$\frac{d^2y}{dx^2} - 6\frac{dy}{dx} + 13y = 0,$$

and show that its roots are $\lambda_1 = 3 + 2i$ and $\lambda_2 = 3 - 2i$.

(b) Confirm that $y_1 = e^{3x}\cos 2x$ and $y_2 = e^{3x}\sin 2x$ are both solutions of the differential equation.

(c) Deduce that $y = e^{3x}(C\cos 2x + D\sin 2x)$ is also a solution of the differential equation, for any values of the two constants C and D.

Solution

(a) The characteristic equation is

$$\lambda^2 - 6\lambda + 13 = 0.$$

The formula method gives

$$\lambda = \frac{6 \pm \sqrt{36 - 4 \times 1 \times 13}}{2} = \frac{6 \pm \sqrt{-16}}{2} = 3 \pm 2i,$$

so the two complex conjugate roots are $\lambda_1 = 3 + 2i$ and $\lambda_2 = 3 - 2i$.

> With the previous notation we have $\alpha = 3$ and $\beta = 2$.

(b) To confirm that $y_1 = e^{3x}\cos 2x$ is a solution of the differential equation, we differentiate and substitute into the differential equation. Differentiating to obtain the first and second derivatives of y_1 gives

$$\frac{dy_1}{dx} = 3e^{3x}\cos 2x + e^{3x}(-2\sin 2x)$$
$$= e^{3x}(3\cos 2x - 2\sin 2x),$$

$$\frac{d^2y_1}{dx^2} = 3e^{3x}(3\cos 2x - 2\sin 2x) + e^{3x}(-6\sin 2x - 4\cos 2x)$$
$$= e^{3x}(5\cos 2x - 12\sin 2x).$$

Substituting these into the left-hand side of the differential equation gives

$$\frac{d^2y_1}{dx^2} - 6\frac{dy_1}{dx} + 13y_1 = e^{3x}(5\cos 2x - 12\sin 2x)$$
$$- 6e^{3x}(3\cos 2x - 2\sin 2x) + 13e^{3x}\cos 2x$$
$$= e^{3x}\left[(5 - 18 + 13)\cos 2x + (-12 + 12)\sin 2x\right]$$
$$= 0.$$

Hence $y_1 = e^{3x}\cos 2x$ is a solution.

Similarly, for $y_2 = e^{3x}\sin 2x$ we have

$$\frac{dy_2}{dx} = e^{3x}(2\cos 2x + 3\sin 2x),$$

$$\frac{d^2y_2}{dx^2} = e^{3x}(12\cos 2x + 5\sin 2x),$$

and substituting into the left-hand side of the differential equation gives

$$\frac{d^2y_2}{dx^2} - 6\frac{dy_2}{dx} + 13y_2 = e^{3x}\left[(12 - 12)\cos 2x + (5 - 18 + 13)\sin 2x\right]$$
$$= 0.$$

Hence $y_2 = e^{3x}\sin 2x$ is also a solution.

(c) Since $y_1 = e^{3x}\cos 2x$ and $y_2 = e^{3x}\sin 2x$ are both solutions of the differential equation, the principle of superposition (Theorem 1.1) tells us that so is

$$y = Ce^{3x}\cos 2x + De^{3x}\sin 2x$$
$$= e^{3x}(C\cos 2x + D\sin 2x),$$

for any values of C and D. ∎

Exercise 1.5

Use the auxiliary equation to find the general solution of each of the following differential equations.

(a) $\dfrac{d^2y}{dx^2} + 4\dfrac{dy}{dx} + 8y = 0$

(b) $\dfrac{d^2\theta}{dt^2} + 9\theta = 0$

We now summarize the method of solving these differential equations as a procedure.

Procedure 1.1   The solution of homogeneous linear constant-coefficient second-order differential equations

The general solution of the homogeneous linear constant-coefficient second-order differential equation

$$a\frac{d^2y}{dx^2} + b\frac{dy}{dx} + cy = 0, \tag{1.3}$$

where a, b, c are (real) constants and $a \neq 0$, may be found as follows.

(a) Write down the auxiliary equation

$$a\lambda^2 + b\lambda + c = 0, \tag{1.5}$$

and find its roots λ_1 and λ_2.

(b) (i) If the auxiliary equation has two distinct real roots λ_1 and λ_2, the general solution of the differential equation is

$$y = Ce^{\lambda_1 x} + De^{\lambda_2 x}.$$

(ii) If the auxiliary equation has two equal real roots $\lambda_1 = \lambda_2$, the general solution of the differential equation is

$$y = (C + Dx)e^{\lambda_1 x}.$$

(iii) If the auxiliary equation has a pair of complex conjugate roots $\lambda_1 = \alpha + \beta i$ and $\lambda_2 = \alpha - \beta i$, the general solution of the differential equation is

$$y = e^{\alpha x}(C\cos\beta x + D\sin\beta x).$$

In each case, C and D are arbitrary constants.

It is worth noting that the three cases in part (b) of Procedure 1.1 correspond to three different possibilities that arise when solving the characteristic equation $a\lambda^2 + b\lambda + c = 0$. These three different possibilities relate to the value of the **discriminant** $b^2 - 4ac$: $b^2 - 4ac > 0$ corresponds to case (i), $b^2 - 4ac = 0$ to case (ii), and $b^2 - 4ac < 0$ to case (iii).

*Exercise 1.6 ───────────────────────────────

Find the general solution of each of the following differential equations.

(a) $\dfrac{d^2y}{dx^2} + 4y = 0$

(b) $u''(x) - 6u'(x) + 8u(x) = 0$

(c) $\dfrac{d^2y}{dx^2} + 2\dfrac{dy}{dx} = 0$

(d) $\dfrac{d^2y}{dx^2} - 2\dfrac{dy}{dx} + y = 0$

(e) $\dfrac{d^2y}{dx^2} - \omega^2 y = 0$, where ω is a real constant

(f) $\dfrac{d^2y}{dx^2} + 4\dfrac{dy}{dx} + 29y = 0$

Exercise 1.7

Small oscillations of the pendulum of a clock can be modelled by the differential equation

$$\ddot{\theta} = -\frac{g}{l}\theta,$$

where g is the magnitude of the acceleration due to gravity, l is the length of the pendulum, and θ is the angle the pendulum makes with the vertical (see Figure 1.1). Solve the differential equation to obtain an expression for θ in terms of g and l.

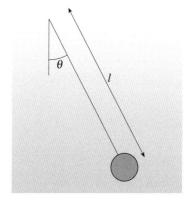

Figure 1.1

1.3 The general solution

In this subsection we prove that the solutions we discovered in Subsection 1.2 are indeed the most general solutions of Equation (1.3). This proof is included for completeness, and you will not be expected to reproduce it; however, it does provide some useful revision of the integrating factor method from *Unit 2*.

Theorem 1.2

Suppose that the roots of the equation

$$a\lambda^2 + b\lambda + c = 0$$

are λ_1 and λ_2. Then the general solution of the second-order linear constant-coefficient differential equation

$$a\frac{d^2y}{dx^2} + b\frac{dy}{dx} + cy = 0 \qquad (1.3)$$

can always be written in the form

$$y(x) = \begin{cases} Ce^{\lambda_1 x} + De^{\lambda_2 x} & (\lambda_1 \neq \lambda_2), \\ (C + Dx)e^{\lambda x} & (\lambda_1 = \lambda_2 = \lambda). \end{cases}$$

In order to prove this it will be convenient to divide through Equation (1.3) by a, obtaining the equivalent form

$$\frac{d^2y}{dx^2} + \frac{b}{a}\frac{dy}{dx} + \frac{c}{a}y = 0. \qquad (1.9)$$

Now we resort to a trick, in order to obtain a *first-order* differential equation in $w = \dfrac{dy}{dx} - ky$, where k is a constant yet to be determined.

Noting that $\dfrac{dw}{dx} = \dfrac{d^2y}{dx^2} - k\dfrac{dy}{dx}$, Equation (1.9) can be written first as

$$\frac{dw}{dx} + \left(\frac{b}{a} + k\right)\frac{dy}{dx} + \frac{c}{a}y = 0,$$

Note that we have eliminated the $\dfrac{d^2y}{dx^2}$ term.

and then, substituting $\dfrac{dy}{dx} = w + ky$, as

$$\frac{dw}{dx} + \left(\frac{b}{a} + k\right)(w + ky) + \frac{c}{a}y = 0.$$

Simplifying, this yields

$$\frac{dw}{dx} + \left(\frac{b}{a} + k\right)w + \left(\frac{c}{a} + k\left(\frac{b}{a} + k\right)\right)y = 0.$$

121

Now, *choosing* k to be a root of the quadratic equation

$$k^2 + \frac{b}{a}k + \frac{c}{a} = 0,$$

which simplifies to

$$ak^2 + bk + c = 0, \tag{1.10}$$

we indeed arrive at a first-order differential equation for w:

$$\frac{dw}{dx} + \left(\frac{b}{a} + k\right)w = 0. \tag{1.11}$$

Of course, Equation (1.10) is the auxiliary equation associated with Equation (1.3), with roots

$$\lambda_1, \lambda_2 = \frac{-b \pm \sqrt{b^2 - 4ac}}{2a},$$

so these are the values of k that we may choose. Before proceeding, notice that the sum of the two roots satisfies

$$\lambda_1 + \lambda_2 = -\frac{b}{a}.$$

For the sake of definiteness, choose $k = \lambda_1$. The above differential equation (1.11) for w may therefore be written as

It does not matter which root we choose, since there is no particular significance in the labelling of λ_1 and λ_2.

$$\frac{dw}{dx} + \left(\frac{b}{a} + \lambda_1\right)w = 0.$$

But since $\lambda_1 + \lambda_2 = -b/a$, we have

$$\frac{b}{a} + \lambda_1 = -\lambda_2.$$

Thus Equation (1.11) becomes

$$\frac{dw}{dx} - \lambda_2 w = 0.$$

This is a first-order linear differential equation, and in principle we could solve it using the integrating factor technique from *Unit 2*. However, the equation is of a particularly simple form that we have seen before, so we can write down the solution as

$$w = Ae^{\lambda_2 x},$$

where A is an arbitrary constant. Now, remembering that

$$w = \frac{dy}{dx} - ky = \frac{dy}{dx} - \lambda_1 y,$$

we arrive at a first-order differential equation for y:

$$\frac{dy}{dx} - \lambda_1 y = Ae^{\lambda_2 x}. \tag{1.12}$$

This is a non-homogeneous linear first-order differential equation that we can solve, once again using the integrating factor method of *Unit 2*. The integrating factor is

$$\exp\left(\int -\lambda_1 \, dx\right) = e^{-\lambda_1 x}.$$

Multiplying through Equation (1.12) by this factor produces the equation

$$e^{-\lambda_1 x}\frac{dy}{dx} - \lambda_1 e^{-\lambda_1 x}y = Ae^{(\lambda_2 - \lambda_1)x},$$

or

$$\frac{d}{dx}\left(ye^{-\lambda_1 x}\right) = Ae^{(\lambda_2-\lambda_1)x}. \tag{1.13}$$

We now have two cases to consider. If $\lambda_2 - \lambda_1 \neq 0$, then integrating both sides yields

This is the case when the auxiliary equation has distinct roots.

$$ye^{-\lambda_1 x} = \frac{A}{\lambda_2 - \lambda_1}e^{(\lambda_2-\lambda_1)x} + C,$$

where C is an arbitrary constant. Multiplying through by $e^{\lambda_1 x}$, we arrive at the explicit form of the general solution

$$y = \frac{A}{\lambda_2 - \lambda_1}e^{\lambda_2 x} + Ce^{\lambda_1 x}.$$

Finally, replacing the arbitrary constant $A/(\lambda_2 - \lambda_1)$ by D gives the required result:

$$y = Ce^{\lambda_1 x} + De^{\lambda_2 x}.$$

If $\lambda_1 = \lambda_2 = \lambda$, say, then Equation (1.13) becomes

This is the case when the auxiliary equation has equal roots.

$$\frac{d}{dx}\left(ye^{-\lambda x}\right) = A,$$

and integrating gives

$$ye^{-\lambda x} = Ax + C,$$

where C is an arbitrary constant. Re-labelling A as D, and multiplying through by $e^{\lambda x}$, we arrive at the explicit form of the general solution

$$y = (C + Dx)e^{\lambda x}.$$

This completes the proof of Theorem 1.2.

End-of-section Exercises

Exercise 1.8

(a) Write down the auxiliary equation of the differential equation

$$3\frac{dy}{dx} - y - 2\frac{d^2y}{dx^2} = 0.$$

(b) Solve this auxiliary equation.

(c) Write down the general solution of the differential equation.

Exercise 1.9

Find the general solution of each of the following differential equations.

(a) $\dfrac{d^2y}{dx^2} + 2\dfrac{dy}{dx} + 2y = 0$ (b) $\dfrac{d^2y}{dx^2} - 16y = 0$

(c) $\dfrac{d^2y}{dx^2} + 4y = 4\dfrac{dy}{dx}$ (d) $\dfrac{d^2\theta}{dt^2} + 3\dfrac{d\theta}{dt} = 0$

Exercise 1.10

For which values of the constant k does the differential equation

$$\frac{d^2y}{dx^2} + 4k\frac{dy}{dx} + 4y = 0$$

have a general solution with oscillating behaviour, that is, a general solution which involves sines and cosines?

2 Inhomogeneous differential equations

Section 1 was concerned with finding the general solution of homogeneous linear constant-coefficient second-order differential equations. This section concerns *inhomogeneous* linear constant-coefficient second-order differential equations, i.e. equations of the form

$$a\frac{d^2y}{dx^2} + b\frac{dy}{dx} + cy = f(x), \tag{2.1}$$

where a, b, c are real constants, $a \neq 0$, and $f(x)$ is a given continuous real-valued function of x.

Subsection 2.1 gives the general method for constructing solutions of Equation (2.1). Subsection 2.2 shows how to find an appropriate particular solution of the differential equation, for use in constructing the general solution, in cases where the function $f(x)$ takes one of a few particular forms. Subsection 2.3 deals with certain cases where complications can arise. Subsection 2.4 shows how to deal with cases where $f(x)$ is a combination of the functions discussed in Subsection 2.2.

2.1 General method of solution

The basic method used for finding the general solution of Equation (2.1) depends on the principle of superposition (Theorem 1.1), and is illustrated in the following example.

Example 2.1

Show that $y = Ce^{-2x} + De^{-3x} + 2$ is a solution of the inhomogeneous differential equation

$$\frac{d^2y}{dx^2} + 5\frac{dy}{dx} + 6y = 12 \tag{2.2}$$

for any values of the constants C and D.

Solution

We know from Exercise 1.3(a) that the homogeneous differential equation

$$\frac{d^2y}{dx^2} + 5\frac{dy}{dx} + 6y = 0 \tag{2.3}$$

has a general solution $y_c = Ce^{-2x} + De^{-3x}$, where C and D are arbitrary constants.

Now consider the constant function $y_p = 2$. This is a particular solution of Equation (2.2) since $d^2y_p/dx^2 = dy_p/dx = 0$ and $6y_p = 12$.

The notation y_c and y_p will be explained shortly.

Therefore, by the principle of superposition (Theorem 1.1),

$$y = y_c + y_p = Ce^{-2x} + De^{-3x} + 2$$

is a solution of Equation (2.2), for any values of C and D. ■

Equation (2.3) is an example of an *associated homogeneous equation* — i.e. the homogeneous equation associated with the inhomogeneous equation (2.2) by making its right-hand side zero. The solutions y_c and y_p also have special names in this context: y_c, the general solution of the associated homogeneous equation (2.3), is called the *complementary function*, and y_p, a particular solution of the inhomogeneous equation (2.2), is called a *particular integral*.

Definitions

Let

$$a\frac{d^2y}{dx^2} + b\frac{dy}{dx} + cy = f(x) \qquad (2.1)$$

be an inhomogeneous linear constant-coefficient second-order differential equation.

(a) Its **associated homogeneous equation** is

$$a\frac{d^2y}{dx^2} + b\frac{dy}{dx} + cy = 0.$$

(b) The general solution y_c of the associated homogeneous equation is known as the **complementary function** for the original inhomogeneous equation (2.1).

(c) Any particular solution y_p of the original inhomogeneous equation (2.1) is referred to as a **particular integral** for that equation.

The term *particular integral* is used here, rather than the term particular solution used in some other texts, to distinguish it from the particular solution to Equation (2.1) that satisfies given initial or boundary conditions (see Section 3).

Later in this section we shall show how to find particular integrals for a wide variety of equations. Before we do that, it is important to realize the full significance of finding just one particular integral.

*Exercise 2.1

Suppose that we have found two different particular integrals y_{p_1}, y_{p_2} for Equation (2.1). Use the principle of superposition to show that the function $y_{p_1} - y_{p_2}$ is then a solution of the associated homogeneous equation.

The result of Exercise 2.1 shows the true significance of finding a particular integral. For if we do so then, since from Section 1 we know how to solve the associated homogeneous equation, we can find *all* particular integrals simply by adding the complementary function. We have proved the following important result.

That is, we can find the complementary function.

Theorem 2.1

If y_c is the complementary function for an inhomogeneous linear constant-coefficient second-order differential equation, and y_p is a particular integral for that equation, then $y_c + y_p$ is the general solution of that equation.

Note that y_c, being the general solution of the associated homogeneous equation, will contain *two* arbitrary constants, whereas y_p, being a particular solution, will contain none.

Let us now see how the method based on Theorem 2.1 can be applied.

Example 2.2

Find the general solution of the differential equation

$$\frac{d^2y}{dx^2} + 9y = 9x + 9. \tag{2.4}$$

Solution

The associated homogeneous equation is

$$\frac{d^2y}{dx^2} + 9y = 0,$$

which has the general solution

$$y_c = C\cos 3x + D\sin 3x.$$

This is the complementary function for Equation (2.4).

A particular integral for Equation (2.4) is

$$y_p = x + 1.$$

This may be verified by differentiation and substitution: $y_p' = 1$ and $y_p'' = 0$, and substituting into the left-hand side of Equation (2.4) gives

$$y_p'' + 9y_p = 0 + 9(x + 1) = 9x + 9,$$

which is the same as the right-hand side of Equation (2.4), as required.

The general solution of Equation (2.4) is, therefore, by Theorem 2.1,

$$y = y_c + y_p = C\cos 3x + D\sin 3x + x + 1,$$

where C and D are arbitrary constants.   ∎

See Exercise 1.5(b), although there different symbols were used for the variables.

You will see in the next subsection how to find such a particular integral.

The method of Example 2.2 may be summarized as follows.

Procedure 2.1   The solution of inhomogeneous linear constant-coefficient second-order differential equations

To find the general solution of the inhomogeneous linear constant-coefficient second-order differential equation

$$a\frac{d^2y}{dx^2} + b\frac{dy}{dx} + cy = f(x):$$

(a) find its complementary function y_c, i.e. the general solution of the associated homogeneous differential equation

$$a\frac{d^2y}{dx^2} + b\frac{dy}{dx} + cy = 0,$$

using Procedure 1.1;

(b) find a particular integral y_p.

The general solution is $y = y_c + y_p$.

The reason why y_c is found first will become clear in Subsection 2.3.

It is worth noting that, by Theorem 2.1, *any* choice of particular integral in Procedure 2.1 gives the *same* general solution. The formula obtained for the general solution may look different for different choices of particular integral, but they are in fact always equivalent. For example, in Example 2.2 the particular integral $y_p = x + 1$ was chosen, and the form of the general solution was obtained as $y = C\cos 3x + D\sin 3x + x + 1$. It would have been equally valid to have chosen, as a particular integral, $y_p = x + 1 + \sin 3x$.

In that case, the form of the general solution would have been obtained as $y = C \cos 3x + D \sin 3x + x + 1 + \sin 3x$. This looks a little different, but it may be written in the form $y = C \cos 3x + (D + 1) \sin 3x + x + 1$; and, since C and D are arbitrary constants, this form of the general solution represents exactly the same family of solutions.

Exercise 2.2

Consider the following differential equations.

(a) $\dfrac{d^2 y}{dx^2} + 4y = 8$ (b) $\dfrac{d^2 y}{dx^2} - 3\dfrac{dy}{dx} + 2y = 6$

See Exercise 1.6(a) and Example 1.3.

For each equation:

- write down its associated homogeneous equation and its complementary function y_c;
- find a particular integral of the form $y_p = p$, where p is a constant;
- write down the general solution.

When using Procedure 2.1, the complementary function is found by using Procedure 1.1. However, the procedures for finding a particular integral are another matter. In Exercise 2.2, where the right-hand sides of the equations are constants, it was possible to find a particular integral almost 'by inspection'; but this method is generally inadequate. Fortunately, there exist procedures for finding a particular integral for equations involving wide classes of right-hand-side functions $f(x)$. The remainder of this section considers some of the simpler cases, where it is possible to determine the *form* of a particular integral by inspection, although some manipulation is required in order to determine the values of certain coefficients.

2.2 Finding a particular integral by the method of undetermined coefficients

In the previous subsection you saw that the inhomogeneous linear constant-coefficient second-order differential equation

$$a\frac{d^2 y}{dx^2} + b\frac{dy}{dx} + cy = f(x) \tag{2.1}$$

can be solved by first solving the associated homogeneous equation, using the methods of Section 1, and then finding a particular integral of Equation (2.1), which depends upon the function $f(x)$. This and the next two subsections show you how to find a particular integral when $f(x)$ is a polynomial, exponential or sinusoidal function, or a sum of such functions.

You saw an example of the approach in Exercise 2.2. There the functions $f(x)$ were *constants* and you tried a *constant* function $y = p$ as a particular integral, substituting into the differential equation to find a suitable value for p. In general, we try a function of the same form as $f(x)$ as a particular integral, and substitute into the differential equation to find suitable values for its unknown coefficients. The function that we try is known as a **trial solution**, and the method is known as the method of **undetermined coefficients**.

There exist procedures for finding a particular integral for fairly general types of continuous function $f(x)$, but these are not considered in this course.

The following examples illustrate the method. Bear in mind, though, that the method (and hence these examples) finds only a particular integral for the differential equation; to find the general solution you would need to find the complementary function and combine it with the particular integral, according to Procedure 2.1.

A polynomial function $(f(x) = m_n x^n + m_{n-1} x^{n-1} + \cdots + m_1 x + m_0)$

Let us first consider a case where $f(x)$ is a linear function (i.e. a polynomial of degree 1).

Example 2.3

Find a particular integral for

$$3\frac{d^2y}{dx^2} - 2\frac{dy}{dx} + y = 4x + 2.$$

Solution

We try a solution of the form

$$y = p_1 x + p_0,$$

where p_1 and p_0 are coefficients to be determined so that the differential equation is satisfied. To try this solution, we need the first and second derivatives of y:

$$\frac{dy}{dx} = p_1, \quad \frac{d^2y}{dx^2} = 0.$$

Substituting these into the left-hand side of the differential equation gives

$$3\frac{d^2y}{dx^2} - 2\frac{dy}{dx} + y = 3 \times 0 - 2p_1 + (p_1 x + p_0) = p_1 x + (p_0 - 2p_1).$$

Therefore, for $y = p_1 x + p_0$ to be a solution of the differential equation, we require that

$$p_1 x + (p_0 - 2p_1) = 4x + 2 \quad \text{for all } x. \tag{2.5}$$

To find the two unknown coefficients p_1 and p_0, we compare the coefficients on both sides of Equation (2.5). Comparing the terms in x gives $p_1 = 4$. Comparing the constant terms gives $p_0 - 2p_1 = 2$, so that $p_0 = 2 + 2p_1 = 2 + 2 \times 4 = 10$. Therefore we have the particular integral

$$y_{\mathrm{p}} = 4x + 10.$$

Comparing coefficients works because two polynomials are equal if and only if all their corresponding coefficients are the same.

Checking: if $y = 4x + 10$, then $dy/dx = 4$, $d^2y/dx^2 = 0$, and substituting into the left-hand side of the differential equation gives

$$3\frac{d^2y}{dx^2} - 2\frac{dy}{dx} + y = 3 \times 0 - 2 \times 4 + (4x + 10) = 4x + 2,$$

as required. ∎

You will have noticed in Example 2.3 that substituting a *linear* trial solution $y = p_1 x + p_0$ into the left-hand side of the differential equation resulted in a *linear* function, namely $p_1 x + (p_0 - 2p_1)$, whose coefficients could be compared with those of the *linear* target function $4x + 2$ to obtain values for p_1 and p_0. This is really the key to the method. If the target function is linear, choosing a linear trial solution ensures that substituting into the left-hand side of the differential equation results in a linear function whose coefficients can be compared with those of the target function. Similarly, as you will see below, if the target function belongs to certain other classes of functions, choosing as a trial solution a *general* function from that class ensures that substitution into the left-hand side of the differential equation produces another function from the same class, whose coefficients can be compared with those of the target function, thus enabling values to be given to the coefficients of the trial solution. The method will work provided that *all* the derivatives of functions in the class are also in the class.

*Exercise 2.3

Find particular integrals of the form $y = p_1 x + p_0$ for each of the following differential equations.

(a) $\dfrac{d^2y}{dx^2} - 2\dfrac{dy}{dx} + 2y = 2x + 3$ 　　(b) $\dfrac{d^2y}{dx^2} + 2\dfrac{dy}{dx} + y = 2x$

Note that, in Exercise 2.3(b), although $f(x)$ is just a multiple of x, it is not possible to find a solution of the form $y(x) = p_1 x$. It is necessary for the trial solution to contain terms like those in $f(x)$ *and all its derivatives*, so that in this case the trial solution must be of the form $y = p_1 x + p_0$. So, in general, even if $m_0 = 0$ in $f(x) = m_1 x + m_0$, so that $f(x) = m_1 x$, you should use a trial solution of the form $y = p_1 x + p_0$.

> Try it and see what goes wrong.

However, if $f(x) = m_0$ is a constant function, then the trial solution need only be a constant function $y = p_0$.

> You saw examples of this in Exercise 2.2.

In general, if $f(x) = m_n x^n + m_{n-1} x^{n-1} + \cdots + m_1 x + m_0$, where $m_n \neq 0$, then a trial solution of the form $y = p_n x^n + p_{n-1} x^{n-1} + \cdots + p_1 x + p_0$ should be used.

*Exercise 2.4

Find a particular integral for

$$y'' - y = t^2.$$

An exponential function $\left(f(x) = me^{kx}\right)$

Example 2.4

Find a particular integral for

$$\frac{d^2y}{dx^2} + 9y = 2e^{3x}.$$

Solution

We try a solution of the form

$$y = pe^{3x},$$

where p is a coefficient to be determined so that the differential equation is satisfied. Differentiating $y = pe^{3x}$ gives

> Since the derivative of e^{3x} is $3e^{3x}$, the exponent $(3x)$ appearing in $y(x)$ should be the same as that appearing in $f(x)$, and only the coefficient p is to be determined.

$$\frac{dy}{dx} = 3pe^{3x}, \quad \frac{d^2y}{dx^2} = 9pe^{3x}.$$

Substituting these into the left-hand side of the differential equation gives

$$\frac{d^2y}{dx^2} + 9y = 9pe^{3x} + 9pe^{3x} = 18pe^{3x}.$$

Therefore, for $y = pe^{3x}$ to be a solution of the differential equation, we require that $18pe^{3x} = 2e^{3x}$ for all x. Hence $p = \frac{1}{9}$, and

$$y_\mathrm{p} = \tfrac{1}{9}e^{3x}$$

is a particular integral for the given differential equation. ■

*Exercise 2.5

Find a particular integral for

$$2\frac{d^2y}{dx^2} - 2\frac{dy}{dx} + y = 2e^{-x}.$$

A sinusoidal function $(f(x) = m\cos\Omega x + n\sin\Omega x)$

This type of function $f(x)$ is particularly important in many practical applications.

Following on from earlier ideas, the trial solution must contain terms like those in $f(x)$ *and all its derivatives*; so, even if $f(x)$ contains only a sine or only a cosine, the trial solution $y(x)$ must contain both a sine and a cosine. However, the value of the parameter Ω appearing in $y(x)$ should be the same as that appearing in $f(x)$.

Example 2.5

Find a particular integral for

$$\frac{d^2y}{dx^2} + 2\frac{dy}{dx} + 2y = 10\sin 2x.$$

Solution

We try a solution of the form

$$y = p\cos 2x + q\sin 2x,$$

where p and q are coefficients to be determined so that the differential equation is satisfied. Differentiating y gives

$$\frac{dy}{dx} = -2p\sin 2x + 2q\cos 2x, \quad \frac{d^2y}{dx^2} = -4p\cos 2x - 4q\sin 2x.$$

Substituting these into the left-hand side of the differential equation gives

$$\begin{aligned}
\frac{d^2y}{dx^2} + 2\frac{dy}{dx} + 2y = {}& (-4p\cos 2x - 4q\sin 2x) \\
& + 2(-2p\sin 2x + 2q\cos 2x) \\
& + 2(p\cos 2x + q\sin 2x) \\
= {}& (-2p + 4q)\cos 2x + (-4p - 2q)\sin 2x.
\end{aligned}$$

Therefore, for $y = p\cos 2x + q\sin 2x$ to be a solution of the differential equation, we require that

$$(-2p + 4q)\cos 2x + (-4p - 2q)\sin 2x = 10\sin 2x \quad \text{for all } x. \qquad (2.6)$$

To find p and q, we compare the coefficients of cos and sin on both sides of Equation (2.6). Comparing cos terms gives $-2p + 4q = 0$. Comparing sin terms gives $-4p - 2q = 10$. Solving these simultaneous equations gives $p = -2$, $q = -1$. Hence

Comparing coefficients works because the cosine and sine functions are *linearly independent*: if $a\sin rx + b\cos rx = 0$ for all x, then $a = b = 0$.

$$y_p = -2\cos 2x - \sin 2x$$

is a particular integral for the given differential equation. ∎

*Exercise 2.6

Find a particular integral for

$$\frac{d^2y}{dt^2} - \frac{dy}{dt} = \cos 3t + \sin 3t.$$

The following procedure summarizes the results of this subsection.

Procedure 2.2   Method of undetermined coefficients

To find a particular integral for the inhomogeneous linear constant-coefficient second-order differential equation

$$a\frac{d^2y}{dx^2} + b\frac{dy}{dx} + cy = f(x),$$

use a trial solution $y(x)$ that has a form similar to that of $f(x)$. For simple forms of $f(x)$, the following table gives the appropriate form of trial solution.

Note that there are exceptional cases where these trial solutions do not work. See Subsection 2.3.

$f(x)$	Trial solution $y(x)$
$m_n x^n + m_{n-1} x^{n-1} + \cdots + m_1 x + m_0$	$p_n x^n + p_{n-1} x^{n-1} + \cdots + p_1 x + p_0$
$m e^{kx}$	$p e^{kx}$
$m \cos \Omega x + n \sin \Omega x$	$p \cos \Omega x + q \sin \Omega x$

To determine the coefficient(s) in $y(x)$, differentiate $y(x)$ twice, substitute into the left-hand side of the differential equation, and equate coefficients of corresponding terms.

Exercise 2.7

What form of trial solution y should you use in order to find a particular integral for each of the following differential equations?

(a) $\dfrac{d^2y}{dx^2} - y = e^{3x}$ (b) $\dfrac{d^2y}{dx^2} + 2\dfrac{dy}{dx} - 4y = \sin 3x$

*Exercise 2.8

Find the *general* solution of each of the following differential equations.

(a) $\dfrac{d^2y}{dx^2} + 2\dfrac{dy}{dx} + 2y = 4$ (b) $\dfrac{d^2\theta}{dt^2} + 3\dfrac{d\theta}{dt} = 9\cos 3t$

The complementary functions were obtained in Exercise 1.9 parts (a) and (d).

Exercise 2.9

A long horizontal rectangular beam of length l rests on rigid supports at each end. It is important in civil engineering to determine how much such a beam 'sags'. A simple model of this 'sag', or vertical displacement y, is the differential equation

$$Ry'' - Sy + \tfrac{1}{2}Q(l - x)x = 0,$$

where R, S and Q are constants related to the structure of the beam, and x is the distance from one end of the beam (as illustrated in Figure 2.1). Find the *general* solution of the differential equation in the case where R, S and Q are all equal to 1.

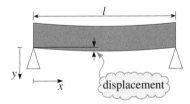

Figure 2.1

In Subsection 2.4 you will see how the principle of superposition can be used in combination with Procedure 2.2 to solve differential equations whose right-hand-side functions $f(x)$ are sums of polynomial, exponential and sinusoidal functions. But first let us look at some exceptional cases for which Procedure 2.2 does not work and needs to be adapted.

2.3 Exceptional cases

There are some exceptional cases for which Procedure 2.2 fails. The aim of this subsection is to indicate when such difficulties arise, and how a particular integral may be found in those circumstances. Let us begin with an example.

Example 2.6

Find a particular integral for

$$\frac{d^2y}{dx^2} - 4y = 2e^{2x}.$$

Solution

Using Procedure 2.2, let us try $y = pe^{2x}$. Differentiating this gives

$$\frac{dy}{dx} = 2pe^{2x}, \quad \frac{d^2y}{dx^2} = 4pe^{2x}.$$

Substituting these into the left-hand side of the differential equation gives

$$\frac{d^2y}{dx^2} - 4y = 4pe^{2x} - 4pe^{2x} = 0.$$

So there is no value of p that gives a particular integral of the form $y = pe^{2x}$.

The trouble is that the complementary function, i.e. the general solution of the associated homogeneous equation

$$\frac{d^2y}{dx^2} - 4y = 0,$$

is $y = Ce^{-2x} + De^{2x}$, thus the trial solution is a solution of the associated homogeneous equation (with $C = 0$, $D = p$). Hence, on substituting the trial solution $y = pe^{2x}$ into the inhomogeneous equation, the left-hand side is zero for any value of p, so it cannot be equal to the non-zero right-hand side.

See Exercise 1.3(c).

In such circumstances, the difficulty can generally be overcome by multiplying the trial solution suggested in Procedure 2.2 by x. Thus, in this case, the trial solution should be modified to take the form $y = pxe^{2x}$. Differentiating this gives

$$\frac{dy}{dx} = pe^{2x} + 2pxe^{2x} = p(1 + 2x)e^{2x},$$

$$\frac{d^2y}{dx^2} = 2pe^{2x} + 2p(1 + 2x)e^{2x} = 4p(1 + x)e^{2x}.$$

There is an analogy here with the case of the homogeneous differential equation when the characteristic equation has equal roots; in that case, when $e^{\lambda x}$ is one solution of the equation, another solution is given by $xe^{\lambda x}$.

Substituting these into the left-hand side of the differential equation gives

$$\frac{d^2y}{dx^2} - 4y = 4p(1 + x)e^{2x} - 4pxe^{2x} = 4pe^{2x}.$$

Therefore $y = pxe^{2x}$ is a solution of the differential equation provided that $4pe^{2x} = 2e^{2x}$ for all x. Hence $p = \frac{1}{2}$, and

$$y_{\mathrm{p}} = \tfrac{1}{2}xe^{2x}$$

is a particular integral for the given differential equation. ∎

The problem with the trial solution being a solution of the associated homogeneous equation can occur irrespective of the form of the trial solution (i.e. polynomial, exponential or sinusoidal), but in most cases it can be overcome by multiplying the trial solution suggested in Procedure 2.2 by x.

When using Procedure 2.2, you should check whether the proposed trial solution is a solution of the associated homogeneous equation, and if so try multiplying it by x. (This is why it is important to find y_c before y_p in Procedure 2.1.)

Exercise 2.10

Find a particular integral for each of the following differential equations.

(a) $\dfrac{d^2y}{dx^2} - 3\dfrac{dy}{dx} + 2y = 4e^x$ (b) $2\dfrac{d^2y}{dx^2} + 3\dfrac{dy}{dx} = 1$

The complementary functions are given in the solutions to Example 1.3 and Exercise 1.3(b).

Exercise 2.11

The motion of a marble dropped from the Clifton Suspension Bridge into the River Avon can be modelled by the differential equation

$$m\ddot{x} + r\dot{x} - mg = 0,$$

where m is the mass of the marble, r is a constant related to air resistance, g is the magnitude of the acceleration due to gravity, and x is the vertical distance from the point of dropping (as shown in Figure 2.2). Find an expression for x in terms of the time t.

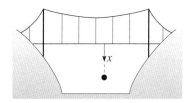

Figure 2.2

We have seen that Procedure 2.2 fails if the trial solution is a solution of the associated homogeneous differential equation: in such cases we multiply the suggested trial solution by x and use this as the trial solution. Another situation in which it is necessary to multiply the suggested trial solution by x is illustrated in the following example.

Example 2.7

Find a particular integral for

$$\frac{d^2y}{dx^2} + 2\frac{dy}{dx} = 2x + 2.$$

Solution

Using Procedure 2.2, let us try $y = p_1x + p_0$. Differentiating this gives

$$\frac{dy}{dx} = p_1, \quad \frac{d^2y}{dx^2} = 0.$$

Substituting these into the left-hand side of the differential equation gives

$$\frac{d^2y}{dx^2} + 2\frac{dy}{dx} = 2p_1.$$

But there is no value of p_1 that satisfies $2p_1 = 2x + 2$ for *all* x.

The problem this time is that the complementary function is $y = C + De^{-2x}$, so the p_0 part of the trial solution is a solution of the associated homogeneous equation (with $C = p_0$, $D = 0$). Hence, on substituting the trial solution $y = p_1x + p_0$ into the inhomogeneous equation, the p_0 part disappears, and the trial solution effectively reduces to $y = p_1x$. The result in this case is that, after substituting the trial solution and its derivatives into the left-hand side of the equation, there are not enough terms on the left-hand side to compare with the terms in the right-hand-side function.

See Exercise 1.6(c).

Again, the difficulty can be overcome by multiplying the trial solution suggested by Procedure 2.2 by x, to give $y = p_1x^2 + p_0x$. Differentiating this gives

$$\frac{dy}{dx} = 2p_1x + p_0, \quad \frac{d^2y}{dx^2} = 2p_1.$$

Substituting these into the left-hand side of the differential equation gives

$$\frac{d^2y}{dx^2} + 2\frac{dy}{dx} = 2p_1 + 2(2p_1x + p_0) = 4p_1x + (2p_1 + 2p_0).$$

Therefore $y = p_1x^2 + p_0x$ is a solution of the differential equation provided that $4p_1x + (2p_1 + 2p_0) = 2x + 2$ for all x. This gives $p_1 = \frac{1}{2}$, $p_0 = \frac{1}{2}$, so

$$y_p = \tfrac{1}{2}(x^2 + x)$$

is a particular integral for the given differential equation.   ∎

To summarize, Procedure 2.2 will fail if *all* or *part* of the suggested trial solution is a solution of the associated homogeneous equation. In such cases, a particular integral can usually be found by multiplying the trial solution by x.

However, it may sometimes be necessary to multiply the trial function by x more than once, as explained in Procedure 2.3 and Exercise 2.12.

Procedure 2.3   *Exceptional cases*

Suppose that you try using the method of undetermined coefficients (described in Procedure 2.2) for finding a particular integral for an inhomogeneous linear constant-coefficient second-order differential equation.

If this fails because all or part of the trial solution is a solution of the associated homogeneous equation, then try multiplying the trial solution by the independent variable x.

If all or part of the resulting trial solution is still a solution of the associated homogeneous equation, then try multiplying by x again.

Exercise 2.12

Find a particular integral for

$$\frac{d^2y}{dx^2} - 2\frac{dy}{dx} + y = e^x.$$

You found the complementary function in Exercise 1.6(d).

2.4   Combining cases

You have seen how to find a particular integral when the right-hand-side function $f(x)$ is polynomial, exponential or sinusoidal. In this subsection you will see how to find a particular integral when $f(x)$ is a combination of such functions, by using the principle of superposition.

Example 2.8

Find a particular integral for

$$\frac{d^2y}{dx^2} + 9y = 2e^{3x} + 18x + 18. \tag{2.7}$$

Solution

In Example 2.4 (page 129) you saw that $y_p = \frac{1}{9}e^{3x}$ is a particular integral for

$$\frac{d^2y}{dx^2} + 9y = 2e^{3x},$$

and in Example 2.2 (page 126) you saw that $y_p = x + 1$ is a particular integral for

$$\frac{d^2y}{dx^2} + 9y = 9x + 9.$$

Therefore, by the principle of superposition (Theorem 1.1), a particular integral for Equation (2.7) is

$$y_p = \tfrac{1}{9}e^{3x} + 2 \times (x + 1) = \tfrac{1}{9}e^{3x} + 2x + 2. \quad \blacksquare$$

The approach of Example 2.8 is to find particular integrals for differential equations involving each part of $f(x)$ separately, and then to use the principle of superposition to combine the two.

Exercise 2.13

Find particular integrals for each of the following differential equations.

(a) $\dfrac{d^2y}{dx^2} - 2\dfrac{dy}{dx} + y = 4e^x - 3e^{2x}$ See Exercise 2.12.

(b) $2\dfrac{d^2x}{dt^2} + 3\dfrac{dx}{dt} + 2x = 12\cos 2t + 10$

End-of-section Exercise

*Exercise 2.14

Find the *general* solution of each of the following differential equations.

You will find some help for parts (a), (d), (e) and (f) in Exercises 1.3 and 1.6, and Example 1.3.

(a) $\dfrac{d^2\theta}{dt^2} + 4\theta = 2t$ (b) $u''(t) + 4u'(t) + 5u(t) = 5$

(c) $3\dfrac{d^2Y}{dx^2} - 2\dfrac{dY}{dx} - Y = e^{2x} + 3$ (d) $\dfrac{d^2y}{dx^2} - 4y = e^{-2x}$

(e) $\dfrac{d^2y}{dx^2} + 4y = \sin 2x + 3x$ (f) $\dfrac{d^2y}{dx^2} - 3\dfrac{dy}{dx} + 2y = 2e^x - 5e^{2x}$

3 Initial conditions and boundary conditions

In Section 2 you saw how to find the general solution of an inhomogeneous linear constant-coefficient second-order differential equation as a combination of a complementary function and a particular integral. In practice, however, we usually want a *particular* solution that satisfies certain additional conditions. Recall that a particular solution is one that does not involve arbitrary constants. In *Unit 2* you saw how one additional condition (called an initial condition) was needed to find a value for the single arbitrary constant in the general solution of a first-order differential equation in order to obtain a particular solution. In the case of second-order differential equations, in order to obtain a particular solution *two* additional conditions are needed to obtain values for the *two* arbitrary constants in the general solution.

There are two types of additional conditions for second-order differential equations: *initial conditions* and *boundary conditions*. Problems involving such conditions are called *initial-value problems* and *boundary-value problems*, respectively, and are discussed in Subsections 3.1 and 3.2.

3.1   Initial-value problems

For a *first-order* differential equation, an initial condition consists of specifying the value of the dependent variable ($y = y_0$, say) at a given value of the independent variable ($x = x_0$), and is often written in the form $y(x_0) = y_0$. One fairly obvious way of specifying *two* additional conditions for a *second-order* differential equation is to give the values of both the dependent variable ($y = y_0$) and its derivative ($dy/dx = z_0$) for the *same* given value of the independent variable ($x = x_0$).

See *Unit 2.*

There are many examples of such a pair of initial conditions occurring naturally as part of a problem. One example is provided by the marble being dropped from the Clifton Suspension Bridge, in Exercise 2.11. In that example, x is the vertical distance from the point of dropping. The obvious choice of origin for the time t is the time at which the marble is dropped. Therefore a naturally occurring pair of initial conditions is that, at time $t = 0$, we know both the position $x = 0$ and the speed $\dot{x} = 0$ (since the marble is dropped, i.e. is released with zero initial velocity). Another example is provided by the clock pendulum in Exercise 1.7. In this example, when the pendulum changes direction, its rate of change of angle θ is momentarily zero; also, when it changes direction, it makes its greatest angle θ_0 with the vertical (see Figure 3.1). Therefore, if we measure time t from the moment the pendulum changes direction, we have the initial conditions $\theta = \theta_0$ and $\dot{\theta} = 0$ when $t = 0$.

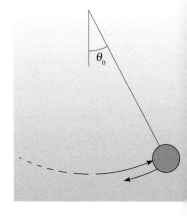

Figure 3.1

Definitions

(a) **Initial conditions** associated with a second-order differential equation with dependent variable y and independent variable x specify that y and dy/dx take values y_0 and z_0, respectively, when x takes the value x_0. These conditions can be written as

$$y = y_0 \text{ and } \frac{dy}{dx} = z_0 \text{ when } x = x_0$$

or as

$$y(x_0) = y_0, \quad y'(x_0) = z_0.$$

The numbers x_0, y_0 and z_0 are often referred to as **initial values**.

(b) The combination of a second-order differential equation and initial conditions is called an **initial-value problem**.

Let us now see how initial conditions can be used to determine values for the two arbitrary constants and hence find a particular solution.

Example 3.1

Find the particular solution of the differential equation

$$\frac{d^2y}{dx^2} - 3\frac{dy}{dx} + 2y = 0$$

that satisfies the initial conditions $y = 0$ and $dy/dx = 1$ when $x = 0$.

Solution

From Example 1.3 we know that the general solution is

$$y = Ce^x + De^{2x}, \tag{3.1}$$

where C and D are two arbitrary constants. One of the initial conditions involves the derivative of the solution, so we need to obtain the derivative of the general solution:

$$\frac{dy}{dx} = Ce^x + 2De^{2x}. \tag{3.2}$$

The initial conditions state that $y(0) = 0$, $y'(0) = 1$. Substituting $x = 0$, $y = 0$ into Equation (3.1) gives

$$0 = Ce^0 + De^0 = C + D,$$

while substituting $x = 0$, $dy/dx = 1$ into Equation (3.2) gives

$$1 = Ce^0 + 2De^0 = C + 2D.$$

Solving these equations gives $C = -1$, $D = 1$, so the required particular solution is

$$y = -e^x + e^{2x}. \quad \blacksquare$$

Note that, when checking a particular solution, you should check that it satisfies the initial or boundary conditions as well as the differential equation.

Exercise 3.1

Find the solutions of the following initial-value problems.

(a) $u''(t) + 9u(t) = 0$, $u\left(\frac{\pi}{2}\right) = 0$, $u'\left(\frac{\pi}{2}\right) = 1$.

See Exercise 1.5(b).

(b) $\dfrac{d^2y}{dx^2} - 3\dfrac{dy}{dx} + 2y = 4e^x$, $y(0) = 4$, $y'(0) = 2$.

See Example 1.3 and Exercise 2.10(a).

(c) $\dfrac{d^2y}{dx^2} - 2\dfrac{dy}{dx} + y = 4e^x - 3e^{2x}$, $y(0) = 4$, $y'(0) = -1$.

See Exercises 1.6(d) and 2.13(a).

You saw in *Unit 2* that an initial-value problem involving a linear first-order differential equation has a unique solution under certain circumstances. (Such circumstances hold for nearly every such initial-value problem that you are likely to come across in practice.) The same is true of initial-value problems involving a linear constant-coefficient second-order differential equation, as the following theorem makes clear.

Theorem 3.1

The initial-value problem

$$a\frac{d^2y}{dx^2} + b\frac{dy}{dx} + cy = f(x), \qquad y(x_0) = y_0, \quad y'(x_0) = z_0,$$

where a, b, c are real constants with $a \neq 0$, and $f(x)$ is a given continuous real-valued function on an interval (r, s), with $x_0 \in (r, s)$, has a unique solution on that interval.

Note that one consequence of this theorem is that if the differential equation is *homogeneous* and the initial conditions are of the form $y(x_0) = 0$ and $y'(x_0) = 0$, then the unique solution must be the zero function $y = 0$, since it satisfies the differential equation and the initial conditions.

3.2 Boundary-value problems

The two conditions in an initial-value problem (the value of the dependent variable y and its derivative dy/dx) both relate to the same value of x. However, the two conditions needed to determine values for the arbitrary constants need not relate to the same value of x. We could have one condition for $x = x_0$ and another for $x = x_1$, say. For example, consider again the 'sagging' beam from Exercise 2.9. Two known conditions on this beam are its zero displacements at the ends of the beam, where it rests on the rigid supports: that is, its *boundary* conditions are $y(0) = 0$ and $y(l) = 0$ (where l is the length of the beam). This pair of boundary conditions gives the value of y at two different points, but in general each boundary condition could specify the value of either y or dy/dx (or even a relationship between them).

Definitions

(a) **Boundary conditions** associated with a second-order differential equation with dependent variable y and independent variable x specify that y or dy/dx (or some combination of the two) takes values y_0 and y_1 at two different values x_0 and x_1, respectively, of x. The numbers x_0, x_1, y_0 and y_1 are often referred to as **boundary values**.

(b) The combination of a second-order differential equation and boundary conditions is called a **boundary-value problem**.

The conditions are referred to as 'boundary' conditions because, as in the beam example, they often relate to conditions at the endpoints x_0 and x_1 of an interval $[x_0, x_1]$ on which we are interested in exploring the differential equation.

Let us now see how boundary conditions can be used to determine values for the two arbitrary constants and hence find a particular solution.

Example 3.2

Find the particular solution of the differential equation

$$\frac{d^2y}{dx^2} + 9y = 0$$

that satisfies the boundary conditions $y = 0$ when $x = 0$ and $dy/dx = 1$ when $x = \frac{\pi}{3}$.

Solution

From Exercise 1.5(b), we know that the general solution is

$$y = C\cos 3x + D\sin 3x, \tag{3.3}$$

where C and D are two arbitrary constants.

One of the boundary conditions involves the derivative of the solution, so we need to obtain the derivative of the general solution:

$$\frac{dy}{dx} = -3C\sin 3x + 3D\cos 3x. \tag{3.4}$$

The boundary conditions state that $y(0) = 0$, $y'\left(\frac{\pi}{3}\right) = 1$. Substituting $x = 0$, $y = 0$ into Equation (3.3) gives

$$0 = C\cos 0 + D\sin 0 = C,$$

i.e. $C = 0$. Substituting $x = \frac{\pi}{3}$, $y' = 1$ and $C = 0$ into Equation (3.4) gives

$$1 = 3D\cos\pi = -3D.$$

Therefore $C = 0$, $D = -\frac{1}{3}$, so the required particular solution is

$$y = -\frac{1}{3}\sin(3x). \quad \blacksquare$$

Exercise 3.2

Find the solution of the following boundary-value problem:

$$\frac{d^2y}{dx^2} - 3\frac{dy}{dx} + 2y = 4e^x, \qquad y'(0) = 2, \quad y(1) = 0.$$

See Exercise 3.1(b).

Exercise 3.3

Use the differential equation of Exercise 2.9, with $R = S = Q = 1$, namely

$$y'' - y + \frac{1}{2}(l - x)x = 0, \tag{3.5}$$

to determine the vertical displacement at the centre of a beam of length 2 metres resting on rigid supports at its ends.

Unlike the case of initial-value problems, boundary-value problems may not have solutions even when the differential equation is linear and constant-coefficient with a continuous real-valued right-hand-side function, as the following example illustrates.

Example 3.3

Try to find a solution of the boundary-value problem

$$\frac{d^2y}{dx^2} + 4y = 0, \qquad y(0) = 0, \quad y\left(\frac{\pi}{2}\right) = 1.$$

Solution

From Exercise 1.6(a), the general solution is

$$y = C\cos 2x + D\sin 2x,$$

where C and D are two arbitrary constants.

The boundary conditions state that $y(0) = 0$, $y\left(\frac{\pi}{2}\right) = 1$. Substituting each of these into the general solution in turn gives

$$0 = C\cos 0 + D\sin 0 = C,$$
$$1 = C\cos\pi + D\sin\pi = -C.$$

There is no solution for which $C = 0$ and $C = -1$, so there is no solution of the differential equation that satisfies the given boundary conditions. $\quad \blacksquare$

Fortunately it is rare for a boundary-value problem that models a real-life situation to have no solution (and in such cases it is usually possible to reformulate the model to overcome the difficulty).

Not only is it possible for boundary-value problems to have no solution, but it is also possible for them to have solutions that are not unique, as the following example illustrates.

Example 3.4

Find the solution of the boundary-value problem

$$\frac{d^2y}{dx^2} + 4\frac{dy}{dx} + 5y = 5, \qquad y(0) = 1, \quad y(\pi) = 1.$$

Solution

From Exercise 2.14(b), the general solution is

$$y = e^{-2x}(C\cos x + D\sin x) + 1,$$

where C and D are two arbitrary constants.

The boundary conditions state that $y(0) = 1$, $y(\pi) = 1$. Substituting each of these into the general solution in turn gives

$$1 = e^0(C\cos 0 + D\sin 0) + 1 = C + 1,$$
$$1 = e^{-2\pi}(C\cos \pi + D\sin \pi) + 1 = -Ce^{-2\pi} + 1.$$

Both of these equations reduce to $C = 0$, but D can take any value, so any solution of the form

$$y = De^{-2x}\sin x + 1$$

satisfies the differential equation and the boundary conditions. ■

In Example 3.4, there is not a unique solution of the differential equation that satisfies the given boundary conditions, but instead there is an infinite family of possible solutions.

Finally, a word of reassurance: most of the boundary-value problems that you will come across in this course will have a unique solution.

End-of-section Exercises

*Exercise 3.4

For each of the following problems, identify the conditions as either initial conditions or boundary conditions, and find the solution of each problem.

(a) $u''(x) + 4u(x) = 0$, $\quad u(0) = 1$, $\quad u'(0) = 0$.

(b) $u''(x) + 4u(x) = 0$, $\quad u(0) = 0$, $\quad u\left(\frac{\pi}{2}\right) = 0$.

(c) $u''(x) + 4u(x) = 0$, $\quad u\left(\frac{\pi}{2}\right) = 0$, $\quad u'\left(\frac{\pi}{2}\right) = 0$.

(d) $u''(x) + 4u(x) = 0$, $\quad u(-\pi) = 1$, $\quad u\left(\frac{\pi}{4}\right) = 2$.

(e) $u''(x) + 4u(x) = 0$, $\quad u'(0) = 0$, $\quad u'\left(\frac{\pi}{4}\right) = 1$.

You found the general solution of the differential equation in Exercise 1.6(a).

Exercise 3.5

Find the solution (if any) of each of the following problems.

(a) $u''(t) + 4u'(t) + 5u(t) = 0$, $\quad u(0) = 0$, $\quad u'(0) = 2$.

See Exercise 2.14(b).

(b) $\dfrac{d^2y}{dx^2} + 2\dfrac{dy}{dx} + 2y = 0$, $\quad$ where $y = 0$ and $\dfrac{dy}{dx} = 0$ when $x = 0$.

See Exercise 1.9(a).

(c) $\ddot{x} + 9x = 3(1 - \pi t)$, $\quad x(0) = \frac{1}{3}$, $\quad \dot{x}\left(\frac{\pi}{3}\right) = 0$.

See Exercise 1.5(b).

4 The nature of solutions

This section is intended principally to assist in the understanding of the nature of oscillatory solutions to problems involving linear constant-coefficient second-order differential equations. For the whole of this section we shall assume that the differential equation has the form

$$a\frac{d^2y}{dx^2} + b\frac{dy}{dx} + cy = f(x),$$

in which a, b and c are *positive*. (This is almost always the case for equations arising in mechanics.)

4.1 Transients

Consider the equation

$$a\frac{d^2y}{dx^2} + b\frac{dy}{dx} + cy = 0 \qquad \text{with} \quad a > 0,\ b > 0,\ c > 0.$$

The nature of the general solution depends on the nature of the roots of the auxiliary equation $a\lambda^2 + b\lambda + c = 0$. More specifically, you saw in Procedure 1.1 that

λ_1, λ_2 real and distinct $\quad\Rightarrow\quad$ solution $y(x) = Ce^{\lambda_1 x} + De^{\lambda_2 x}$,

λ_1, λ_2 real and equal $\quad\Rightarrow\quad$ solution $y(x) = (C + Dx)e^{\lambda_1 x}$,

λ_1, λ_2 complex $(= \alpha \pm i\beta)$ $\quad\Rightarrow\quad$ solution $y(x) = e^{\alpha x}(C\cos\beta x + D\sin\beta x)$,

where in each case C and D are arbitrary real constants.

Since the auxiliary equation has λ_1 and λ_2 as roots, it may be written as

$$(\lambda - \lambda_1)(\lambda - \lambda_2) = 0,$$

or

$$\lambda^2 - (\lambda_1 + \lambda_2)\lambda + \lambda_1\lambda_2 = 0.$$

When we divide through the original auxiliary equation by a, we obtain

$$\lambda^2 + \frac{b}{a}\lambda + \frac{c}{a} = 0.$$

Comparing the coefficients of λ in these two versions of the same quadratic equation, we find that

$$\lambda_1 + \lambda_2 = -\frac{b}{a} \quad \text{and} \quad \lambda_1\lambda_2 = \frac{c}{a}.$$

Now, using the fact that a, b and c are positive, we can make some interesting deductions. First, c/a must be positive so, if they are real, λ_1 and λ_2 have the same sign. Also, since $-b/a$ is negative, the sum $\lambda_1 + \lambda_2$ must be negative. There is only one conclusion to draw from this: if λ_1 and λ_2 are real, then both are negative. If on the other hand λ_1 and λ_2 form the complex conjugate pair $\alpha \pm i\beta$, then their sum is

$$\lambda_1 + \lambda_2 = 2\alpha.$$

Now $\lambda_1 + \lambda_2 = -b/a$ being negative implies that α must be negative.

The upshot is that, in the above list of solutions, all the exponential terms have a *negative* index. Thus for large values of x, the magnitude of all the above solutions will become small. This phenomenon represents *damping*, and you will meet it again in *Unit 17*.

The graphs of typical complementary functions in the three cases are shown in Figure 4.1.

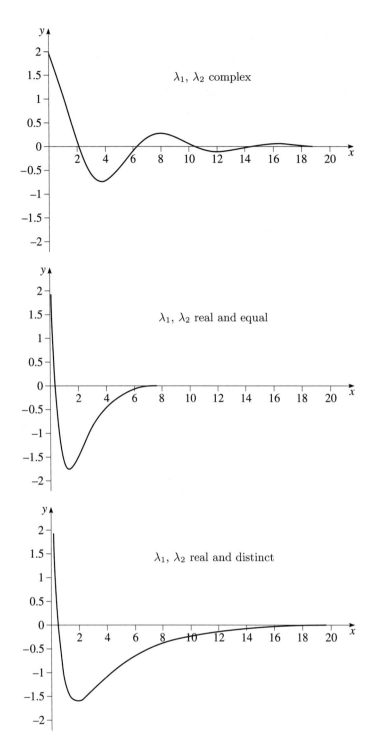

Figure 4.1

In such cases, when the complementary function tends to zero, it is known as the **transient** or the **transient solution**, in that it essentially disappears for large enough x.

If we now turn to the inhomogeneous equation

$$a\frac{d^2y}{dx^2} + b\frac{dy}{dx} + cy = f(x),$$

the above discussion shows that when a, b and c are positive, the complementary function is transient and will not affect the long-term behaviour of the solution.

For this reason, a particular integral not involving part of the transient solution is known as the **steady-state solution**. In most cases, for large x, because the transient solution then has little effect, the solution settles down to a 'steady state' given by the contribution from that particular integral. Two typical solutions to initial-value problems of this type are sketched at the top of Figure 4.2. Here you can see the two examples of a particular solution, followed by the contributions made to each by the transient and the steady-state solution.

However, it is still possible that a particular integral may decay at an even faster rate than the complementary function!

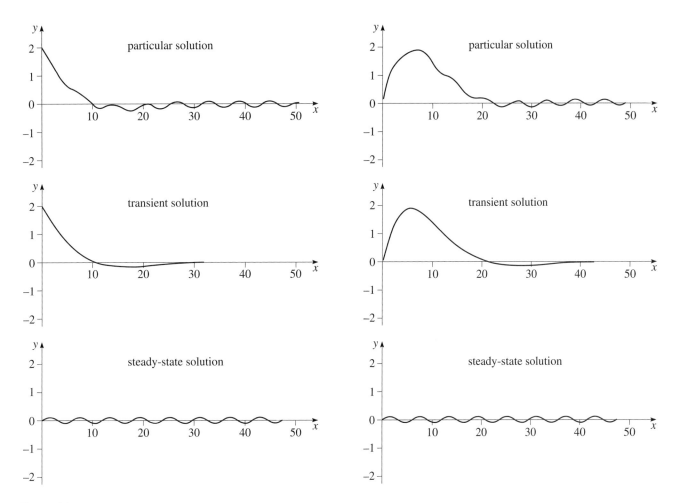

Figure 4.2

Example 4.1

Consider the differential equation of Example 2.5 (page 130),

$$\frac{d^2y}{dx^2} + 2\frac{dy}{dx} + 2y = 10\sin 2x,$$

together with the initial conditions $y(0) = -1$ and $y'(0) = -2$. Find the particular solution and the steady-state behaviour of the solution.

Solution

The auxiliary equation is

$$\lambda^2 + 2\lambda + 2 = 0,$$

with roots $-1 \pm i$. In Example 2.5 we found a particular integral

$$y(x) = -2\cos 2x - \sin 2x.$$

143

Therefore the general solution of the differential equation is

$$y(x) = e^{-x}(C\cos x + D\sin x) - 2\cos 2x - \sin 2x.$$

Substituting the initial conditions shows that $C = D = 1$, so the particular solution to the initial-value problem is

$$y(x) = e^{-x}(\cos x + \sin x) - 2\cos 2x - \sin 2x.$$

This is made up of the transient $e^{-x}(\cos x + \sin x)$, which quickly dies away, and the steady-state solution $-2\cos 2x - \sin 2x$, which determines the long-term behaviour.

We say that the terms $-2\cos 2x$ and $-\sin 2x$ **dominate** the solution for large positive values of x.   ■

In the remainder of this section you are invited to investigate these ideas using the computer algebra package.

4.2   Solving initial-value problems on the computer

The computer algebra package for the course allows you to solve initial-value problems involving linear constant-coefficient second-order differential equations in general, and not just when all the coefficients are positive. The following activity asks you to solve such problems, and to examine the nature and behaviour of the solutions by means of graphs.

Use your computer to complete the following activity.

PC

Activity 4.1 ───────────────────────────────────

Solve each of the following initial-value problems.

(a) $\dfrac{d^2y}{dx^2} + 3\dfrac{dy}{dx} + 2y = 4e^x$, $y(0) = 4$, $y'(0) = 2$.

(b) $2\dfrac{d^2y}{dx^2} + 3\dfrac{dy}{dx} = \sin x$, $y(0) = 0$, $y'(0) = -1$.

(c) $4\dfrac{d^2y}{dx^2} + 4\dfrac{dy}{dx} + y = 2\cos 2x$, $y(1) = 0$, $y'(1) = 1$.

(d) $5\dfrac{d^2y}{dx^2} + 6\dfrac{dy}{dx} + 5y = 4\sin x$, $y(0) = 1$, $y'(0) = -2$.

(e) $\dfrac{d^2y}{dx^2} - 4\dfrac{dy}{dx} + 4y = 3\cos 3x$, $y(\frac{\pi}{2}) = 0$, $y'(\frac{\pi}{2}) = \frac{1}{2}$.

In each case, consider the long-term behaviour of the solution, and try to identify which terms will dominate the solution for large positive values of x.

───────────────────────────────────

Outcomes

After studying this unit you should be able to:

- understand and use the terminology relating to linear constant-coefficient second-order differential equations;
- understand the key role of the principle of superposition in the solution of linear constant-coefficient second-order differential equations;
- obtain the general solution of a homogeneous linear constant-coefficient second-order differential equation using the solutions of its auxiliary equation;
- use the method of undetermined coefficients to find a particular integral for an inhomogeneous linear constant-coefficient second-order differential equation with certain simple forms of right-hand-side function;
- obtain the general solution of an inhomogeneous linear constant-coefficient second-order differential equation by combining its complementary function and a particular integral;
- use the general solution together with a pair of initial or boundary conditions to obtain, when possible, a particular solution of a linear constant-coefficient second-order differential equation;
- understand the nature of the solutions of linear constant-coefficient second-order differential equations with positive coefficients, particularly those involving transient and steady-state parts;
- use the computer algebra package for the course to solve a second-order differential equation.

Solutions to the exercises

Section 1

1.1 (a) Equations (i), (ii), (iii), (vii), (viii) and (ix) are linear and constant-coefficient. (Equations (v) and (vi) are non-linear; (iv) is linear but not constant-coefficient.)

(b) Of the linear constant-coefficient equations, only (iii) and (ix) are homogeneous.

(c) In Equations (i)–(vi) the (dependent, independent) variable pairs are all (y, x). In Equations (vii), (viii) and (ix) they are (t, θ), (x, t) and (x, t), respectively.

1.2 (a) $\lambda^2 - 5\lambda + 6 = 0$

(b) $\lambda^2 - 9 = 0$

(c) $\lambda^2 + 2\lambda = 0$

1.3 (a) The auxiliary equation is $\lambda^2 + 5\lambda + 6 = 0$. Solving this by factorization as $(\lambda + 2)(\lambda + 3) = 0$ gives the roots $\lambda_1 = -2$ and $\lambda_2 = -3$. The general solution is therefore

$$y = Ce^{-2x} + De^{-3x}.$$

(b) The auxiliary equation is $2\lambda^2 + 3\lambda = 0$. This can be factorized as $\lambda(2\lambda + 3) = 0$, so its roots are $\lambda_1 = 0$ and $\lambda_2 = -\frac{3}{2}$. The general solution is therefore

$$y = Ce^0 + De^{-3x/2} = C + De^{-3x/2}.$$

(c) The auxiliary equation is $\lambda^2 - 4 = 0$, i.e. $\lambda^2 = 4$, so its roots are $\lambda_1 = -2$ and $\lambda_2 = 2$. The general solution is therefore

$$z = Ce^{-2u} + De^{2u}.$$

1.4 (a) The auxiliary equation is $\lambda^2 + 2\lambda + 1 = 0$, which can be factorized as $(\lambda + 1)^2 = 0$, giving equal roots $\lambda_1 = \lambda_2 = -1$. The general solution is therefore

$$y = (C + Dx)e^{-x}.$$

(b) The auxiliary equation factorizes as $(\lambda - 2)^2 = 0$, which has equal roots $\lambda_1 = \lambda_2 = 2$. The general solution is therefore

$$s = (C + Dt)e^{2t}.$$

1.5 (a) The auxiliary equation is $\lambda^2 + 4\lambda + 8 = 0$, which has solutions

$$\lambda = \frac{-4 \pm \sqrt{16 - 32}}{2} = -2 \pm 2i.$$

The general solution is therefore

$$y = e^{-2x}(C \cos 2x + D \sin 2x).$$

(b) The auxiliary equation is $\lambda^2 + 9 = 0$, which has solutions

$$\lambda = \pm 3i.$$

The general solution is therefore

$$\theta = e^0(C \cos 3t + D \sin 3t) = C \cos 3t + D \sin 3t.$$

(Note how simple the solution is when there is no first-derivative term in the differential equation. In general, the solution of an equation of the form $y'' + \omega^2 y = 0$, where ω is a constant and x is the independent variable, is $y = C \cos \omega x + D \sin \omega x$.)

1.6 (a) The auxiliary equation is $\lambda^2 + 4 = 0$, which has solutions $\lambda = \pm 2i$. The general solution is therefore

$$y = C \cos 2x + D \sin 2x.$$

(You could also have written down this general solution directly using the remark in Solution 1.5(b).)

(b) The auxiliary equation is $\lambda^2 - 6\lambda + 8 = 0$, which has solutions $\lambda_1 = 4$ and $\lambda_2 = 2$. The general solution is therefore

$$u = Ce^{4x} + De^{2x}.$$

(c) The auxiliary equation is $\lambda^2 + 2\lambda = 0$, which has solutions $\lambda_1 = 0$ and $\lambda_2 = -2$. The general solution is therefore

$$y = C + De^{-2x}.$$

(d) The auxiliary equation is $\lambda^2 - 2\lambda + 1 = 0$, which has solutions $\lambda_1 = \lambda_2 = 1$. The general solution is therefore

$$y = (C + Dx)e^x.$$

(e) The auxiliary equation is $\lambda^2 - \omega^2 = 0$, which has solutions $\lambda = \pm \omega$. The general solution is therefore

$$y = Ce^{\omega x} + De^{-\omega x}.$$

(f) The auxiliary equation is $\lambda^2 + 4\lambda + 29 = 0$, which has solutions $\lambda = -2 \pm 5i$. The general solution is therefore

$$e^{-2x}(C \cos 5x + D \sin 5x).$$

1.7 The auxiliary equation is $\lambda^2 + g/l = 0$, which has solutions $\lambda = \pm i\sqrt{g/l}$. The general solution is therefore

$$\theta = C \cos\left(\sqrt{\frac{g}{l}}\, t\right) + D \sin\left(\sqrt{\frac{g}{l}}\, t\right).$$

(This is another example of an equation involving no first-derivative term. So you could have written down the general solution directly using the remark in Solution 1.5(b).)

1.8 (a) The required auxiliary equation is

$$3\lambda - 1 - 2\lambda^2 = 0,$$

or, equivalently,

$$2\lambda^2 - 3\lambda + 1 = 0.$$

(b) The two solutions of the auxiliary equation are $\lambda_1 = \frac{1}{2}$ and $\lambda_2 = 1$.

(c) By Procedure 1.1, the general solution is

$$y = Ce^{\frac{1}{2}x} + De^x,$$

where C and D are arbitrary constants.

1.9 **(a)** $\lambda^2 + 2\lambda + 2 = 0$ has solutions $-1 \pm i$, so the general solution is $y = e^{-x}(C\cos x + D\sin x)$.

(b) $\lambda^2 - 16 = 0$ has solutions ± 4, so the general solution is $y = Ce^{4x} + De^{-4x}$.

(c) $\lambda^2 - 4\lambda + 4 = 0$ has solutions $\lambda_1 = \lambda_2 = 2$, so the general solution is $y = (C + Dx)e^{2x}$.

(d) $\lambda^2 + 3\lambda = 0$ has solutions $\lambda_1 = 0$ and $\lambda_2 = -3$, so the general solution is $\theta = C + De^{-3t}$.

1.10 The auxiliary equation $\lambda^2 + 4k\lambda + 4 = 0$ can be solved using the formula method to give $\lambda = -2k \pm 2\sqrt{k^2 - 1}$. So there are complex conjugate solutions, leading to a general solution involving sines and cosines, when $k^2 < 1$, i.e. when $|k| < 1$.

Section 2

2.1 We could check this directly, by substituting $y = y_{\mathrm{p}_1} - y_{\mathrm{p}_2}$ into the associated homogeneous equation. However, it is easier to appeal to the principle of superposition. Since y_{p_1} and y_{p_2} both satisfy

$$a\frac{d^2y}{dx^2} + b\frac{dy}{dx} + cy = f(x),$$

Theorem 1.1 shows that the combination $y = y_{\mathrm{p}_1} - y_{\mathrm{p}_2}$ indeed satisfies

$$a\frac{d^2y}{dx^2} + b\frac{dy}{dx} + cy = f(x) - f(x) = 0,$$

as required.

2.2 **(a)** The associated homogeneous equation is $d^2y/dx^2 + 4y = 0$. The complementary function (see Exercise 1.6(a)) is $y_{\mathrm{c}} = C\cos 2x + D\sin 2x$.

Trying a solution of the form $y_{\mathrm{p}} = p$, where p is a constant, in the original equation $d^2y/dx^2 + 4y = 8$ gives $0 + 4p = 8$, so that $p = 2$. Thus a particular integral is $y_{\mathrm{p}} = 2$.

By Procedure 2.1, the general solution is

$$y = C\cos 2x + D\sin 2x + 2.$$

(b) The associated homogeneous equation is $d^2y/dx^2 - 3dy/dx + 2y = 0$. The complementary function (see Example 1.3) is $y_{\mathrm{c}} = Ce^{x} + De^{2x}$.

Trying a solution of the form $y_{\mathrm{p}} = p$ in the original equation $d^2y/dx^2 - 3dy/dx + 2y = 6$ gives $0 - 0 + 2p = 6$, so that $p = 3$. Thus a particular integral is $y_{\mathrm{p}} = 3$.

By Procedure 2.1, the general solution is

$$y = Ce^{x} + De^{2x} + 3.$$

2.3 **(a)** Substituting $y = p_1 x + p_0$ and its derivatives into the differential equation gives

$$0 - 2p_1 + 2(p_1 x + p_0) = 2p_1 x + (2p_0 - 2p_1) = 2x + 3.$$

Equating coefficients gives $p_1 = 1$, $p_0 = \frac{5}{2}$. Therefore a particular integral is

$$y_{\mathrm{p}} = x + \tfrac{5}{2}.$$

(b) Substituting $y = p_1 x + p_0$ and its derivatives into the differential equation gives

$$0 + 2p_1 + (p_1 x + p_0) = p_1 x + (2p_1 + p_0) = 2x.$$

Hence $p_1 = 2$, $p_0 = -4$, and a particular integral is

$$y_{\mathrm{p}} = 2x - 4.$$

2.4 We try $y = p_2 t^2 + p_1 t + p_0$, which has derivatives $y' = 2p_2 t + p_1$, $y'' = 2p_2$. Substituting these into the differential equation gives

$$2p_2 - (p_2 t^2 + p_1 t + p_0) = -p_2 t^2 - p_1 t + (2p_2 - p_0)$$
$$= t^2.$$

Hence $p_2 = -1$, $p_1 = 0$, $p_0 = -2$, and a particular integral is

$$y_{\mathrm{p}} = -t^2 - 2.$$

2.5 We try a solution of the form $y = pe^{-x}$, which has derivatives $dy/dx = -pe^{-x}$, $d^2y/dx^2 = pe^{-x}$. Substituting these into the differential equation gives

$$2pe^{-x} + 2pe^{-x} + pe^{-x} = 5pe^{-x} = 2e^{-x}.$$

Hence $p = \frac{2}{5}$, and a particular integral is

$$y_{\mathrm{p}} = \tfrac{2}{5}e^{-x}.$$

2.6 We try $y = p\cos 3t + q\sin 3t$, which has derivatives

$$\frac{dy}{dt} = -3p\sin 3t + 3q\cos 3t,$$
$$\frac{d^2y}{dt^2} = -9p\cos 3t - 9q\sin 3t.$$

Substituting into the differential equation gives

$$(-9p\cos 3t - 9q\sin 3t) - (-3p\sin 3t + 3q\cos 3t)$$
$$= -(9p + 3q)\cos 3t + (3p - 9q)\sin 3t$$
$$= \cos 3t + \sin 3t.$$

Hence we have a pair of simultaneous equations

$$-9p - 3q = 1,$$
$$3p - 9q = 1.$$

Adding three times the second equation to the first shows that $q = -\frac{2}{15}$, whence $p = -\frac{1}{15}$. A particular integral is thus

$$y_{\mathrm{p}} = -\tfrac{1}{15}\cos 3t - \tfrac{2}{15}\sin 3t.$$

2.7 **(a)** Try $y = pe^{3x}$.

(b) Try $y = p\cos 3x + q\sin 3x$.

2.8 **(a)** From Exercise 1.9(a), the complementary function is $y_{\mathrm{c}} = e^{-x}(C\cos x + D\sin x)$. To find a particular integral, try $y = p_0$. Substituting into the differential equation gives

$$0 + 0 + 2p_0 = 2p_0 = 4.$$

Hence $p_0 = 2$, and a particular integral is $y_{\mathrm{p}} = 2$. Therefore the general solution is

$$y = e^{-x}(C\cos x + D\sin x) + 2.$$

(b) From Exercise 1.9(d), $\theta_c = C + De^{-3t}$. To find a particular integral, try $\theta = p\cos 3t + q\sin 3t$. Differentiating gives

$$\frac{d\theta}{dt} = -3p\sin 3t + 3q\cos 3t,$$

$$\frac{d^2\theta}{dt^2} = -9p\cos 3t - 9q\sin 3t.$$

Substituting into the differential equation gives

$$(-9p\cos 3t - 9q\sin 3t) + 3(-3p\sin 3t + 3q\cos 3t)$$
$$= (9q - 9p)\cos 3t - (9q + 9p)\sin 3t$$
$$= 9\cos 3t.$$

This gives a pair of simultaneous equations to solve:

$$-9p + 9q = 9,$$
$$-9p - 9q = 0.$$

Hence $p = -\frac{1}{2}$, $q = \frac{1}{2}$, and a particular integral is $\theta_p = -\frac{1}{2}\cos 3t + \frac{1}{2}\sin 3t$. Therefore the general solution is

$$\theta = C + De^{-3t} - \tfrac{1}{2}\cos 3t + \tfrac{1}{2}\sin 3t.$$

2.9 Putting the equation into standard form and using $R = S = Q = 1$ gives

$$y'' - y = -\tfrac{1}{2}(l - x)x = -\tfrac{1}{2}lx + \tfrac{1}{2}x^2.$$

The associated homogeneous equation is $y'' - y = 0$, which has auxiliary equation $\lambda^2 - 1 = 0$. This has roots $\lambda = \pm 1$, so the complementary function is

$$y_c = Ce^x + De^{-x}.$$

To obtain a particular integral, we try a function of the form $y = p_2x^2 + p_1x + p_0$. Its derivatives are $y' = 2p_2x + p_1$, $y'' = 2p_2$. Substituting into the differential equation gives

$$2p_2 - (p_2x^2 + p_1x + p_0) = -p_2x^2 - p_1x + (2p_2 - p_0)$$
$$= \tfrac{1}{2}x^2 - \tfrac{1}{2}lx.$$

Hence $p_2 = -\frac{1}{2}$, $p_1 = \frac{1}{2}l$, $p_0 = -1$, and a particular integral is

$$y_p = -\tfrac{1}{2}x^2 + \tfrac{1}{2}lx - 1.$$

Therefore the general solution is

$$y = Ce^x + De^{-x} - \tfrac{1}{2}x^2 + \tfrac{1}{2}lx - 1.$$

2.10 (a) From Example 1.3, the associated homogeneous equation has general solution $y = Ce^x + De^{2x}$, and the trial solution $y = pe^x$ suggested by Procedure 2.2 is a solution of this equation (with $C = p$, $D = 0$). So we try $y = pxe^x$ instead. Differentiating twice gives

$$\frac{dy}{dx} = pe^x + pxe^x = p(1 + x)e^x,$$

$$\frac{d^2y}{dx^2} = pe^x + p(1 + x)e^x = p(2 + x)e^x.$$

Substituting into the left-hand side of the differential equation gives

$$p(2 + x)e^x - 3p(1 + x)e^x + 2pxe^x = -pe^x = 4e^x.$$

Hence $p = -4$, and a particular integral is

$$y_p = -4xe^x.$$

(b) From Exercise 1.3(b), the associated homogeneous equation has general solution $y = C + De^{-3x/2}$, and the trial solution $y = p_0$ suggested by Procedure 2.2 is a solution of this equation (with $C = p_0$, $D = 0$). So we try $y = p_0x$. Differentiating twice gives

$$\frac{dy}{dx} = p_0, \qquad \frac{d^2y}{dx^2} = 0.$$

Substituting into the left-hand side of the differential equation gives $3p_0 = 1$, so $p_0 = \frac{1}{3}$, and a particular integral is

$$y_p = \tfrac{1}{3}x.$$

2.11 The associated homogeneous equation is

$$m\lambda^2 + r\lambda = 0,$$

with solutions $\lambda = 0$ and $\lambda = -r/m$. The complementary function is therefore

$$x_c = C + De^{-rt/m}.$$

The inhomogeneous term is mg, so Procedure 2.2 suggests a trial solution $x = p_0$. However, this is a solution of the associated homogeneous equation (with $C = p_0$, $D = 0$). Hence we try $x = p_0t$ instead. Differentiating and substituting gives

$$rp_0 = mg,$$

so

$$p_0 = \frac{mg}{r}.$$

Hence a particular integral is

$$x_p = \frac{mgt}{r},$$

and the general solution is

$$x = C + De^{-rt/m} + \frac{mgt}{r}.$$

2.12 From Exercise 1.6(d), the associated homogeneous equation has general solution $y = (C + Dx)e^x$, so not only is the trial solution $y = pe^x$ suggested by Procedure 2.2 a solution of the associated homogeneous differential equation (with $C = p$, $D = 0$), but so is $y = pxe^x$ (with $C = 0$, $D = p$). So we try $y = px^2e^x$. Differentiating twice gives

$$\frac{dy}{dx} = 2pxe^x + px^2e^x = p(2x + x^2)e^x,$$

$$\frac{d^2y}{dx^2} = p(2 + 2x)e^x + p(2x + x^2)e^x$$
$$= p(2 + 4x + x^2)e^x.$$

Substituting into the differential equation gives

$$p(2 + 4x + x^2)e^x - 2p(2x + x^2)e^x + px^2e^x = 2pe^x$$
$$= e^x.$$

Hence $p = \frac{1}{2}$, and a particular integral is

$$y_p = \tfrac{1}{2}x^2e^x.$$

2.13 (a) From Exercise 2.12, $y_\mathrm{p} = \frac{1}{2}x^2 e^x$ is a particular integral for
$$\frac{d^2 y}{dx^2} - 2\frac{dy}{dx} + y = e^x.$$
So, using the principle of superposition, we can find a particular integral for the given differential equation if we can find one for
$$\frac{d^2 y}{dx} - 2\frac{dy}{dx} + y = -3e^{2x}.$$
We try $y = pe^{2x}$, which has derivatives
$$\frac{dy}{dx} = 2pe^{2x}, \quad \frac{d^2 y}{dx^2} = 4pe^{2x}.$$
Substituting into the differential equation gives
$$4pe^{2x} - 4pe^{2x} + pe^{2x} = pe^{2x} = -3e^{2x}.$$
Hence $p = -3$, and $y_\mathrm{p} = -3e^{2x}$ is a particular integral for the differential equation with right-hand side $-3e^{2x}$.

Thus, using the principle of superposition, a particular integral for the given differential equation is
$$y_\mathrm{p} = 4(\tfrac{1}{2}x^2 e^x) - 3e^{2x} = 2x^2 e^x - 3e^{2x}.$$

(b) This time we do not have a particular integral for any part of the right-hand-side function, so we need to start from scratch.

First consider the $12\cos 2t$ term on the right-hand side, and try $x = p\cos 2t + q\sin 2t$ as a trial solution. This has derivatives
$$\frac{dx}{dt} = -2p\sin 2t + 2q\cos 2t,$$
$$\frac{d^2 x}{dt^2} = -4p\cos 2t - 4q\sin 2t.$$
Substituting into the differential equation gives
$$2(-4p\cos 2t - 4q\sin 2t) + 3(-2p\sin 2t + 2q\cos 2t)$$
$$+ 2(p\cos 2t + q\sin 2t)$$
$$= 6(q - p)\cos 2t - 6(p + q)\sin 2t$$
$$= 12\cos 2t.$$
So $p + q = 0$, $q - p = 2$, hence $p = -1$, $q = 1$, and a particular integral is
$$x_\mathrm{p} = -\cos 2t + \sin 2t.$$
Now consider the 10 term, and try $x = p_0$. Substituting into the differential equation gives $2p_0 = 10$, so $p_0 = 5$, and a particular integral is
$$x_\mathrm{p} = 5.$$
Therefore, using the principle of superposition, a particular integral for the differential equation with $f(t) = 12\cos 2t + 10$ is
$$x_\mathrm{p} = -\cos 2t + \sin 2t + 5.$$

2.14 (a) From Exercise 1.6(a), the complementary function is
$$\theta_\mathrm{c} = C\cos 2t + D\sin 2t.$$
To find a particular integral, try $\theta = p_1 t + p_0$. Substituting this and its derivatives into the differential equation gives
$$4(p_1 t + p_0) = 2t.$$

Hence $p_1 = \frac{1}{2}$, $p_0 = 0$, and a particular integral is
$$\theta_\mathrm{p} = \tfrac{1}{2}t.$$
Therefore the general solution is
$$\theta = C\cos 2t + D\sin 2t + \tfrac{1}{2}t.$$

(b) The auxiliary equation is $\lambda^2 + 4\lambda + 5 = 0$, which has solutions $\lambda = -2 \pm i$. So the complementary function is
$$u_\mathrm{c} = e^{-2t}(C\cos t + D\sin t).$$
To find a particular integral, try $u = p_0$. Substituting gives $5p_0 = 5$. Hence $p_0 = 1$, and a particular integral is
$$u_\mathrm{p} = 1.$$
Therefore the general solution is
$$u = e^{-2t}(C\cos t + D\sin t) + 1.$$

(c) The auxiliary equation is $3\lambda^2 - 2\lambda - 1 = 0$, which has solutions $\lambda_1 = 1$ and $\lambda_2 = -\frac{1}{3}$. So the complementary function is
$$Y_\mathrm{c} = Ce^x + De^{-x/3}.$$
Consider first the e^{2x} term on the right-hand side of the equation. To find a particular integral, try $Y = pe^{2x}$. The derivatives are $dY/dx = 2pe^{2x}$ and $d^2 Y/dx^2 = 4pe^{2x}$. Substituting gives
$$3(4pe^{2x}) - 2(2pe^{2x}) - pe^{2x} = 7pe^{2x} = e^{2x}.$$
Hence $p = \frac{1}{7}$, and a particular integral is
$$Y_\mathrm{p} = \tfrac{1}{7}e^{2x}.$$
Now consider the 3 term on the right-hand side of the equation, and try $Y = p_0$. Substituting gives $-p_0 = 3$, so $p_0 = -3$, and a particular integral is
$$Y_\mathrm{p} = -3.$$
Therefore, using the principle of superposition, a particular integral for the differential equation with $f(x) = e^{2x} + 3$ is
$$Y_\mathrm{p} = \tfrac{1}{7}e^{2x} - 3.$$
Therefore the general solution is
$$Y = Ce^x + De^{-x/3} + \tfrac{1}{7}e^{2x} - 3.$$

(d) From Exercise 1.3(c), the complementary function is
$$y_\mathrm{c} = Ce^{-2x} + De^{2x}.$$
To find a particular integral, since e^{-2x} is a solution of the associated homogeneous equation, try $y = pxe^{-2x}$. The derivatives are $dy/dx = p(1 - 2x)e^{-2x}$ and $d^2 y/dx^2 = 4p(x - 1)e^{-2x}$. Substituting gives
$$4p(x - 1)e^{-2x} - 4pxe^{-2x} = -4pe^{-2x} = e^{-2x}.$$
Hence $p = -\frac{1}{4}$, and a particular integral is
$$y_\mathrm{p} = -\tfrac{1}{4}xe^{-2x}.$$
Therefore the general solution is
$$y = Ce^{-2x} + De^{2x} - \tfrac{1}{4}xe^{-2x}.$$

(e) From Exercise 1.6(a), the complementary function is

$$y_c = C\cos 2x + D\sin 2x.$$

To find a particular integral, we note that, from part (a), a particular integral for $d^2y/dx^2 + 4y = 2x$ is $y_p = \frac{1}{2}x$. So we need to consider only the $\sin 2x$ term, and then use the principle of superposition. For this term, noting the form of the complementary function, try $y = x(p\cos 2x + q\sin 2x)$. The derivatives are

$$\frac{dy}{dx} = (p + 2qx)\cos 2x + (q - 2px)\sin 2x,$$

$$\frac{d^2y}{dx^2} = (4q - 4px)\cos 2x - (4p + 4qx)\sin 2x.$$

Substituting gives

$$(4q - 4px)\cos 2x - (4p + 4qx)\sin 2x$$
$$+ 4x(p\cos 2x + q\sin 2x)$$
$$= 4q\cos 2x - 4p\sin 2x$$
$$= \sin 2x.$$

Hence $p = -\frac{1}{4}$, $q = 0$, and a particular integral is $y_p = -\frac{1}{4}x\cos 2x$.

So, using the principle of superposition, a particular integral for the given differential equation is

$$y_p = -\frac{1}{4}x\cos 2x + \frac{3}{2}(\frac{1}{2}x) = -\frac{1}{4}x\cos 2x + \frac{3}{4}x.$$

Therefore the general solution is

$$y = C\cos 2x + D\sin 2x - \frac{1}{4}x\cos 2x + \frac{3}{4}x.$$

(f) From Example 1.3, the complementary function is

$$y_c = Ce^x + De^{2x}.$$

Consider first the $2e^x$ term on the right-hand side of the equation. To find a particular integral, since e^x appears in the complementary function, try $y = pxe^x$, which has derivatives

$$\frac{dy}{dx} = p(1 + x)e^x, \quad \frac{d^2y}{dx^2} = p(2 + x)e^x.$$

Substituting into the differential equation gives

$$p(2 + x)e^x - 3p(1 + x)e^x + 2pxe^x = -pe^x = 2e^x.$$

Hence $p = -2$, and a particular integral is

$$y_p = -2xe^x.$$

Now consider the $-5e^{2x}$ term on the right-hand side of the equation. To find a particular integral, since e^{2x} appears in the complementary function, try $y = pxe^{2x}$, which has derivatives

$$\frac{dy}{dx} = p(1 + 2x)e^{2x}, \quad \frac{d^2y}{dx^2} = p(4 + 4x)e^{2x}.$$

Substituting into the differential equation gives

$$p(4 + 4x)e^{2x} - 3p(1 + 2x)e^{2x} + 2pxe^{2x} = pe^{2x}$$
$$= -5e^{2x}.$$

Hence $p = -5$, and a particular integral is

$$y_p = -5xe^{2x}.$$

Therefore, using the principle of superposition, a particular integral for the differential equation with $f(x) = 2e^x - 5e^{2x}$ is

$$y_p = -2xe^x - 5xe^{2x}.$$

Therefore the general solution is

$$y = Ce^x + De^{2x} - 2xe^x - 5xe^{2x}.$$

Section 3

3.1 (a) From Exercise 1.5(b), the general solution is

$$u = C\cos 3t + D\sin 3t.$$

Its derivative is

$$u' = -3C\sin 3t + 3D\cos 3t.$$

Substituting the initial condition $t = \frac{\pi}{2}$, $u = 0$ into the general solution gives $D = 0$. Substituting the initial condition $t = \frac{\pi}{2}$, $u' = 1$ into the derivative gives $C = \frac{1}{3}$. Hence the required particular solution is

$$u = \frac{1}{3}\cos 3t.$$

(b) From Example 1.3 and Exercise 2.10(a), the general solution is

$$y = Ce^x + De^{2x} - 4xe^x.$$

Its derivative is

$$y' = Ce^x + 2De^{2x} - 4(1 + x)e^x.$$

Substituting the initial condition $x = 0$, $y = 4$ into the general solution gives $C + D = 4$. Substituting the initial condition $x = 0$, $y' = 2$ into the derivative gives $C + 2D - 4 = 2$. Hence $C = 2$, $D = 2$, and the required particular solution is

$$y = 2e^x + 2e^{2x} - 4xe^x.$$

(c) From Exercises 1.6(d) and 2.13(a), the general solution is

$$y = (C + Dx)e^x + 2x^2e^x - 3e^{2x}.$$

Its derivative is

$$y' = (C + D + Dx)e^x + (4x + 2x^2)e^x - 6e^{2x}.$$

Substituting the initial condition $x = 0$, $y = 4$ into the general solution gives $C - 3 = 4$. Substituting the initial condition $x = 0$, $y' = -1$ into the derivative gives $C + D - 6 = -1$. Hence $C = 7$, $D = -2$, and the required particular solution is

$$y = (7 - 2x)e^x + 2x^2e^x - 3e^{2x}$$
$$= (7 - 2x + 2x^2)e^x - 3e^{2x}.$$

3.2 From Exercise 3.1(b), the general solution is

$$y = Ce^x + De^{2x} - 4xe^x,$$

and its derivative is

$$y' = Ce^x + 2De^{2x} - 4(1 + x)e^x.$$

Substituting the boundary condition $x = 0$, $y' = 2$ into the derivative gives $C + 2D = 6$. Substituting $x = 1$, $y = 0$ into the general solution gives $Ce + De^2 - 4e = 0$, which can be rearranged to give $C + eD = 4$. Hence $C = (8 - 6e)/(2 - e)$, $D = 2/(2 - e)$, and the required particular solution is

$$y = \frac{8 - 6e}{2 - e}e^x + \frac{2}{2 - e}e^{2x} - 4xe^x.$$

3.3 From Exercise 2.9, the general solution of Equation (3.5) is $y = Ce^x + De^{-x} - \frac{1}{2}x^2 + \frac{1}{2}lx - 1$, which for $l = 2$ becomes

$$y = Ce^x + De^{-x} - \frac{1}{2}x^2 + x - 1.$$

The boundary conditions, resulting from the beam resting on supports at its two ends, are $y(0) = 0$, $y(2) = 0$.

Substitution of these into the differential equation gives $C + D - 1 = 0$ and $Ce^2 + De^{-2} - 1 = 0$. Multiplying the second equation by e^2 gives $C + D = 1$ and $Ce^4 + D = e^2$ as the equations to solve. Subtracting the equations gives $C(e^4 - 1) = e^2 - 1$. This gives

$$C = \frac{e^2 - 1}{e^4 - 1} = \frac{e^2 - 1}{(e^2 + 1)(e^2 - 1)} = \frac{1}{e^2 + 1},$$

$$D = 1 - C = 1 - \frac{1}{e^2 + 1} = \frac{e^2 + 1 - 1}{e^2 + 1} = \frac{e^2}{e^2 + 1}.$$

Hence the required particular solution is

$$y = \frac{1}{e^2 + 1}(e^x + e^{2-x}) - \tfrac{1}{2}x^2 + x - 1.$$

At the centre of the beam, $x = 1$, so $y \simeq 0.148$. The displacement or 'sag' at the centre of the beam is approximately $0.148\,\mathrm{m}$ or about $14.8\,\mathrm{cm}$.

3.4 Problems (a) and (c) are initial-value problems; problems (b), (d) and (e) are boundary-value problems.

The differential equation is the same in each case, and from Exercise 1.6(a) its general solution is

$$u = C\cos 2x + D\sin 2x.$$

The derivative is

$$u' = -2C\sin 2x + 2D\cos 2x.$$

(a) The condition $u(0) = 1$ gives $C = 1$. The condition $u'(0) = 0$ gives $D = 0$. The required solution is therefore

$$u = \cos 2x.$$

(b) The condition $u(0) = 0$ gives $C = 0$. The condition $u\left(\frac{\pi}{2}\right) = 0$ gives $C = 0$ also. D therefore remains arbitrary, so there is an infinite number of solutions, of the form

$$u = D\sin 2x.$$

(c) The condition $u\left(\frac{\pi}{2}\right) = 0$ gives $C = 0$. The condition $u'\left(\frac{\pi}{2}\right) = 0$ gives $D = 0$. The required solution is therefore the zero function

$$u = 0.$$

(Alternatively, since the differential equation is homogeneous and the initial conditions are both equal to zero, by the remarks after Theorem 3.1 the solution is the zero function $u = 0$.)

(d) The condition $u(-\pi) = 1$ gives $C = 1$. The condition $u\left(\frac{\pi}{4}\right) = 2$ gives $D = 2$. The required solution is therefore

$$u = \cos 2x + 2\sin 2x.$$

(e) The condition $u'(0) = 0$ gives $D = 0$. The condition $u'\left(\frac{\pi}{4}\right) = 1$ gives $C = -\tfrac{1}{2}$. The required solution is therefore

$$u = -\tfrac{1}{2}\cos 2x.$$

3.5 Parts (a) and (b) are initial-value problems, and therefore by Theorem 3.1 each has a unique solution. However, part (c) is a boundary-value problem, which may have no solution, a unique solution, or an infinite number of solutions.

(a) From Exercise 2.14(b), the general solution is

$$u = e^{-2t}(C\cos t + D\sin t).$$

Its derivative is

$$u' = e^{-2t}((-2C + D)\cos t - (C + 2D)\sin t).$$

The condition $u(0) = 0$ gives $C = 0$. The condition $u'(0) = 2$ gives $D = 2$. The solution is therefore

$$u = 2e^{-2t}\sin t.$$

(b) The differential equation is homogeneous and the initial conditions are both equal to zero. Hence the solution is the zero function $y = 0$.

(c) From Exercise 1.5(b), the complementary function is

$$x_c = C\cos 3t + D\sin 3t.$$

To find a particular integral, try $x = p_1 t + p_0$. Substituting into the differential equation gives

$$9(p_1 t + p_0) = 3(1 - \pi t).$$

Hence $p_1 = -\tfrac{\pi}{3}$, $p_0 = \tfrac{1}{3}$, and a particular integral is

$$x_p = -\tfrac{\pi}{3}t + \tfrac{1}{3}.$$

Therefore the general solution is

$$x = C\cos 3t + D\sin 3t - \tfrac{\pi}{3}t + \tfrac{1}{3},$$

and its derivative is

$$\dot{x} = -3C\sin 3t + 3D\cos 3t - \tfrac{\pi}{3}.$$

The condition $x(0) = \tfrac{1}{3}$ gives $C = 0$. The condition $\dot{x}\left(\frac{\pi}{3}\right) = 0$ gives $D = -\tfrac{\pi}{9}$. The solution is therefore

$$x = -\tfrac{\pi}{9}\sin 3t - \tfrac{\pi}{3}t + \tfrac{1}{3}.$$

UNIT 4 Vector algebra

Study guide for Unit 4

This unit assumes no previous knowledge of vectors. You will need to know only basic algebra and trigonometry, and how to use Cartesian coordinates for specifying a point in a plane.

The recommended study pattern is to study one section per study session, and to study the sections in the order in which they appear.

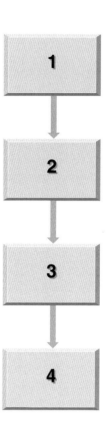

Introduction

We often need to represent physical quantities such as mass, force, velocity, acceleration, time, etc., mathematically. Most of the physical quantities that we need can be classified into two types: *scalars* and *vectors*. *Scalar quantities* are quantities, like mass, temperature, energy, volume and time, that can be represented by a single real number. Other quantities, like force, velocity and acceleration, possess *magnitude* and *direction* in space, and cannot be represented by a single real number; they are called *vector quantities*.

The definitive vector quantity is *displacement*. The displacement of a point specifies the position of the point in space relative to some reference point. We use the concept of displacement whenever we want to describe spatial relationships. Consider, for example, the instructions written in blood on a pirate's treasure map:

> Take five paces due north from the big oak tree, then seven paces due west, and then dig down for three metres.

This is a specification of a displacement vector — the displacement of the treasure from a reference point (the big oak tree). In fact, this particular way of specifying the displacement of the treasure is known as the *Cartesian* description of a displacement, although the pirate probably didn't know that. Alternatively, there is the so-called *polar* description of the *same* displacement (equating paces with metres):

> Starting at the big oak tree, dig for 9.1 paces along a straight sloping line inclined at 19° below the horizontal at a bearing of 54° west of north.

This 'distance (or magnitude) plus direction' specification will also get you to the treasure, although less conveniently because it is more difficult to dig along a sloping line. These two different specifications are shown in Figure 0.1.

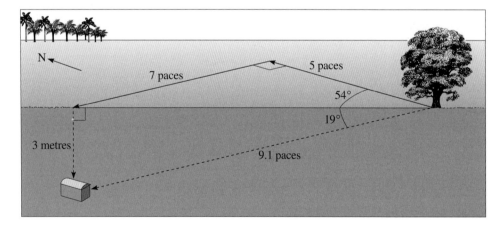

Figure 0.1

Section 1 defines a vector and discusses ways of representing vectors in two dimensions. Section 3 discusses another way of representing vectors, one that easily generalizes from two to three (or more) dimensions. Sections 2 and 4 consider ways of operating on and combining vectors — that is, they provide the fundamentals of *vector algebra*.

1 Describing and representing vectors

Subsection 1.1 explains what scalars and vectors are. Subsections 1.2 and 1.3 then explain how to denote vectors symbolically (i.e. algebraically) and how to show them in diagrams. Subsection 1.4 explains what is meant by saying that two vectors are equal to one another, which is a necessary first step in the development of an algebra for vectors. Subsection 1.5 introduces a method for representing vectors in two dimensions that can be useful in a variety of physical situations.

1.1 Scalars and vectors

A **scalar** is any quantity, such as mass, time, volume and temperature, that can be represented mathematically by a single real number (and often a unit of measurement). Real numbers themselves are examples of scalars, and you can regard the terms *scalar* and *real number* as synonymous. Examples of scalar quantities, quoted to some convenient degree of accuracy, are:

the mass of the Earth, 5.975×10^{24} kilograms;

the temperature of melting ice, 0 degrees Celsius;

my current bank account balance, -153.12 pounds sterling;

pi (π), $3.141\,59\ldots$.

A real number x is defined by two properties: its *modulus* $|x|$ and its *sign*. Thus the **magnitude** of a scalar x is $|x|$. For example, the magnitude of my current account balance is $|-153.12|$ pounds $= 153.12$ pounds, which sounds a lot better since it doesn't remind me that I'm in debt. Note that magnitudes are always non-negative (i.e. positive or zero).

> The modulus of a real number is also called its *magnitude*.

A *vector* quantity is any quantity, such as force, velocity, displacement, etc., that has a magnitude *and* a direction in space (or, in two dimensions, a direction in a plane). An example is the velocity of a motor car travelling on the M4 motorway from London to Bristol with a speed of 95 km per hour in a westerly direction. The magnitude of the velocity vector is 95 (dropping units for convenience), and the direction of the velocity vector is due west. Thus the specification of a **vector** consists of:

> The familiar term *speed* is used to mean the magnitude of a velocity. Speed is a non-negative scalar.

(a) a non-negative real number, called its modulus or **magnitude**;

(b) a **direction** in space.

This unit is mainly concerned with just two vector quantities: displacement and velocity. Later in the course you will come across other vector quantities such as force, torque and momentum. Fortunately, *all* vector quantities obey exactly the *same* laws of algebra. Thus what you learn about displacements and velocities in this unit can be carried over to all vector quantities.

1.2 Vector notation

Vectors are denoted in printed text by bold letters, e.g. **v**, **F**. In your written work, you should denote vectors by drawing either a straight line or a squiggly line under the letter, e.g. $\underline{v}$, $\underline{F}$ or $\underset{\sim}{v}$, $\underset{\sim}{F}$. Thus if a symbol is used to represent the velocity of an object, then it must be handwritten by you as either $\underline{v}$ or $\underset{\sim}{v}$ (but will be printed in the text as **v**).

> It is *important* that you learn to write vectors using the underlining: if you do not do so, someone reading your work may not be able to tell that you are referring to a vector. In particular, you may lose marks!

The modulus or magnitude of the vector **v** is denoted by $|\mathbf{v}|$ or, sometimes, where there is no possibility of ambiguity, by v; $|\mathbf{v}|$ is a non-negative scalar.

We read $|\mathbf{v}|$ as 'the modulus of v' or 'the magnitude of v', or simply 'mod v'.

1.3   Using arrows to represent vectors

A vector can be conveniently represented in a diagram by an arrow, i.e. a straight line with an arrowhead on it. The tail of the arrow may be placed at some fixed origin, the direction of the arrow is chosen to represent that of the vector, and its length is chosen to be proportional to the magnitude of the vector. In Figure 1.1, which uses the origin of the Cartesian coordinate system as the fixed origin, the shorter arrow represents a vector of magnitude 1 in the positive x-direction, and the longer arrow represents a vector of magnitude $2\sqrt{2}$ in a direction at $\frac{\pi}{4}$ radians (45°) to the positive x-direction. (Note that we use the convention that positive angles are measured anticlockwise.) If we decide to denote these vectors by letters **a** and **b**, respectively, then we can also put this information on the diagram, by writing **a** and **b** near the arrowheads, as shown in Figure 1.2.

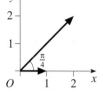

Figure 1.1

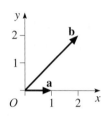

Figure 1.2

Note that in this course, and commonly elsewhere, the arrows representing vectors are drawn using thick lines. This helps to distinguish vector arrows from other arrowed lines such as those representing the coordinate axes (e.g. Figures 1.1 and 1.2) or those representing compass directions (e.g. Figure 1.3).

*Exercise 1.1

Represent the following two vectors on a diagram by arrows:

- vector **a** has magnitude 3 units and points in the positive y-direction;
- vector **b** has magnitude 4 units and points in the direction at $\frac{\pi}{3}$ radians (60°) to the positive x-direction.

Vector notation and the use of arrows in diagrams is now illustrated further by specific reference to displacement vectors and velocity vectors.

Displacement is the position of a point in space relative to some reference point or origin. For example, the city of Leeds is 296 km from the city of Bristol in the direction of 15° east of north (N 15°E). The displacement of Leeds from Bristol can be specified as the vector

$$\mathbf{s} = 296\,\mathrm{km\,N\,15°E}.$$

It would be wrong to write $\mathbf{s} = 296\,\mathrm{km}$, because the left-hand side is a vector symbol and the right-hand side is a scalar.

Here the bold symbol **s** has been used to denote the displacement. Note that both magnitude and direction are specified: the magnitude of the displacement is $|\mathbf{s}| = 296\,\mathrm{km}$, and the direction is specified by the compass bearing N 15°E.

The displacement $\mathbf{s} = 296\,\mathrm{km\,N\,15°E}$ can be represented in a diagram by an arrow, as shown in Figure 1.3. The length of the arrow represents 296 km, which may be shown in the diagram by writing $|\mathbf{s}| = 296$.

For any two points P and Q, we can define the **displacement vector** from P to Q: it is the vector whose magnitude is the distance from P to Q and whose direction is the direction of the straight line from P to Q. A useful notation for this vector is $\overrightarrow{PQ}$ (see Figure 1.4). In this context the symbol PQ (without an arrow) represents the length of the straight line joining P and Q, i.e. $PQ = |\overrightarrow{PQ}|$. Note that $PQ = QP$ but $\overrightarrow{PQ} \neq \overrightarrow{QP}$ (because $\overrightarrow{PQ}$ and $\overrightarrow{QP}$ are in opposite directions).

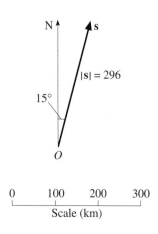

Figure 1.3

Displacement vector

The displacement vector $\overrightarrow{PQ}$ is the vector whose magnitude is the distance from P to Q and whose direction is the direction of the straight line from P to Q.

Figure 1.4

One query may have occurred to you. What is the displacement vector of a point from itself? In other words, what is the vector $\overrightarrow{PP}$? Clearly its length is zero, but what is its direction? The answer is that it does not have one! We define the **zero vector** to be the unique vector with magnitude zero and no direction. It is denoted by **0**. Thus we can conclude that $\overrightarrow{PP} = \mathbf{0}$.

Zero vector

The zero vector is the unique vector with magnitude zero and no direction. It is denoted by **0**.

Be particularly careful to underline the zero vector ($\underline{0}$ or $\underset{\sim}{0}$) in your written work!

A constant **velocity** is also defined by a magnitude and a direction. For instance, in a weather forecast, a typical wind velocity might be 35 knots from the north-west. It is not sufficient to say that 'the wind velocity is 35 knots'; the obvious question about such a statement would be 'from which direction?'. The vector **v** representing this velocity has magnitude 35 and direction from the north-west and towards the south-east (since the air is travelling in the south-easterly direction). It can be represented on a diagram as shown in Figure 1.5. The length of the arrow represents a wind speed of 35 knots.

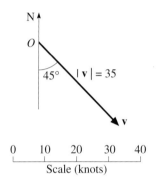

Note that the *direction* of a vector consists of two attributes:

(a) an *orientation*, represented by the *slope* of the arrow in diagrams like Figures 1.1 to 1.5;

Figure 1.5

(b) a *sense*, represented by the *arrowhead*.

For instance, the arrow representing the velocity 35 knots from the north-west in Figure 1.5 is a line making an angle of 45° anticlockwise from the south direction (the orientation) and an arrowhead pointing towards south-east as opposed to north-west (the sense).

*Exercise 1.2

The displacement of Birmingham from Derby is 57 km in the direction S 30°W. The displacement of Leicester from Derby is 32 km in the direction S 45°E.

Draw a diagram, to a suitable scale, representing these two displacements by arrows.

Exercise 1.3

A car travelling from London along the M1 with speed 70 mph heads in the direction N 60°W near Junction 14.

Represent the velocity of the car by an arrow, drawn to a suitable scale.

1.4 Equality of vectors

> **Definition**
>
> Two vectors are said to be **equal** if they have the same magnitude *and* the same direction.

You have seen how to represent a vector by an arrow. This definition of equality of vectors tells us that the two features needed to define a vector uniquely are its magnitude and direction. This means that any two arrows drawn at different places on the page but which are equal in length, parallel and have the same sense, can be used to represent the same vector. For instance, the two arrows in Figure 1.6 are each of length 2 units and point in the positive x-direction. They represent two equal vectors, and we write **b** = **d**. In other words, the arrow representing a vector does not have to be drawn so that its tail is at any particular point.

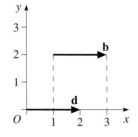

Figure 1.6

Example 1.1

Figure 1.7 shows several vectors represented by arrows drawn to scale. Find the vector equal to the vector **a**.

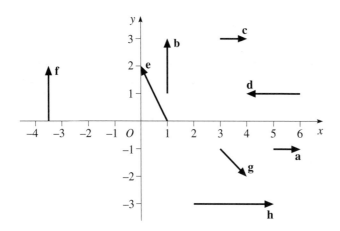

Figure 1.7

Solution

We are looking for a vector that is equal in length to **a** (i.e. one unit), parallel to **a** and points in the same direction (i.e. the positive x-direction). There are two arrows (and thus vectors) other than **a** that point in the positive x-direction; they are **c** and **h**. (The arrow representing **d** points in the negative x-direction.) The magnitudes of **c** and **h** are 1 unit and 3 units, respectively. Since the magnitude of **a** is 1 unit, **c** = **a** but **h** ≠ **a**.

Note that although **a** and **c** are drawn at different places in the (x, y)-plane, they are equal in magnitude and have the same direction, so they are equal vectors. ■

Exercise 1.4 ───────────────────────────

Which vector in Figure 1.7 is equal to vector **b**?

───

1.5 Polar representation of two-dimensional vectors

This subsection introduces a systematic way of specifying the magnitude and direction of a vector in a coordinate system.

You should be familiar with using a two-dimensional *Cartesian coordinate system* for specifying the position (x, y) of a point in a plane, and indeed the same system is commonly used for displaying vectors (as in Figures 1.1, 1.2, 1.6 and 1.7). The **plane polar coordinate system**, however, is in some sense a more natural one for specifying vectors since it effectively regards *magnitude* and *direction* as two *coordinates*.

Let **r** be a vector on a plane surface. Introduce a Cartesian coordinate system, and draw the vector as an arrow with its tail at the origin O, as in Figure 1.8. The magnitude of **r** is $|\mathbf{r}| = r$, the distance of the tip P of the arrow from O. The direction of **r** is specified by the angle ϕ measured (usually in radians) anticlockwise from the positive x-axis.

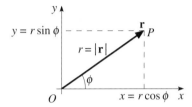

Figure 1.8

We have not quite finished the description, because a vector now has many representations (since rotating the line segment OP through $2n\pi$, where n is any integer, leaves it unchanged). To avoid this ambiguity, we shall normally take ϕ to lie in the range $-\pi < \phi \le \pi$. (Note that under this convention a vector below the x-axis has a negative value for ϕ — see Figure 1.9.)

In fact, a vector has an infinite number of representations!

Thus the endpoint P of a vector **r** is specified by the two numbers r (a distance) and ϕ (an angle). These two numbers r and ϕ are the **plane polar coordinates** (or simply **polar coordinates**) of the endpoint P of the vector **r**, when the tail of its arrow is at O. We use the notation $\langle r, \phi \rangle$ in order to distinguish polar coordinates from the Cartesian variety, so the vector is now specified as

$$\mathbf{r} = \langle r, \phi \rangle.$$

You can see from Figure 1.8 that the polar coordinates $\langle r, \phi \rangle$ of P are related to the Cartesian coordinates (x, y) of P by the following formulae:

$$x = r \cos \phi, \quad y = r \sin \phi;$$
$$r = (x^2 + y^2)^{1/2}, \quad \tan \phi = y/x.$$

However, the statement $\tan \phi = y/x$ does not define ϕ uniquely since, for example, $\tan \phi = \tan(\pi + \phi)$. To pin down the value of ϕ in the range $-\pi < \phi \le \pi$, we can use the two equations

$$\sin \phi = y/r \quad \text{and} \quad \cos \phi = x/r.$$

In practice, when finding the angle ϕ from the values of x and y, it usually helps to sketch the Cartesian coordinates in the (x, y)-plane so that you can see in which quadrant ϕ must lie. The signs of sin and cos for angles in the four quadrants are shown in Figure 1.10: you will find it useful to know these. (A simple acronym to aid the memory is 'CAST': starting from the lower right, and working anticlockwise round the quadrants, the following are positive: Cos, All (of sin, cos, tan), Sin and Tan.)

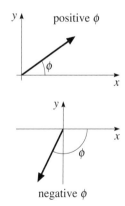

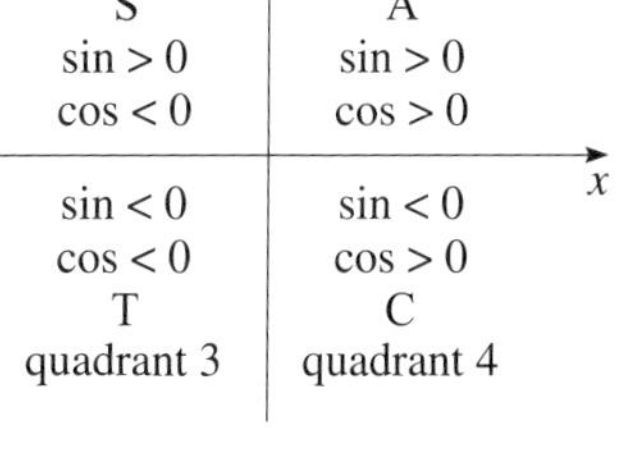

Figure 1.9

quadrant 2	quadrant 1
S	A
sin > 0	sin > 0
cos < 0	cos > 0
sin < 0	sin < 0
cos < 0	cos > 0
T	C
quadrant 3	quadrant 4

Figure 1.10

159

Example 1.2

Give the polar representation of the vectors **a**, **b**, **e** and **g** in Figure 1.11.

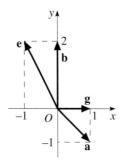

Figure 1.11

Solution

In Figure 1.11 each vector is drawn as an arrow from the origin, so the polar representation of each vector is given by the polar coordinates of its endpoint. In some cases we can specify r and ϕ simply from inspection of Figure 1.11, but we shall use the above formulae in order to illustrate the general method.

The endpoint of **a** has Cartesian coordinates $(1, -1)$, so we have

$$r = (1^2 + (-1)^2)^{1/2} = \sqrt{2},$$
$$\sin\phi = y/r = -1/\sqrt{2} \quad \text{and} \quad \cos\phi = x/r = 1/\sqrt{2}.$$

Thus $\phi = -\frac{\pi}{4}$ radians, i.e. $\mathbf{a} = \langle\sqrt{2}, -\frac{\pi}{4}\rangle$. (Since $-\frac{\pi}{2} < -\frac{\pi}{4} < 0$, the angle coordinate $-\frac{\pi}{4}$ indicates that **a** should lie in the fourth quadrant, which is confirmed by Figure 1.11.)

Vector **b** is of length 2 units and points in the positive y-direction. The Cartesian coordinates of its endpoint are $(0, 2)$, so we have

$$r = (0^2 + 2^2)^{1/2} = 2,$$
$$\sin\phi = y/r = 2/2 = 1 \quad \text{and} \quad \cos\phi = x/r = 0/2 = 0.$$

Hence $\phi = \frac{\pi}{2}$ radians (which is obvious from the fact that **b** points in the positive y-direction). Hence $\mathbf{b} = \langle 2, \frac{\pi}{2}\rangle$.

The endpoint of vector **e** has Cartesian coordinates $(-1, 2)$, so

$$r = ((-1)^2 + 2^2)^{1/2} = \sqrt{5}, \quad \sin\phi = 2/\sqrt{5} \quad \text{and} \quad \cos\phi = -1/\sqrt{5},$$

giving $\phi = 2.034$ radians. Hence $\mathbf{e} = \langle\sqrt{5}, 2.034\rangle$. (Since $\frac{\pi}{2} < 2.034 < \pi$, the angle coordinate 2.034 indicates that **e** should lie in the second quadrant, which is confirmed by Figure 1.11.)

Finally, **g** is of unit length (i.e. of length 1 unit) and points in the positive x-direction. The Cartesian coordinates of its endpoint are $(1, 0)$, so

$$r = (1^2 + 0^2)^{1/2} = 1, \quad \sin\phi = 0 \quad \text{and} \quad \cos\phi = 1.$$

Thus $\mathbf{g} = \langle 1, 0\rangle$. (This is an exceptional case where the numerical values of the coordinates are the same in the two coordinate systems.) ∎

*Exercise 1.5

Complete Table 1.1. Each row should show the Cartesian and corresponding polar coordinates of a particular point. If any entry is invalid, say so and explain why.

Table 1.1

Cartesian coordinates (x, y)	Polar coordinates $\langle r, \phi \rangle$
$(0, -1)$	$\langle 1, -\frac{\pi}{2} \rangle$
$(1, 1)$	
	$\langle 4, -\frac{\pi}{4} \rangle$
	$\langle 6, \pi \rangle$
$(-1, -1)$	
	$\langle -1, \pi \rangle$
	$\langle 10^8, \exp(0.1\pi) \rangle$

*Exercise 1.6

As you saw earlier, the displacement of Leeds from Bristol can be expressed as $\mathbf{s} = 296\,\text{km N}\,15°\text{E}$ (see Figure 1.3 on page 156). Express this vector in polar form $\langle r, \phi \rangle$ using a suitable coordinate system.

The polar representation of vectors can be a useful representation in a variety of physical situations, as you will see later in the course. (It is generalized to three dimensions in *Unit 23.*)

End-of-section Exercises

Exercise 1.7

The following is a list of some physical quantities: temperature, velocity, volume, energy, force, displacement, time, acceleration. Decide which are scalar and which are vector quantities.

Exercise 1.8

What are the polar coordinates of a point Q whose Cartesian coordinates are $(0, -3)$? What is the magnitude of the vector $\overrightarrow{OQ}$ where O is the origin of coordinates?

2 Scaling and adding vectors

This section defines two arithmetic or algebraic operations involving vectors. The first and simpler of these is the *multiplication of a vector by a scalar*, or *scaling of a vector*. The second is the *addition of two vectors* to give a third vector called the *resultant* of the two vectors.

2.1 Scaling of a vector

Consider vectors $\mathbf{c}$ and $\mathbf{h}$ in Figure 1.7 (page 158). Both vectors point in the same direction, but $\mathbf{h}$ has a length three times that of $\mathbf{c}$. We say that $\mathbf{h}$ is a *scaling* of $\mathbf{c}$ by the number 3, and we write $\mathbf{h} = 3\mathbf{c}$.

Generally, if **v** is a vector and m is a positive number, then the product $m\mathbf{v}$ is a vector in the same direction as **v** but with magnitude $m|\mathbf{v}|$, i.e. m times the magnitude of **v**. This multiplication of a vector by a scalar is called *scaling* or *scalar multiplication*, and $m\mathbf{v}$ is called a *scalar multiple* of **v**. For example, if **v** has magnitude 4 and points in the positive x-direction, then $3\mathbf{v}$ has magnitude 12 and points in the positive x-direction also. This is illustrated in Figure 2.1.

Note that there is no multiplication sign between the m and the **v**. In vector algebra the dot and cross symbols are reserved for other products, to be discussed in Section 4.

Figure 2.1

We can also scale a vector **v** by a negative number. When m is negative, the vector $m\mathbf{v}$ has magnitude $|m||\mathbf{v}|$ and points in the *opposite* direction to **v**. A special case is when $m = -1$. Then the vector $(-1)\mathbf{v}$ has the same magnitude as **v** but points in the opposite direction; see Figure 2.2. We normally write $(-1)\mathbf{v}$ simply as $-\mathbf{v}$, i.e. $(-1)\mathbf{v} = -\mathbf{v}$.

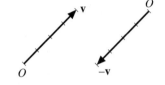

Figure 2.2

What happens when we multiply a vector by zero ($m = 0$)? The above definitions imply that the result should be a vector with magnitude zero. You will recall from Section 1 that there is a special vector with magnitude zero, namely the zero vector, **0**. Thus $0\mathbf{v} = \mathbf{0}$.

Definition

For any vector **v** and any real number m, the **scalar multiple** $m\mathbf{v}$ is the vector with magnitude $|m||\mathbf{v}|$ which is:

- in the same direction as **v** if $m > 0$;
- in the opposite direction to **v** if $m < 0$;
- the zero vector (i.e. with unspecified direction) if $m = 0$.

The multiplication of **v** by m is called **scaling** or **scalar multiplication**.

Example 2.1

(a) Let **u** represent the velocity of my car travelling with a speed of 30 mph along a straight road due north. Write down, in terms of **u**, the velocity of a car overtaking me and travelling at 45 mph. If another car is travelling in the opposite direction to me with speed 60 mph, write down this car's velocity in terms of **u**.

(b) If $ABCDEF$ is a regular hexagon (Figure 2.3) and, for example, $\overrightarrow{AB}$ represents the displacement vector from A to B, write down algebraic relations connecting:

   (i) $\overrightarrow{AB}$ and $\overrightarrow{ED}$;   (ii) $\overrightarrow{AF}$ and $\overrightarrow{DC}$.

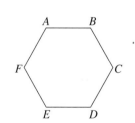

Figure 2.3

Solution

(a) The velocity vector **u** has magnitude 30 mph and points due north. The car overtaking me is travelling in the same direction but has a velocity of magnitude 45 mph; suppose that its velocity vector is denoted by **v** (see Figure 2.4). Then **v** is parallel to **u** and has the same sense as **u**, and $|\mathbf{v}| = \frac{45}{30}|\mathbf{u}|$. Therefore **v** is just a scaling of **u**, i.e.

$$\mathbf{v} = 1.5\mathbf{u}.$$

Two vectors are *parallel* if they have either the same, or opposite, directions.

Now suppose that the velocity of the car travelling in the opposite direction is denoted by **w**. Then **w** is parallel to **u** but has the *opposite* sense to **u**, and $|\mathbf{w}| = \frac{60}{30}|\mathbf{u}|$. So we can write

$$\mathbf{w} = -2\mathbf{u},$$

where the negative sign indicates the opposite sense.

(b) The opposite sides of a regular hexagon are parallel, and all the sides have the same length.

(i) Thus the displacement vectors $\overrightarrow{AB}$ and $\overrightarrow{ED}$ have equal magnitudes and the same direction. So we have

$$\overrightarrow{AB} = \overrightarrow{ED}.$$

(ii) The displacement vectors $\overrightarrow{AF}$ and $\overrightarrow{DC}$ have equal magnitudes but opposite directions, thus

$$\overrightarrow{AF} = -\overrightarrow{DC} \quad (\text{or, equivalently, } \overrightarrow{DC} = -\overrightarrow{AF}). \quad \blacksquare$$

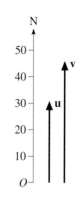

Figure 2.4

Exercise 2.1

(a) If **d** is the displacement vector from Bristol to Leeds, write down in terms of **d** the displacement vectors from Leeds to Bristol and from Leeds to Leeds.

(b) If **v** represents the velocity of a wind of 35 knots from the north-east, what vectors represent the following?

(i) A wind of 70 knots from the north-east.

(ii) A wind of 35 knots from the south-west.

(iii) Still air.

(c) Relate the direction and magnitude of $-1.5\mathbf{v}$ to those of **v**, where **v** is any given non-zero vector. Do the same for $-k\mathbf{v}$, where k is an arbitrary positive number.

(d) If $ABCD$ is a parallelogram (Figure 2.5) and, for example, $\overrightarrow{AB}$ represents the displacement vector from A to B, write down algebraic relations connecting:

(i) $\overrightarrow{AB}$ and $\overrightarrow{DC}$;   (ii) $\overrightarrow{BC}$ and $\overrightarrow{DA}$.

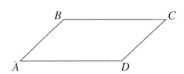

Figure 2.5

(e) If **v** is any non-zero vector, what are the magnitude and direction of the vector $\dfrac{1}{|\mathbf{v}|}\mathbf{v}$?

Unit vectors

The vector $\dfrac{1}{|\mathbf{v}|}\mathbf{v}$ in Exercise 2.1(e) is a vector that has magnitude 1 and points in the direction of **v**. It is called the *unit vector* in the direction of **v**. The unit vector in the direction of **v** is often denoted by the symbol $\widehat{\mathbf{v}}$.

Definition

For any non-zero vector **v**, the **unit vector** in the direction of **v** is the vector

$$\widehat{\mathbf{v}} = \frac{1}{|\mathbf{v}|}\mathbf{v}.$$

Unit vectors are often used to denote directions in the plane, or in space.

A particular example is provided by the unit vectors in the positive directions of the x- and y-axes in the plane Cartesian coordinate system. These unit vectors are denoted by **i** and **j**, respectively, and are called **Cartesian unit vectors**.

We shall develop the Cartesian representation of vectors in Section 3.

Figure 2.6 shows these Cartesian unit vectors and two other vectors, **a** and **b**. The vector **a** has magnitude 2 and points in the positive x-direction; **b** has magnitude 3.5 and points in the positive y-direction. The unit vector **i** has magnitude 1 and points in the same direction as **a**. Thus we can write **a** in terms of **i** by a scaling:

$$\mathbf{a} = 2\mathbf{i}.$$

Similarly, we can write **b** in terms of **j**:

$$\mathbf{b} = 3.5\mathbf{j}.$$

Any vector parallel to the x- or y-axis can be written as a scaling of **i** or **j**.

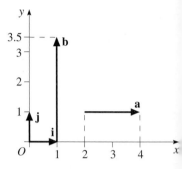

Figure 2.6

Note that although **i** and **j** are shown in Figure 2.6 with their tails at the origin, this is not necessary. They can be drawn at any convenient position, provided only that they are of unit magnitude and point in the positive x- and y-directions, respectively — see, for example, Figure 2.7.

Exercise 2.2

Four vectors, **a**, **b**, **c** and **d**, of magnitudes 2, 2.5, 3 and 1, respectively, are shown in Figure 2.7. The directions of the four vectors are defined by the arrows. Write down **a**, **b**, **c** and **d** as scalings of the Cartesian unit vectors **i** and **j**.

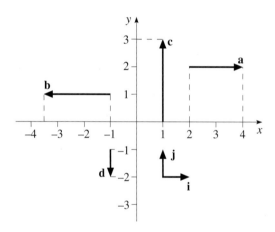

Figure 2.7

Exercise 2.3

Let the unit vectors **i** and **j** denote the directions of east and north, respectively. Specify the following vectors as scalings of **i** and **j**.

(a) The wind velocity of 35 km per hour due south.

(b) The displacement of Bristol from London (112 miles due west).

(c) The displacement of London from Bristol.

2.2 Addition of vectors

What is meant by the addition of vectors? Suppose that we make a journey from Bristol to Leeds, and then another journey from Leeds to Norwich. The first journey produces a displacement of $\mathbf{d}_1$ and the second a displacement of $\mathbf{d}_2$. The net result of the two journeys is a displacement of $\mathbf{d}_3$ from Bristol to Norwich. This is illustrated by the triangle of displacements shown in Figure 2.8. Displacements are said to add by the *triangle rule*, and we write $\mathbf{d}_3 = \mathbf{d}_1 + \mathbf{d}_2$. The vector $\mathbf{d}_3$ is called the *resultant* of $\mathbf{d}_1$ and $\mathbf{d}_2$.

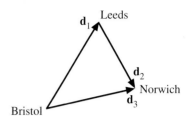

Figure 2.8

Velocities also add by the triangle rule, and so do forces, accelerations and all other vector quantities. Thus the triangle rule is also called the *vector addition rule*.

Triangle rule or vector addition rule

To add any two vectors $\mathbf{a}$ and $\mathbf{b}$: choose an origin O; draw the line OP in the direction of $\mathbf{a}$ and with length equal to the magnitude of $\mathbf{a}$; and draw the line PQ in the direction of $\mathbf{b}$ and with length equal to the magnitude of $\mathbf{b}$ (as in Figure 2.9). Then $\mathbf{a} + \mathbf{b}$ is the vector with magnitude equal to the length of OQ and with the direction from O to Q. The vector $\mathbf{a} + \mathbf{b}$ is called the **sum** or **resultant** of $\mathbf{a}$ and $\mathbf{b}$.

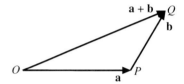

Figure 2.9

Note that the sum of two displacement vectors can also be written using the notation

$$\overrightarrow{OP} + \overrightarrow{PQ} = \overrightarrow{OQ}.$$

Now recall that when discussing displacements we mentioned the zero vector $\mathbf{0}$ (representing no displacement). Once addition of vectors is introduced, we *need* the zero vector in order to answer questions such as 'what is $\mathbf{i} + (-1)\mathbf{i}$?'. Geometrically, no construction is needed when adding the zero vector, which obeys the rather obvious rule

$$\mathbf{a} + \mathbf{0} = \mathbf{a}.$$

Exercise 2.4

Three vectors $\mathbf{a}$, $\mathbf{b}$ and $\mathbf{c}$ of magnitudes 3, 2 and 4 are shown in Figure 2.10.

(a) Draw a rough sketch to show the vectors $\mathbf{a} + \mathbf{b}$ and $\mathbf{a} + \mathbf{c}$.

(b) Sketch the vector $-\mathbf{b}$, and draw a rough sketch to show the addition of $\mathbf{a}$ and $-\mathbf{b}$.

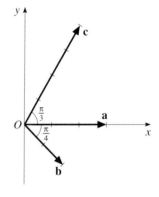

Figure 2.10

Exercise 2.4(b) suggests a definition of **vector subtraction**. To subtract the vector $\mathbf{b}$ from the vector $\mathbf{a}$, we *add* the vectors $\mathbf{a}$ and $-\mathbf{b}$ by the triangle rule of vector addition; that is, in symbols,

$$\mathbf{a} - \mathbf{b} = \mathbf{a} + (-\mathbf{b}).$$

*Exercise 2.5

A vector $\mathbf{a}$ has magnitude 3 units and points in the positive x-direction. A vector $\mathbf{b}$ has magnitude 4 units and points in the positive y-direction. Draw a diagram showing the vectors $\mathbf{a} + \mathbf{b}$ and $\mathbf{a} - \mathbf{b}$.

Vector addition is *commutative*, i.e. the order in which we add two vectors does not matter. This can be illustrated by reference to vectors **a** and **c** of Exercise 2.4 (see Figure 2.11). The triangle OP_1Q illustrates the addition **a** + **c**, while triangle OP_2Q illustrates **c** + **a**. The same resultant $\overrightarrow{OQ}$ is obtained in both cases. Thus

$$\mathbf{a} + \mathbf{c} = \mathbf{c} + \mathbf{a}.$$

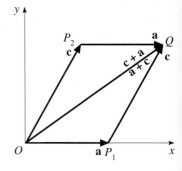

Figure 2.11

Exercise 2.6

For the particular cases of the vectors **a**, **b**, **c** defined in Exercise 2.4, and for the scalar $m = 2$, draw sketches to illustrate the *associative* property of vector addition,

$$(\mathbf{a} + \mathbf{b}) + \mathbf{c} = \mathbf{a} + (\mathbf{b} + \mathbf{c}),$$

and the *distributive* property of scaling over vector addition,

$$m(\mathbf{a} + \mathbf{b}) = m\mathbf{a} + m\mathbf{b}.$$

An alternative geometrical construction for adding two vectors can be seen from Figure 2.11. It is called the **parallelogram rule**. Draw the two vectors $\overrightarrow{OP_1}$ and $\overrightarrow{OP_2}$ with the same beginning point O. Complete the parallelogram OP_1QP_2. Then the resultant vector is the vector $\overrightarrow{OQ}$ on the diagonal of the parallelogram. The parallelogram rule gives the same resultant as the triangle rule.

2.3   Algebraic rules for scaling and adding vectors

Subsections 2.1 and 2.2 showed how to multiply a vector by a scalar and how to add vectors, i.e. what is meant by $m\mathbf{v}$ and $\mathbf{a} + \mathbf{b}$. We also saw illustrations of the commutative, associative and distributive rules. These are only some of the algebraic rules for manipulating vectors by addition and scaling. A complete list of these rules, which apply whether or not the vectors are confined to a plane, is given below.

Algebraic rules for scaling and adding vectors

Let **a**, **b** and **c** be vectors, and let m, m_1 and m_2 be scalars.

1   Addition is commutative: $\mathbf{a} + \mathbf{b} = \mathbf{b} + \mathbf{a}$.

2   Addition is associative: $(\mathbf{a} + \mathbf{b}) + \mathbf{c} = \mathbf{a} + (\mathbf{b} + \mathbf{c})$.

3   $m\mathbf{a}$ is a vector with magnitude $|m||\mathbf{a}|$, in the same direction as **a** when $m > 0$ and in the opposite direction when $m < 0$.

4   Scaling is associative: $m_1(m_2\mathbf{a}) = (m_1 m_2)\mathbf{a}$.

5   Scaling is distributive: $(m_1 + m_2)\mathbf{a} = m_1\mathbf{a} + m_2\mathbf{a}$.

6   Scaling is distributive over vector addition: $m(\mathbf{a} + \mathbf{b}) = m\mathbf{a} + m\mathbf{b}$.

7   Addition and scaling involving the zero vector are as expected: $\mathbf{0} + \mathbf{a} = \mathbf{a}$ and $0\mathbf{a} = \mathbf{0}$.

8   Subtraction is defined by $\mathbf{a} - \mathbf{b} = \mathbf{a} + (-1)\mathbf{b}$.

Notice that these rules say nothing about the multiplication of one vector by another: vector multiplication is defined in Section 4. Nor has anything been said about division by a vector: in fact, division by a vector is not defined.

A more abstract approach would be to define a vector to be something that obeys these rules, then explore the consequences. This is the approach taken in the second-level pure mathematics course.

These rules allow us to manipulate algebraic expressions involving scalings and vector addition in a familiar way.

Example 2.2

Simplify the expression

$$2(\mathbf{a} + \mathbf{b}) + 3(\mathbf{b} + \mathbf{c}) - 5(\mathbf{a} + \mathbf{b} - \mathbf{c}).$$

Solution

Strict use of the rules requires us to write the expression solely in terms of addition. So we have

$$2(\mathbf{a} + \mathbf{b}) + 3(\mathbf{b} + \mathbf{c}) - 5(\mathbf{a} + \mathbf{b} - \mathbf{c})$$

$$= 2(\mathbf{a} + \mathbf{b}) + 3(\mathbf{b} + \mathbf{c}) + (-5)(\mathbf{a} + \mathbf{b} + (-1)\mathbf{c}) \qquad \text{(using Rule 8)}$$

$$= 2(\mathbf{a} + \mathbf{b}) + 3(\mathbf{b} + \mathbf{c}) + (-5)((\mathbf{a} + \mathbf{b}) + (-1)\mathbf{c}) \qquad \text{(using Rule 2)}$$

$$= 2\mathbf{a} + 2\mathbf{b} + 3\mathbf{b} + 3\mathbf{c} + (-5)(\mathbf{a} + \mathbf{b}) + (-5)((-1)\mathbf{c}) \qquad \text{(using Rule 6 three times)}$$

$$= 2\mathbf{a} + 2\mathbf{b} + 3\mathbf{b} + 3\mathbf{c} + (-5)(\mathbf{a} + \mathbf{b}) + 5\mathbf{c} \qquad \text{(using Rule 4)}$$

$$= 2\mathbf{a} + 2\mathbf{b} + 3\mathbf{b} + 3\mathbf{c} + (-5)\mathbf{a} + (-5)\mathbf{b} + 5\mathbf{c} \qquad \text{(using Rule 6)}$$

$$= 2\mathbf{a} + (-5)\mathbf{a} + 2\mathbf{b} + 3\mathbf{b} + (-5)\mathbf{b} + 3\mathbf{c} + 5\mathbf{c} \qquad \text{(using Rule 1 several times)}$$

$$= (2 - 5)\mathbf{a} + (2 + 3 - 5)\mathbf{b} + (3 + 5)\mathbf{c} \qquad \text{(using Rule 5 four times)}$$

$$= (-3)\mathbf{a} + \mathbf{0} + 8\mathbf{c} \qquad \text{(using Rule 7)}$$

$$= (-3)\mathbf{a} + 8\mathbf{c} \qquad \text{(using Rule 7)}$$

$$= 8\mathbf{c} + (-3)\mathbf{a} \qquad \text{(using Rule 1)}$$

$$= 8\mathbf{c} + (-1)(3\mathbf{a}) \qquad \text{(using Rule 4)}$$

$$= 8\mathbf{c} - 3\mathbf{a} \qquad \text{(using Rule 8)}.$$

However, because Rules 1, 2, 4, 5, 6, 7 and 8 are exactly the same as the familiar rules for manipulating algebraic expressions involving scalar quantities, we would usually write the solution more succinctly as

$$2(\mathbf{a} + \mathbf{b}) + 3(\mathbf{b} + \mathbf{c}) - 5(\mathbf{a} + \mathbf{b} - \mathbf{c})$$

$$= 2\mathbf{a} + 2\mathbf{b} + 3\mathbf{b} + 3\mathbf{c} - 5\mathbf{a} - 5\mathbf{b} + 5\mathbf{c}$$

$$= (2 - 5)\mathbf{a} + (2 + 3 - 5)\mathbf{b} + (3 + 5)\mathbf{c}$$

$$= 8\mathbf{c} - 3\mathbf{a}. \quad \blacksquare$$

In the following exercises, use the more succinct method.

Exercise 2.7 _____

Simplify the expression $4(\mathbf{a} - \mathbf{c}) + 3(\mathbf{c} - \mathbf{b}) + 2(2\mathbf{a} - \mathbf{b} - 3\mathbf{c})$.

*Exercise 2.8 _____

Find the vector $\mathbf{x}$ in terms of $\mathbf{a}$ and $\mathbf{b}$ in the following vector equations.

(a) $2\mathbf{b} + 4\mathbf{x} = 7\mathbf{a}$ (b) $n(\mathbf{b} - \mathbf{a}) + \mathbf{x} = m(\mathbf{a} - \mathbf{b})$

In Subsection 1.1 a vector was defined as a quantity having a magnitude and a direction. In fact, this definition is incomplete in that it does not include a rule for combining two such quantities. Hence a complete definition of a vector is as follows.

Vectors
- A vector has magnitude and direction.
- Any two vectors can be added by the triangle rule.
- A vector can be scaled by a real number in such a way that the above rules apply.

It is a rather surprising fact that so many physical quantities — displacement, velocity, acceleration, force, torque, momentum, to name but a few — all qualify as vectors under the above simple definition. This is one reason why the subject of vectors is so important.

End-of-section Exercises

Exercise 2.9

The vectors **a** and **b** are represented by the arrows shown in Figure 2.12. The magnitudes of **a** and **b** are 4 and 6, respectively. Draw a sketch to show the vectors $\mathbf{a} + \mathbf{b}$, $\mathbf{a} - \mathbf{b}$ and $2\mathbf{a} + \frac{1}{2}\mathbf{b}$.

Exercise 2.10

If $\mathbf{v} = -4.7\mathbf{u}$, what can you say about the magnitude and direction of **v** in terms of the magnitude and direction of the non-zero vector **u**?

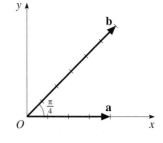

Figure 2.12

Exercise 2.11

If $ABCD$ is a quadrilateral, with $\overrightarrow{AB}$ denoting the displacement vector from A to B, and $\overrightarrow{BC}$, $\overrightarrow{CD}$, $\overrightarrow{DA}$ defined similarly, show that

$$\overrightarrow{AB} + \overrightarrow{BC} + \overrightarrow{CD} + \overrightarrow{DA} = \mathbf{0}.$$

*Exercise 2.12

Two vectors **p** and **q** are defined in polar form: $\mathbf{p} = \langle 3, \frac{\pi}{2} \rangle$, $\mathbf{q} = \langle 4, \pi \rangle$. Sketch **p**, **q** and $\mathbf{p} + \mathbf{q}$, and give the polar forms of $5\mathbf{p}$, $-\mathbf{q}$ and $\mathbf{p} + \mathbf{q}$.

Exercise 2.13

(a) Which of the following proposed general rules is true for the scalar multiplication of a vector in polar form? (Assume $m > 0$.)

$$m\langle r, \phi \rangle \overset{?}{=} \langle mr, \phi \rangle,$$

$$m\langle r, \phi \rangle \overset{?}{=} \langle mr, m\phi \rangle.$$

(b) Does the following proposed general rule hold for the addition of vectors in polar form?

$$\langle r_1, \phi_1 \rangle + \langle r_2, \phi_2 \rangle \overset{?}{=} \langle r_1 + r_2, \phi_1 + \phi_2 \rangle$$

3   Cartesian components of a vector

So far we have approached vectors, and the laws of vector addition and scaling, geometrically. To add vectors geometrically requires drawing diagrams representing the vectors by arrows. An alternative, and sometimes more convenient, *algebraic* approach to representing vectors is developed in this section, first in two dimensions and then in three.

3.1   Vectors in two dimensions

We have already seen in Subsection 2.1 how to write vectors that are parallel to the x-axis or y-axis as scalar multiples of the Cartesian unit vectors **i** and **j**, respectively. (Recall that **i** and **j** are the unit vectors in the directions of the positive x- and y-axes, respectively.) Of course, in general, vectors do not lie parallel to either the x-axis or the y-axis. However, you will see in this subsection how use of the rules for vector addition and for scalar multiplication allows us to write any vector in the (x, y)-plane in terms of the Cartesian unit vectors **i** and **j**.

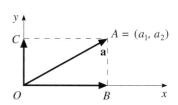

Figure 3.1

Consider an arbitrary vector $\mathbf{a} = \overrightarrow{OA}$ in the (x, y)-plane, whose tail is at the origin O, as shown in Figure 3.1. The vector $\overrightarrow{OA}$ is called the **position vector** of the point A, and its endpoint is determined by the Cartesian coordinates a_1 and a_2 of A, i.e. by the distances OB and OC, respectively.

Note that if A were in one of the other three quadrants of the plane, then one or both of a_1, a_2 would be negative.

Furthermore, the vectors $\overrightarrow{OB}$ and $\overrightarrow{OC}$ can be written as scalings of the Cartesian unit vectors **i** and **j**:

$$\overrightarrow{OB} = a_1\mathbf{i} \quad \text{and} \quad \overrightarrow{OC} = a_2\mathbf{j}.$$

Hence the triangle rule (or parallelogram rule) for the addition of vectors allows the vector **a** to be expressed as the sum of $\overrightarrow{OB}$ and $\overrightarrow{OC}$, i.e. as

$$\mathbf{a} = \overrightarrow{OB} + \overrightarrow{OC} \quad \text{or} \quad \mathbf{a} = a_1\mathbf{i} + a_2\mathbf{j}.$$

The latter is called the *component form* of **a**, and the numbers a_1 and a_2 are called the **i**- and **j**-components of **a**, respectively.

You may also see these numbers referred to as the x- and y-components of **a**.

When the tail of the vector **a** is not at the origin, its components are defined in an obvious way.

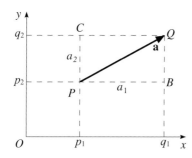

Figure 3.2

Referring to Figure 3.2, the components of **a** are

$$a_1 = q_1 - p_1 \quad \text{and} \quad a_2 = q_2 - p_2.$$

A shorter way of writing a vector in component form is as an *ordered pair of numbers*, (a_1, a_2), where the unit vectors **i** and **j** are not shown explicitly. This notation needs to be used with care because the coordinates of a point in a plane are also denoted in this way, and vectors are conceptually different from points. To avoid such confusion, in this course the **column vector** notation

$$\mathbf{a} = \begin{bmatrix} a_1 \\ a_2 \end{bmatrix}$$

This is the way in which many computer algebra packages display vectors.

will be used instead. In the text, to save space, the column vector will often be written as $\mathbf{a} = [a_1 \quad a_2]^T$, where the *transpose symbol* T here changes the row into a column.

Definition

A vector $\mathbf{a} = \overrightarrow{PQ}$ in the (x, y)-plane, where P is the point (p_1, p_2) and Q is the point (q_1, q_2), has **component form**

$$\mathbf{a} = a_1\mathbf{i} + a_2\mathbf{j},$$

where $a_1 = q_1 - p_1$ and $a_2 = q_2 - p_2$, and **i** and **j** are the Cartesian unit vectors.

The component form may also be written as

$$\mathbf{a} = \begin{bmatrix} a_1 \\ a_2 \end{bmatrix} \quad \text{or} \quad \mathbf{a} = [a_1 \quad a_2]^T.$$

The numbers a_1 and a_2 are the (**Cartesian**) **components of a**.

169

*Exercise 3.1 ———————————————————

Write each of the vectors in Figure 1.7 (page 158) in the form $\mathbf{a} = a_1\mathbf{i} + a_2\mathbf{j}$ and as a column vector.

———————————————————

The magnitude of a vector given in component form is found very easily. For example, the magnitude of the vector $\mathbf{a}$ in Figure 3.2 is just the length of the line PQ. This is found by Pythagoras's Theorem to be $\sqrt{a_1^2 + a_2^2}$.

Magnitude of a two-dimensional vector in component form

If $\mathbf{a} = \overrightarrow{PQ} = a_1\mathbf{i} + a_2\mathbf{j}$, where P and Q have coordinates (p_1, p_2) and (q_1, q_2), respectively, then

$$|\mathbf{a}| = \sqrt{a_1^2 + a_2^2} = \sqrt{(q_1 - p_1)^2 + (q_2 - p_2)^2}.$$

Vectors in component form can also be added and scaled very easily, by making use of the algebraic rules for the scaling and adding of vectors. For example,

$$\begin{aligned}
\mathbf{a} + \mathbf{b} &= (a_1\mathbf{i} + a_2\mathbf{j}) + (b_1\mathbf{i} + b_2\mathbf{j}) \\
&= a_1\mathbf{i} + a_2\mathbf{j} + b_1\mathbf{i} + b_2\mathbf{j} \\
&= (a_1\mathbf{i} + b_1\mathbf{i}) + (a_2\mathbf{j} + b_2\mathbf{j}) \\
&= (a_1 + b_1)\mathbf{i} + (a_2 + b_2)\mathbf{j}.
\end{aligned}$$

So, to add two vectors one adds their respective components. Similarly,

$$\begin{aligned}
m\mathbf{a} &= m(a_1\mathbf{i} + a_2\mathbf{j}) \\
&= (ma_1)\mathbf{i} + (ma_2)\mathbf{j},
\end{aligned}$$

so scaling a vector is achieved by scaling its components.

Adding and scaling two-dimensional vectors in component form

If $\mathbf{a} = a_1\mathbf{i} + a_2\mathbf{j}$, $\mathbf{b} = b_1\mathbf{i} + b_2\mathbf{j}$ and m is a scalar, then

$$\mathbf{a} + \mathbf{b} = (a_1 + b_1)\mathbf{i} + (a_2 + b_2)\mathbf{j}$$

and

$$m\mathbf{a} = (ma_1)\mathbf{i} + (ma_2)\mathbf{j}.$$

Equivalently, using column vector notation,

$$\begin{bmatrix} a_1 \\ a_2 \end{bmatrix} + \begin{bmatrix} b_1 \\ b_2 \end{bmatrix} = \begin{bmatrix} a_1 + b_1 \\ a_2 + b_2 \end{bmatrix}$$

and

$$m\begin{bmatrix} a_1 \\ a_2 \end{bmatrix} = \begin{bmatrix} ma_1 \\ ma_2 \end{bmatrix}.$$

Exercise 3.2 ———————————————————

Figure 3.3 shows four vectors in the (x, y)-plane.

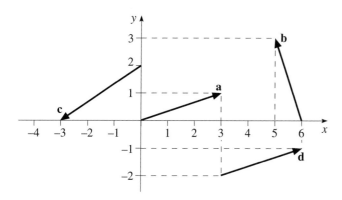

Figure 3.3

(a) Write down the vectors in component form.

(b) Draw a diagram to verify that the scaling $3.5\mathbf{a}$ is the same when obtained geometrically or algebraically using components.

(c) Use the triangle rule to obtain the vector $\mathbf{a} + \mathbf{b}$. Verify that this vector is the same as that obtained by adding the component forms of $\mathbf{a}$ and $\mathbf{b}$.

(d) Find, algebraically, the components of the vector $2\mathbf{a} + \mathbf{b} - \mathbf{c}$. Hence find the magnitude of the vector $2\mathbf{a} + \mathbf{b} - \mathbf{c}$.

Exercise 3.3

(a) Find the numbers p and q if $\mathbf{r} = \begin{bmatrix} p + q \\ p - q \end{bmatrix}$, $\mathbf{s} = \begin{bmatrix} -3 \\ 7 \end{bmatrix}$ and $\mathbf{r} = \mathbf{s}$.

(b) Find the magnitude of the vector $\mathbf{t}$ if $\mathbf{t} = \mathbf{u} + \mathbf{v}$, where $\mathbf{u} = \dfrac{1}{\sqrt{2}} \begin{bmatrix} 1 \\ 1 \end{bmatrix}$ and $\mathbf{v} = \dfrac{1}{\sqrt{2}} \begin{bmatrix} 1 \\ -1 \end{bmatrix}$.

Exercise 3.4

The three vectors $\mathbf{a}$, $\mathbf{b}$ and $\mathbf{c}$ in Figure 3.4 are specified in polar coordinates by

$$\mathbf{a} = \left\langle 2, \tfrac{\pi}{3} \right\rangle, \quad \mathbf{b} = \left\langle 3, \tfrac{3\pi}{4} \right\rangle, \quad \mathbf{c} = \left\langle 1, \tfrac{\pi}{6} \right\rangle.$$

(a) What are the magnitudes of the three vectors?

(b) Write down the vectors $\mathbf{a}$, $\mathbf{b}$ and $\mathbf{c}$ in terms of $\mathbf{i}$ and $\mathbf{j}$.

(c) Obtain the vector $\mathbf{a} + \mathbf{c}$ in terms of $\mathbf{i}$ and $\mathbf{j}$.

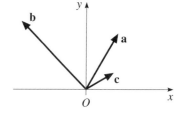

Figure 3.4

In Exercise 3.4 the vectors were given in polar coordinate form, which is just a systematic way of specifying magnitude and direction. The process of finding the Cartesian components of a vector given its magnitude and direction is known as **resolving a vector into its components**. This is essentially what you did in Exercise 3.4(b). Thus given the magnitude $|\mathbf{a}|$ of the vector $\mathbf{a}$ in Figure 3.5, and its direction ϕ, we can resolve it into its components:

$$a_1 = |\mathbf{a}| \cos \phi \quad \text{and} \quad a_2 = |\mathbf{a}| \sin \phi.$$

Conversely, given the components a_1 and a_2 of a vector, we can specify its magnitude and direction:

$$|\mathbf{a}| = (a_1^2 + a_2^2)^{1/2}, \quad \cos \phi = a_1/|\mathbf{a}|, \quad \sin \phi = a_2/|\mathbf{a}|.$$

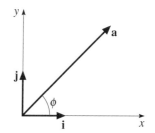

Figure 3.5

You had practice at doing these calculations in Subsection 1.5.

171

You will see this idea again in Section 4. For now, note that if you wish to add two vectors in polar form it will be necessary first to resolve them into their Cartesian components (since there is no convenient formula for vector addition in polar coordinates).

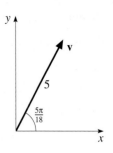

Exercise 3.5 _____

(a) Resolve the vector **v** of magnitude 5 shown in Figure 3.6 into its Cartesian components.

(b) Find the magnitudes and directions of the vectors

$$\mathbf{a} = \sqrt{3}\mathbf{i} - \mathbf{j} \quad \text{and} \quad \mathbf{b} = -3\mathbf{i} + 3\mathbf{j}.$$

Figure 3.6

3.2   Vectors in three dimensions

Thus far we have discussed vectors in the plane, reaching the component representation of such vectors in the previous subsection. However, the world is three-dimensional, and few real problems are restricted to a plane surface. For example, starting at point A at one corner of the cube shown in Figure 3.7, you can reach the opposite corner S by three successive displacements: $\overrightarrow{AQ} + \overrightarrow{QB} + \overrightarrow{BS}$. In order to work with such addition of displacements in three dimensions, it is necessary to introduce a three-dimensional coordinate system.

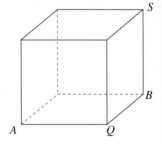

Figure 3.7

A three-dimensional Cartesian coordinate system

Consider a two-dimensional Cartesian coordinate system Oxy. Draw a third axis, the z-axis, through the origin O, perpendicular to both the x- and y-axes of the two-dimensional system. This produces a coordinate system with three mutually perpendicular axes, the x-, y- and z-axes (see Figure 3.8), intersecting at O. Alternatively, the coordinate system can be characterized by three planes:

- the (x, y)-**plane**, which contains the x- and y-axes and is perpendicular to the z-axis;
- the (x, z)-**plane**, analogously defined;
- the (y, z)-**plane**, again analogously defined.

Any point P can be represented uniquely by its perpendicular distances from the (x, y)-, (x, z)- and (y, z)-planes. These distances, called the (**Cartesian**) **coordinates** of P, are shown in Figure 3.8.

The x-axes shown in Figures 3.8 and 3.9 are meant to point *out* of the plane of the page.

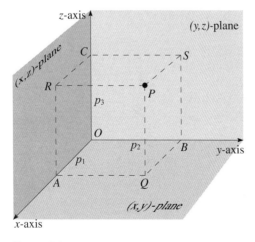

Figure 3.8

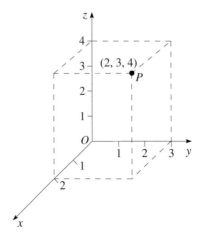

Figure 3.9

QP, RP and SP are perpendicular to the (x, y)-plane, (x, z)-plane and (y, z)-plane, respectively.

We denote the point P by the ordered triple of coordinates (p_1, p_2, p_3), where

$$p_1 = SP = OA,$$
$$p_2 = RP = OB,$$
$$p_3 = QP = OC.$$

For example, the point $(2, 3, 4)$ is shown in Figure 3.9.

When drawing Figure 3.9 it was necessary to choose one of two possible ways for the positive z-direction to be defined; these are shown in Figure 3.10, where in both cases the y-axis is meant to point into the plane of the page, away from you.

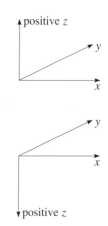

Figure 3.10

The usual convention for relating the positive directions of x, y and z is given by the following rule, called the **right-hand rule**. The right hand is held with the middle finger, first finger and thumb placed (roughly) perpendicular to each other, and the other two fingers closed (see Figure 3.11). If the thumb and first finger are pointing in the directions of the positive x- and y-axes, respectively, then the middle finger is pointing in the direction of the positive z-axis.

Alternatively, you can think of Figure 3.9 as showing a corner of a room (with the z-axis pointing upwards). If you are standing in the corner facing outwards, then the left-hand edge of the floor is the y-axis, and the right-hand edge is the x-axis. A coordinate system defined in this way is called a **right-handed system**. Only right-handed systems will be used in this course. The systems drawn in Figure 3.9 and the top of Figure 3.10 are right-handed systems.

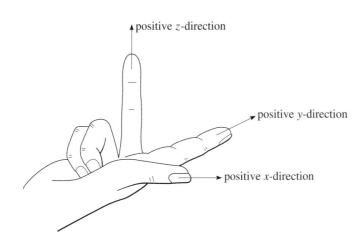

Figure 3.11

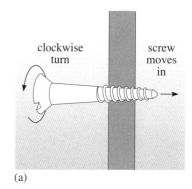

(a)

An alternative definition of the same positive z-direction is given by the **screw rule**, stated as follows. Suppose that we are turning a screw into a piece of wood; then a clockwise rotation makes the screw move into the wood (see Figure 3.12(a)). If we turn the screw in the sense from x to y as shown in Figure 3.12(b), then the direction in which the screw moves is along the positive z-direction.

For the rest of this unit the screw rule will be used to characterize a right-handed system, but you should use whichever rule you find easier to apply.

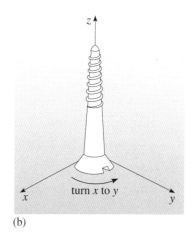

(b)

Figure 3.12

Exercise 3.6

Decide which of the sets of perpendicular axes in Figure 3.13 define right-handed coordinate systems.

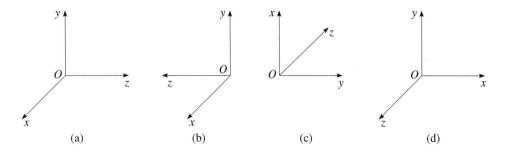

Figure 3.13

(The x-axis points out of the plane of the paper in (a) and (b). The z-axis points into and out of the plane of the paper in (c) and (d), respectively.)

The component form of three-dimensional vectors

The algebraic representation of vectors can be extended to vectors in three dimensions, such as in Figure 3.14. The vector $\mathbf{a}$, drawn from the origin O, is the *position vector* of point A with three-dimensional Cartesian coordinates (a_1, a_2, a_3). A third Cartesian unit vector $\mathbf{k}$ is introduced to represent the positive z-direction. We now have three Cartesian unit vectors, $\mathbf{i}$, $\mathbf{j}$ and $\mathbf{k}$, which are perpendicular to each other. The vector $\mathbf{a}$ may thus be written in *component form* as

$$\mathbf{a} = a_1\mathbf{i} + a_2\mathbf{j} + a_3\mathbf{k} \quad \text{or} \quad \mathbf{a} = \begin{bmatrix} a_1 \\ a_2 \\ a_3 \end{bmatrix} \quad \text{or} \quad \mathbf{a} = [a_1 \quad a_2 \quad a_3]^T.$$

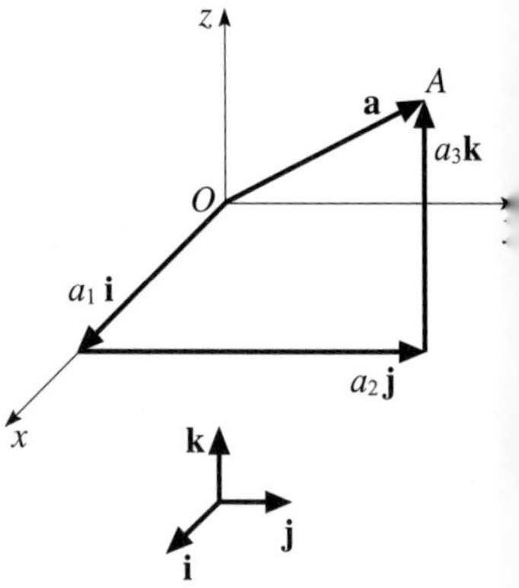

Figure 3.14

> ### Definition
>
> The **position vector** of a point A relative to the origin O of three-dimensional space is the displacement of A from O, i.e. the vector
>
> $$\mathbf{a} = \overrightarrow{OA}.$$
>
> The $\mathbf{i}$-, $\mathbf{j}$- and $\mathbf{k}$-components of the position vector $\mathbf{a}$ are the coordinates a_1, a_2 and a_3 of the point A, respectively.

These may sometimes be referred to as x-, y- and z-components.

The components of vectors not based at the origin are defined similarly, as follows.

> ### Definition
>
> A vector $\mathbf{a} = \overrightarrow{PQ}$ in three-dimensional space, where P is the point (p_1, p_2, p_3) and Q is the point (q_1, q_2, q_3), has **component form**
>
> $$\mathbf{a} = a_1\mathbf{i} + a_2\mathbf{j} + a_3\mathbf{k},$$
>
> where $a_1 = q_1 - p_1$, $a_2 = q_2 - p_2$, $a_3 = q_3 - p_3$, and $\mathbf{i}$, $\mathbf{j}$, $\mathbf{k}$ are the Cartesian unit vectors. The numbers a_1, a_2, a_3 are the (**Cartesian**) **components** of $\mathbf{a}$.

Note that the component form may also be written as

$$\mathbf{a} = \begin{bmatrix} a_1 \\ a_2 \\ a_3 \end{bmatrix}$$

or

$$\mathbf{a} = [a_1 \quad a_2 \quad a_3]^T.$$

As in two dimensions, the operations of vector algebra can be expressed in terms of components.

Adding and scaling three-dimensional vectors in component form

If $\mathbf{a} = a_1\mathbf{i} + a_2\mathbf{j} + a_3\mathbf{k}$, $\mathbf{b} = b_1\mathbf{i} + b_2\mathbf{j} + b_3\mathbf{k}$ and m is a scalar, then

$$\mathbf{a} + \mathbf{b} = (a_1 + b_1)\mathbf{i} + (a_2 + b_2)\mathbf{j} + (a_3 + b_3)\mathbf{k}$$

and

$$m\mathbf{a} = (ma_1)\mathbf{i} + (ma_2)\mathbf{j} + (ma_3)\mathbf{k}.$$

The magnitude of a vector in terms of its components a_1, a_2, a_3 can be found using Pythagoras's Theorem (see Figure 3.15). The length ON is $\sqrt{a_1^2 + a_2^2}$, and $OA^2 = ON^2 + NA^2$. But $OA = |\mathbf{a}|$, thus

$$|\mathbf{a}| = \sqrt{a_1^2 + a_2^2 + a_3^2}.$$

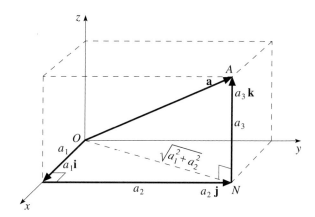

Figure 3.15

This can be summarized as follows.

Magnitude of a three-dimensional vector in component form

If $\mathbf{a} = \overrightarrow{PQ} = a_1\mathbf{i} + a_2\mathbf{j} + a_3\mathbf{k}$, where the points P and Q have coordinates (p_1, p_2, p_3) and (q_1, q_2, q_3), respectively, then

$$|\mathbf{a}| = \sqrt{a_1^2 + a_2^2 + a_3^2} = \sqrt{(q_1 - p_1)^2 + (q_2 - p_2)^2 + (q_3 - p_3)^2}.$$

---

*Exercise 3.7 ───────────────

Given vectors $\mathbf{a} = \mathbf{i} + \mathbf{j} + \mathbf{k}$, $\mathbf{b} = 2\mathbf{i} - 3\mathbf{j} - \mathbf{k}$ and $\mathbf{c} = 3\mathbf{i} + \mathbf{k}$:

(a) express $\mathbf{d} = 2\mathbf{a} - 3\mathbf{b}$ and $\mathbf{e} = \mathbf{a} - 2\mathbf{b} + 4\mathbf{c}$ in component form;

(b) find the magnitudes of the vectors $\mathbf{d}$ and $\mathbf{e}$;

(c) evaluate $|\mathbf{a}|$, and write down a unit vector in the direction of $\mathbf{a}$;

(d) find the components of a vector $\mathbf{x}$ such that $\mathbf{a} + \mathbf{x} = \mathbf{b}$.

Exercise 3.8 ───────────────

Find the magnitude of the vector $\mathbf{p} = 3\begin{bmatrix} 1 \\ 0 \\ 6 \end{bmatrix} - \begin{bmatrix} 2 \\ 3 \\ -1 \end{bmatrix}$.

Vector equation of a straight line

One useful application of position vectors (in two or three dimensions) is in obtaining a vector equation of a straight line.

Example 3.1

Find the position vector of a point T lying on the straight-line segment PQ (see Figure 3.16) in terms of the position vectors of P and Q.

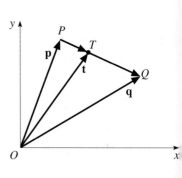

Solution

Let T be any point on PQ (see Figure 3.16). The position vector $\overrightarrow{OT}$ of T relative to the origin can also be written, using the triangle rule, as

$$\overrightarrow{OT} = \overrightarrow{OP} + \overrightarrow{PT}.$$

Now $\overrightarrow{PT} = s\overrightarrow{PQ}$, for some number s, and the point T traces out the line segment PQ as s varies from 0 to 1. Thus the straight-line segment PQ is described by the vector equation

$$\overrightarrow{OT} = \overrightarrow{OP} + s\overrightarrow{PQ} \quad (0 \le s \le 1).$$

Writing $\mathbf{p} = \overrightarrow{OP}$, $\mathbf{q} = \overrightarrow{OQ}$, $\mathbf{t} = \overrightarrow{OT}$, and noting (using the triangle rule) that $\overrightarrow{PQ} = \overrightarrow{OQ} - \overrightarrow{OP} = \mathbf{q} - \mathbf{p}$, this equation can also be written as

$$\mathbf{t} = \mathbf{p} + s(\mathbf{q} - \mathbf{p}) = (1-s)\mathbf{p} + s\mathbf{q} \quad (0 \le s \le 1). \quad \blacksquare$$

Figure 3.16

Note that if the parameter s in Example 3.1 is allowed to range over all the real numbers $(-\infty < s < \infty)$, then the point T traces out the entire straight line of which PQ is a segment. Also note that the ideas in Example 3.1 are easily extended to three dimensions.

Vector equation of a straight line

If P and Q are any two distinct points on a straight line in space, with position vectors $\mathbf{p}$ and $\mathbf{q}$, respectively, with respect to some given origin, then the **vector equation of the straight line** is

$$\mathbf{t} = (1-s)\mathbf{p} + s\mathbf{q} \quad (-\infty < s < \infty),$$

where $\mathbf{t}$ represents the position vector of any point on the line.

If $0 \le s \le 1$, then the equation represents only the line segment PQ.

Exercise 3.9

Write down, in component form, the vector equation of the straight line on which lie the points with Cartesian coordinates $(1, 1, 2)$ and $(2, 3, 1)$.

End-of-section Exercises

Exercise 3.10

Let $\mathbf{a} = 2\mathbf{i} - \mathbf{j}$, $\mathbf{b} = \mathbf{i} + 3\mathbf{j} + 5\mathbf{k}$ and $\mathbf{c} = \mathbf{j} - 2\mathbf{k}$.

(a) Find the magnitudes of $\mathbf{a}$ and $\mathbf{b}$, and describe the direction of $\mathbf{a}$.

(b) Find the vectors $\mathbf{a} + \mathbf{b}$, $2\mathbf{a} - \mathbf{b}$ and $\mathbf{c} + 2\mathbf{b} - 3\mathbf{a}$ in component form.

(c) What is the endpoint Q of the displacement represented by the vector $2\mathbf{a} - \mathbf{b}$ if $(0, 2, 3)$ is its beginning point P?

Exercise 3.11

Write the vectors $\mathbf{0}$, $\mathbf{i}$, $\mathbf{j}$ and $\mathbf{k}$ as column vectors in three dimensions.

---

4 Products of vectors

So far in this unit we have defined two algebraic operations: vector addition (by the triangle rule) and the scaling of a vector. The addition of vectors can be usefully applied only to two vectors representing the same type of physical quantity. For example, the addition of a displacement and a velocity has no physical meaning. However, vectors representing the same or different types of physical quantities can be combined in operations that are called the *dot product* and the *cross product*. They are called products because in some respects they behave like 'multiplications' in the algebra of real numbers. Dot products and cross products of vectors have numerous applications in geometry, mechanics and electromagnetism.

In this section the dot product and cross product are defined geometrically and also in terms of components of vectors. The dot product of two vectors is interpreted in terms of projecting a shadow of one vector onto another, and is applied to the problem of finding the angle between two vectors or lines. The cross product of two vectors is interpreted as a vector whose magnitude is an area. Both dot and cross products can be used in problems involving finding the areas of plane figures and the volumes of solid objects.

4.1 The dot product

> **Definition**
>
> The **dot product** of two vectors $\mathbf{a}$ and $\mathbf{b}$ is
>
> $\mathbf{a} \cdot \mathbf{b} = |\mathbf{a}|\,|\mathbf{b}| \cos\theta,$
>
> where θ $(0 \leq \theta \leq \pi)$ is the angle between the directions of $\mathbf{a}$ and $\mathbf{b}$ (see Figure 4.1).

The product $\mathbf{a} \cdot \mathbf{b}$ is read as 'a dot b'.

The dot product of two vectors is a *scalar quantity*, i.e. it is a real number: $\mathbf{a} \cdot \mathbf{b}$ is the product of the three scalars $|\mathbf{a}|$, $|\mathbf{b}|$ and $\cos\theta$. So the operation of the dot product combines two vectors to define a scalar, and for this reason the dot product is also called the **scalar product**. The angle θ lies in the range $0 \leq \theta \leq \pi$: the value of $\mathbf{a} \cdot \mathbf{b}$ is positive for $0 \leq \theta < \frac{\pi}{2}$, i.e. when θ is an acute angle; the value of $\mathbf{a} \cdot \mathbf{b}$ is negative for $\frac{\pi}{2} < \theta \leq \pi$, i.e. when θ is obtuse; the value of $\mathbf{a} \cdot \mathbf{b}$ is zero for $\theta = \frac{\pi}{2}$, i.e. when θ is a right angle.

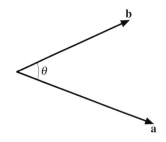

Figure 4.1

> It is important, when writing a dot product, to make sure that the dot between the vectors is clear.

*Exercise 4.1

Three vectors $\mathbf{a}$, $\mathbf{b}$ and $\mathbf{c}$ of magnitudes 2, 4 and 1 units, respectively, lying in the same plane, are represented by arrows as shown in Figure 4.2. The angle between the vectors $\mathbf{a}$ and $\mathbf{b}$ is $\frac{\pi}{3}$ radians, and that between the vectors $\mathbf{b}$ and $\mathbf{c}$ is $\frac{\pi}{6}$ radians. Use the definition of dot product to find the values of $\mathbf{a} \cdot \mathbf{b}$, $\mathbf{b} \cdot \mathbf{c}$, $\mathbf{a} \cdot \mathbf{c}$ and $\mathbf{b} \cdot \mathbf{b}$.

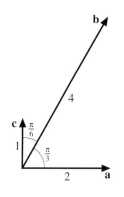

Figure 4.2

This exercise demonstrates two important properties of the dot product.

(a) If two vectors **a** and **b** are perpendicular to each other (i.e. the angle between them is $\frac{\pi}{2}$ radians), then since $\cos\frac{\pi}{2} = 0$,

$$\mathbf{a} \cdot \mathbf{b} = |\mathbf{a}|\,|\mathbf{b}|\cos\frac{\pi}{2} = 0.$$

(b) The dot product of a vector with itself gives the square of the magnitude of the vector, i.e.

$$\mathbf{a} \cdot \mathbf{a} = |\mathbf{a}|\,|\mathbf{a}|\cos 0 = |\mathbf{a}|^2.$$

The converse of (a) also holds: if **a** and **b** are two *non-zero* vectors such that $\mathbf{a} \cdot \mathbf{b} = 0$, then the definition of the dot product tells us that $\cos\theta = 0$; therefore $\theta = \frac{\pi}{2}$ and the vectors are perpendicular.

In the product of real numbers, $xy = 0$ implies that either x or y (or both) is zero. In contrast, for the dot product, $\mathbf{a} \cdot \mathbf{b} = 0$ gives an extra possibility: either **a** or **b** (or both) is the zero vector, or the angle between **a** and **b** is $\frac{\pi}{2}$ radians.

Properties of the dot product

The following are some important properties of the dot product of two vectors. They include the rules for manipulating dot products in algebraic expressions.

Properties of the dot product

Let **a**, **b** and **c** be vectors, and let m be a scalar.

1 $\mathbf{a} \cdot \mathbf{b}$ is a scalar.

2 $\mathbf{a} \cdot \mathbf{b} = \mathbf{b} \cdot \mathbf{a}$, i.e. the dot product is commutative.

3 $\mathbf{a} \cdot (\mathbf{b} + \mathbf{c}) = \mathbf{a} \cdot \mathbf{b} + \mathbf{a} \cdot \mathbf{c}$ and $(\mathbf{a} + \mathbf{b}) \cdot \mathbf{c} = \mathbf{a} \cdot \mathbf{c} + \mathbf{b} \cdot \mathbf{c}$, i.e. the dot product is distributive over vector addition.

4 $(m\mathbf{a}) \cdot \mathbf{b} = m(\mathbf{a} \cdot \mathbf{b}) = \mathbf{a} \cdot (m\mathbf{b})$, i.e. a scalar can be 'moved through' a dot product.

5 If neither **a** nor **b** is the zero vector, then $\mathbf{a} \cdot \mathbf{b} = 0$ if and only if **a** is perpendicular to **b**.

6 $\mathbf{a} \cdot \mathbf{a} = |\mathbf{a}|^2.$

These properties can all be derived from the definition of the dot product, but the derivations are not given here.

The following example shows how these properties can be used to simplify expressions.

Example 4.1

Expand the expression $\mathbf{x} \cdot \mathbf{y}$, given that $\mathbf{x} = 2\mathbf{u} + \mathbf{v}$ and $\mathbf{y} = \mathbf{u} - 5\mathbf{v}$. Calculate its value when **u** and **v** are perpendicular unit vectors.

Solution

$$
\begin{aligned}
\mathbf{x} \cdot \mathbf{y} &= (2\mathbf{u} + \mathbf{v}) \cdot (\mathbf{u} - 5\mathbf{v}) \\
&= (2\mathbf{u}) \cdot (\mathbf{u} - 5\mathbf{v}) + \mathbf{v} \cdot (\mathbf{u} - 5\mathbf{v}) && \text{(Property 3)} \\
&= (2\mathbf{u}) \cdot \mathbf{u} + (2\mathbf{u}) \cdot (-5\mathbf{v}) + \mathbf{v} \cdot \mathbf{u} + \mathbf{v} \cdot (-5\mathbf{v}) && \text{(Property 3)} \\
&= 2(\mathbf{u} \cdot \mathbf{u}) - 10(\mathbf{u} \cdot \mathbf{v}) + \mathbf{v} \cdot \mathbf{u} - 5(\mathbf{v} \cdot \mathbf{v}) && \text{(Property 4)} \\
&= 2(\mathbf{u} \cdot \mathbf{u}) - 9(\mathbf{u} \cdot \mathbf{v}) - 5(\mathbf{v} \cdot \mathbf{v}) && \text{(Property 2)}
\end{aligned}
$$

Now $\mathbf{u} \cdot \mathbf{u} = |\mathbf{u}|^2 = 1$ and $\mathbf{v} \cdot \mathbf{v} = |\mathbf{v}|^2 = 1$ when **u** and **v** are unit vectors. Furthermore, $\mathbf{u} \cdot \mathbf{v} = 0$ when **u** and **v** are perpendicular vectors. So when **u** and **v** are perpendicular unit vectors, we have

$$\mathbf{x} \cdot \mathbf{y} = 2 - 0 - 5 = -3. \quad \blacksquare$$

*Exercise 4.2 ———————————————————————————————

(a) Expand the expression $(\mathbf{a} + \mathbf{b}) \cdot (\mathbf{a} - \mathbf{b})$.

(b) Expand the expression $|\mathbf{a} + \mathbf{b}|^2$.

Recall that $|\mathbf{a}|^2 = \mathbf{a} \cdot \mathbf{a}$.

Exercise 4.3 ———————————————————————————————

Given that $\mathbf{a}$ and $\mathbf{b}$ are perpendicular unit vectors:

(a) find the value of m such that the two vectors $2\mathbf{a} + 3\mathbf{b}$ and $m\mathbf{a} + \mathbf{b}$ are perpendicular;

(b) find the value of $|\mathbf{c}|$ if $\mathbf{c} = 3\mathbf{a} + 5\mathbf{b}$.

Finally, a word of caution: $(\mathbf{a} \cdot \mathbf{b})\mathbf{c}$ is not in general the same as $\mathbf{a}(\mathbf{b} \cdot \mathbf{c})$. The vector $(\mathbf{a} \cdot \mathbf{b})\mathbf{c}$ is a scaling of $\mathbf{c}$ by the number $\mathbf{a} \cdot \mathbf{b}$, whereas $\mathbf{a}(\mathbf{b} \cdot \mathbf{c})$ is a scaling of $\mathbf{a}$ by the number $\mathbf{b} \cdot \mathbf{c}$. Clearly these two vectors are not generally even parallel, let alone equal. For example, if $\mathbf{a} = \mathbf{b} = \mathbf{i}$ and $\mathbf{c} = \mathbf{j}$, then

$$(\mathbf{a} \cdot \mathbf{b})\mathbf{c} = (\mathbf{i} \cdot \mathbf{i})\mathbf{j} = \mathbf{j} \quad \text{but} \quad \mathbf{a}(\mathbf{b} \cdot \mathbf{c}) = \mathbf{i}(\mathbf{i} \cdot \mathbf{j}) = \mathbf{0}.$$

In general, if m is a scalar and $\mathbf{a}$ is a vector, we can write $m\mathbf{a}$ or $\mathbf{a}m$ as convenient, although $m\mathbf{a}$ is more usual; thus $\mathbf{a}(\mathbf{b} \cdot \mathbf{c})$ means the same as $(\mathbf{b} \cdot \mathbf{c})\mathbf{a}$.

The component form of the dot product

We saw in Section 3 that an arbitrary vector $\mathbf{a}$ in three dimensions may be expressed in terms of the Cartesian unit vectors as

$$\mathbf{a} = a_1\mathbf{i} + a_2\mathbf{j} + a_3\mathbf{k} = \begin{bmatrix} a_1 \\ a_2 \\ a_3 \end{bmatrix}.$$

With this representation, vector addition and scaling become simple algebraic operations without any reference to diagrams. The definition of the dot product was expressed in terms of the magnitudes of two vectors and the angle between them. We shall now see how to express the dot product in terms of components of vectors.

First observe that, by definition, $\mathbf{i}$, $\mathbf{j}$ and $\mathbf{k}$ are unit vectors and are perpendicular to one another (see Figure 4.3). Thus:

$$\mathbf{i} \cdot \mathbf{j} = \mathbf{j} \cdot \mathbf{i} = 0, \quad \mathbf{i} \cdot \mathbf{k} = \mathbf{k} \cdot \mathbf{i} = 0, \quad \mathbf{j} \cdot \mathbf{k} = \mathbf{k} \cdot \mathbf{j} = 0;$$

$$\mathbf{i} \cdot \mathbf{i} = 1, \quad \mathbf{j} \cdot \mathbf{j} = 1, \quad \mathbf{k} \cdot \mathbf{k} = 1.$$

If two vectors $\mathbf{a}$ and $\mathbf{b}$ have component forms $\mathbf{a} = a_1\mathbf{i} + a_2\mathbf{j} + a_3\mathbf{k}$ and $\mathbf{b} = b_1\mathbf{i} + b_2\mathbf{j} + b_3\mathbf{k}$, then the dot product of $\mathbf{a}$ and $\mathbf{b}$ may be written as

$$(a_1\mathbf{i} + a_2\mathbf{j} + a_3\mathbf{k}) \cdot (b_1\mathbf{i} + b_2\mathbf{j} + b_3\mathbf{k}).$$

We can now apply Properties 3 and 4 of the dot product and the above rules for combining $\mathbf{i}$, $\mathbf{j}$ and $\mathbf{k}$ to this expression to obtain a very simple formula for the dot product of vectors in component form. Specifically, we have

$$
\begin{aligned}
&(a_1\mathbf{i} + a_2\mathbf{j} + a_3\mathbf{k}) \cdot (b_1\mathbf{i} + b_2\mathbf{j} + b_3\mathbf{k}) \\
&= a_1\mathbf{i} \cdot (b_1\mathbf{i} + b_2\mathbf{j} + b_3\mathbf{k}) + a_2\mathbf{j} \cdot (b_1\mathbf{i} + b_2\mathbf{j} + b_3\mathbf{k}) + a_3\mathbf{k} \cdot (b_1\mathbf{i} + b_2\mathbf{j} + b_3\mathbf{k}) \\
&= a_1\mathbf{i} \cdot b_1\mathbf{i} + a_1\mathbf{i} \cdot b_2\mathbf{j} + a_1\mathbf{i} \cdot b_3\mathbf{k} \\
&\quad + a_2\mathbf{j} \cdot b_1\mathbf{i} + a_2\mathbf{j} \cdot b_2\mathbf{j} + a_2\mathbf{j} \cdot b_3\mathbf{k} \\
&\quad\quad + a_3\mathbf{k} \cdot b_1\mathbf{i} + a_3\mathbf{k} \cdot b_2\mathbf{j} + a_3\mathbf{k} \cdot b_3\mathbf{k} \\
&= a_1 b_1 (\mathbf{i} \cdot \mathbf{i}) + a_1 b_2 (\mathbf{i} \cdot \mathbf{j}) + a_1 b_3 (\mathbf{i} \cdot \mathbf{k}) \\
&\quad + a_2 b_1 (\mathbf{j} \cdot \mathbf{i}) + a_2 b_2 (\mathbf{j} \cdot \mathbf{j}) + a_2 b_3 (\mathbf{j} \cdot \mathbf{k}) \\
&\quad\quad + a_3 b_1 (\mathbf{k} \cdot \mathbf{i}) + a_3 b_2 (\mathbf{k} \cdot \mathbf{j}) + a_3 b_3 (\mathbf{k} \cdot \mathbf{k}) \\
&= a_1 b_1 + a_2 b_2 + a_3 b_3.
\end{aligned}
$$

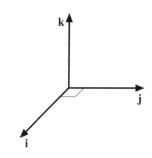

Figure 4.3

Note that for the right-handed system shown, the unit vector $\mathbf{i}$ points out of the plane of the page towards you.

This extremely important formula is worth remembering.

Component form of the dot product

If $\mathbf{a} = a_1\mathbf{i} + a_2\mathbf{j} + a_3\mathbf{k}$ and $\mathbf{b} = b_1\mathbf{i} + b_2\mathbf{j} + b_3\mathbf{k}$, then

$$\mathbf{a} \cdot \mathbf{b} = a_1 b_1 + a_2 b_2 + a_3 b_3.$$

---

*Exercise 4.4

If $\mathbf{a} = 4\mathbf{i} + \mathbf{j} - 5\mathbf{k}$ and $\mathbf{b} = \mathbf{i} - 3\mathbf{j} + \mathbf{k}$, show that $\mathbf{a} \cdot \mathbf{b} = -4$. What does the negative sign tell us?

The angle between two vectors

The component form of the dot product has an important application in calculating the angle between two vectors. You have already seen that if $\mathbf{a} \cdot \mathbf{b} = 0$ and neither $\mathbf{a}$ nor $\mathbf{b}$ is zero, then $\mathbf{a}$ and $\mathbf{b}$ are perpendicular. For instance, if $\mathbf{a} = 2\mathbf{i} - \mathbf{j}$ and $\mathbf{b} = 2\mathbf{i} + 4\mathbf{j}$, then $\mathbf{a} \cdot \mathbf{b} = (2 \times 2) + (-1 \times 4) = 0$, so the angle between $\mathbf{a}$ and $\mathbf{b}$ is $\frac{\pi}{2}$ radians. In general, the equation defining the dot product of $\mathbf{a}$ and $\mathbf{b}$, i.e. $\mathbf{a} \cdot \mathbf{b} = |\mathbf{a}|\,|\mathbf{b}| \cos \theta$, gives the following simple expression for finding the angle between $\mathbf{a}$ and $\mathbf{b}$.

Angle between two vectors

The angle θ between any two non-zero vectors $\mathbf{a}$ and $\mathbf{b}$ is given by

$$\cos \theta = \frac{\mathbf{a} \cdot \mathbf{b}}{|\mathbf{a}|\,|\mathbf{b}|} = \frac{a_1 b_1 + a_2 b_2 + a_3 b_3}{\sqrt{a_1^2 + a_2^2 + a_3^2}\sqrt{b_1^2 + b_2^2 + b_3^2}},$$

where $0 \le \theta \le \pi$.

Example 4.2

(a) Find the angle between the vector $\mathbf{a} = \mathbf{i} + \sqrt{3}\mathbf{k}$ and the x-axis.

(b) Find the angle between the vectors $\mathbf{a} = \mathbf{i} + \sqrt{3}\mathbf{k}$ and $\mathbf{b} = \sqrt{3}\mathbf{i} - 2\mathbf{j} + 3\mathbf{k}$.

(c) Show that $\mathbf{c} = -2\sqrt{3}\mathbf{i} + 2\mathbf{k}$ is perpendicular to $\mathbf{a} = \mathbf{i} + \sqrt{3}\mathbf{k}$.

Solution

(a) The direction of the x-axis is the same as the direction of $\mathbf{i}$, and the angle θ between $\mathbf{a}$ and $\mathbf{i}$ is given by

$$\cos \theta = \frac{\mathbf{a} \cdot \mathbf{i}}{|\mathbf{a}|\,|\mathbf{i}|} = \frac{a_1}{|\mathbf{a}|} = \frac{1}{\sqrt{1+3}} = \frac{1}{2}.$$

Thus the angle between $\mathbf{a}$ and the x-axis is $\frac{\pi}{3}$ radians.

(b) We have $|\mathbf{a}| = \sqrt{1+3} = 2$, $|\mathbf{b}| = \sqrt{3+4+9} = 4$ and

$$\mathbf{a} \cdot \mathbf{b} = (1 \times \sqrt{3}) + (0 \times -2) + (\sqrt{3} \times 3) = 4\sqrt{3}.$$

Therefore the angle θ between $\mathbf{a}$ and $\mathbf{b}$ is given by

$$\cos \theta = \frac{4\sqrt{3}}{2 \times 4} = \frac{\sqrt{3}}{2},$$

so $\theta = \frac{\pi}{6}$ radians.

(c) To test whether **a** and **c** are perpendicular, we calculate their dot product:

$$\mathbf{a} \cdot \mathbf{c} = (\mathbf{i} + \sqrt{3}\mathbf{k}) \cdot (-2\sqrt{3}\mathbf{i} + 2\mathbf{k})$$
$$= (1 \times -2\sqrt{3}) + (0 \times 0) + (\sqrt{3} \times 2)$$
$$= 0.$$

Since $\mathbf{a} \cdot \mathbf{c} = 0$ and **a** and **c** are non-zero vectors, **c** is perpendicular to **a**. ∎

Exercise 4.5

Consider the vectors

$$\mathbf{a} = 2\mathbf{i} - 3\mathbf{j} + \mathbf{k} \quad \text{and} \quad \mathbf{b} = -\mathbf{i} + 2\mathbf{j} + 4\mathbf{k}.$$

Find the magnitudes of **a** and **b**, and the angle between them.

Resolving a vector into components

The dot product has a useful geometric interpretation.

Exercise 4.6

If $\mathbf{a} = a_1\mathbf{i} + a_2\mathbf{j} + a_3\mathbf{k}$, find the values of $\mathbf{a} \cdot \mathbf{i}$, $\mathbf{a} \cdot \mathbf{j}$ and $\mathbf{a} \cdot \mathbf{k}$.

The solution to Exercise 4.6 shows the important fact that the **i**-component of any vector **a** may be found by taking the dot product $\mathbf{a} \cdot \mathbf{i}$. The **j**- and **k**-components can be found similarly (by taking dot products with **j** and **k**, respectively).

We can also find the components of a vector in other directions. Suppose that a vector **a**, represented by $\overrightarrow{OA}$, makes an angle θ with a *unit vector* **u** (see Figure 4.4). Draw the line AP perpendicular to the direction of **u**. Then the distance OP is seen from simple trigonometry to be $|\mathbf{a}| \cos\theta$. Now observe that the dot product of **a** and **u** is

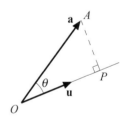

Figure 4.4

$$\mathbf{a} \cdot \mathbf{u} = |\mathbf{a}| \, |\mathbf{u}| \cos\theta = |OP| \quad (\text{since } |\mathbf{u}| = 1).$$

The distance OP represents the *component* of **a** in the direction of **u**.

Note that $\mathbf{a} \cdot \mathbf{u}$ will be negative if $\theta > \frac{\pi}{2}$, i.e. if P and **u** lie on opposite sides of O.

Definition

The **component** of a vector **a** in the direction of an arbitrary *unit vector* **u** is $\mathbf{a} \cdot \mathbf{u}$.

Exercise 4.7

Consider the vectors

$$\mathbf{a} = 2\mathbf{i} - 3\mathbf{j} + \mathbf{k} \quad \text{and} \quad \mathbf{b} = -\mathbf{i} + 2\mathbf{j} + 4\mathbf{k}.$$

(a) Which of the following vectors is perpendicular to **a**?

$$\mathbf{c} = -\mathbf{i} + \mathbf{j} + 3\mathbf{k}, \quad \mathbf{d} = -2\mathbf{i} + \mathbf{k}, \quad \mathbf{e} = -\mathbf{i} - \mathbf{j} - \mathbf{k}.$$

(b) Find the component of the vector $\mathbf{a} + 2\mathbf{b}$ in the direction of the line joining the origin to the point $(1, 1, 1)$.

Resolving vectors will be a vital technique in subsequent units, and sometimes you will need to be able to resolve a vector into components in directions other than horizontal and vertical. For example, suppose that two forces, **N** and **W**, are acting at a point on an inclined plane (see Figure 4.5). These forces can be represented by vectors, and you will see that it may be convenient to take axes as shown, with **i** pointing up the plane. It is then necessary to be able to resolve **N** and **W** into components along and perpendicular to the plane.

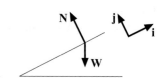

Figure 4.5

The dot product method of obtaining components always works, but a geometric view is also useful. This follows because the component of a vector **a** in the direction of a unit vector **u** is

$$\mathbf{a} \cdot \mathbf{u} = |\mathbf{a}| \cos\theta,$$

where θ is the angle between **a** and **u**. We summarize the method as a procedure.

Procedure 4.1   Resolving a vector into components

Given a vector **a** and a unit vector **u**, to find the component of **a** in the direction of **u**, do the following.

- Find (usually from a diagram) the angle θ between **a** and **u** (with $0 \le \theta \le \pi$).
- The component of the vector **a** in the direction of the unit vector **u** is $|\mathbf{a}| \cos\theta$.
- If necessary (for example, if $\theta > \frac{\pi}{2}$), use the trigonometric formulae from the Handbook to simplify the result.

The following example uses Cartesian unit vectors that are not horizontal and vertical.

Example 4.3

Suppose that the unit vector **i** points up a plane which is inclined at an angle α to the horizontal, and the unit vector **j** is perpendicular to the plane, as shown in Figure 4.6. Find the **i**- and **j**-components of the vectors **N** and **W**.

Solution

It is easy to resolve the vector **N** into its component form:

$$\mathbf{N} = 0\mathbf{i} + |\mathbf{N}|\mathbf{j} = |\mathbf{N}|\mathbf{j}.$$

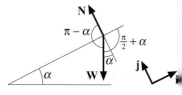

Figure 4.6

For the vector **W**, we note from the geometry of the diagram that the angles between **W** and **i**, and **W** and **j**, are given by $\frac{\pi}{2} + \alpha$ and $\pi - \alpha$, respectively. Applying Procedure 4.1 twice (with $\mathbf{u} = \mathbf{i}$ and then $\mathbf{u} = \mathbf{j}$) allows us to resolve **W** into its component form:

$$\mathbf{W} = |\mathbf{W}|\cos(\tfrac{\pi}{2} + \alpha)\,\mathbf{i} + |\mathbf{W}|\cos(\pi - \alpha)\,\mathbf{j}$$
$$= -|\mathbf{W}|\sin\alpha\,\mathbf{i} - |\mathbf{W}|\cos\alpha\,\mathbf{j}. \quad\blacksquare$$

So the **i**- and **j**-components of **N** are 0 and $|\mathbf{N}|$ respectively, and those of **W** are $-|\mathbf{W}|\sin\alpha$ and $-|\mathbf{W}|\cos\alpha$.

*Exercise 4.8

The two-dimensional vectors **v** and **w** in Figure 4.7 have magnitudes 1.5 and 2, respectively. Resolve **v** and **w** into their **i**- and **j**-components.

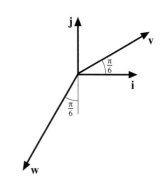

Figure 4.7

Exercise 4.9

In Figure 4.8 the point P lies on a line making an angle α with the x-axis. The vectors **a**, **b**, **c**, **d** have magnitudes 1, 1.5, 1.5 and 2, respectively, and point in the directions shown.

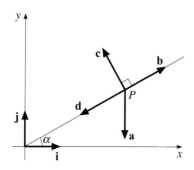

Figure 4.8

Resolve each of these vectors into their **i**- and **j**-components.

Exercise 4.10

Figure 4.9 shows a configuration similar to Figure 4.8, but with the unit vectors **i** and **j** aligned along and perpendicular to the line, respectively.

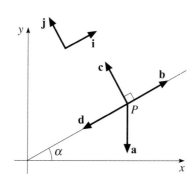

Figure 4.9

Resolve each of the vectors **a**, **b**, **c** and **d** into their **i**- and **j**-components.

Exercise 4.11

The vectors **p**, **q** and **r** in Figure 4.10 have magnitudes 2.5, 3 and 2.5, respectively. Resolve **p**, **q** and **r** into their **i**- and **j**-components.

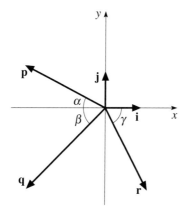

Figure 4.10

Exercise 4.12

The sum of the two-dimensional vectors **a**, **b**, **c** in Figure 4.11 is the zero vector, and $|\mathbf{c}| = 2$. By resolving the vectors into their components, determine the magnitudes of **a** and **b**.

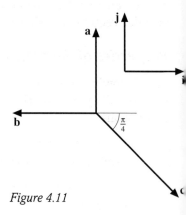

Figure 4.11

4.2 The cross product

You have seen that the dot product of two vectors is a scalar (i.e. a real number). In contrast, the *cross product* of two vectors is a *vector*, whose direction is perpendicular to both. The cross product has numerous applications in geometry and mechanics, as you will see later in the course.

Definition

The **cross product** of two vectors **a** and **b** is

$$\mathbf{a} \times \mathbf{b} = (|\mathbf{a}|\,|\mathbf{b}|\sin\theta)\,\widehat{\mathbf{c}},$$

where θ $(0 \le \theta \le \pi)$ is the angle between the directions of **a** and **b**, and $\widehat{\mathbf{c}}$ is a unit vector perpendicular to both **a** and **b**, whose sense is given by the right-hand screw rule as shown in Figure 4.12.

The product $\mathbf{a} \times \mathbf{b}$ is read as 'a cross b'.

The angle θ between two vectors **a** and **b** lies in the range $0 \le \theta \le \pi$, so $\sin\theta \ge 0$ and hence $|\mathbf{a}|\,|\mathbf{b}|\sin\theta \ge 0$. So the cross product of **a** and **b** is a vector with magnitude $|\mathbf{a}|\,|\mathbf{b}|\sin\theta$ and direction defined by $\widehat{\mathbf{c}}$. The direction of $\widehat{\mathbf{c}}$ is the direction in which the screw in Figure 4.12 would advance when turned from **a** towards **b** through the angle θ. Notice that $\widehat{\mathbf{c}}$ is not defined if **a** and **b** are parallel or if **a** or **b** is the zero vector; but in these cases $|\mathbf{a}|\,|\mathbf{b}|\sin\theta = 0$ so we take $\mathbf{a} \times \mathbf{b} = \mathbf{0}$. The cross product is also called the **vector product**, which stresses the fact that $\mathbf{a} \times \mathbf{b}$ is a vector.

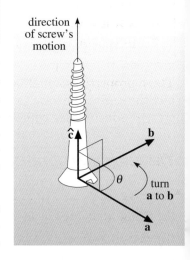

Figure 4.12

The order of writing down **a** and **b** is very important. According to the screw rule, $\mathbf{b} \times \mathbf{a}$ is a vector in the direction opposite to $\mathbf{a} \times \mathbf{b}$. Figure 4.13 shows what would happen to the screw in Figure 4.12 if we turned from **b** to **a**: it would 'unscrew'. The unit vector $\widehat{\mathbf{d}}$ in the direction of $\mathbf{b} \times \mathbf{a}$ is in the opposite sense to $\widehat{\mathbf{c}}$, i.e. $\widehat{\mathbf{d}} = -\widehat{\mathbf{c}}$. Hence

$$\mathbf{b} \times \mathbf{a} = (|\mathbf{b}|\,|\mathbf{a}|\sin\theta)\,\widehat{\mathbf{d}} = -(|\mathbf{b}|\,|\mathbf{a}|\sin\theta)\,\widehat{\mathbf{c}} = -(\mathbf{a} \times \mathbf{b}).$$

*Exercise 4.13

Three vectors **u**, **v** and **w** lie in the (x, y)-plane. Their magnitudes are 2, 3 and 4 units, respectively, their directions make angles $\frac{\pi}{6}$, $\frac{\pi}{3}$ and $\frac{\pi}{6}$ radians, respectively, with the positive x-axis, and they have positive **j**-components. Use the definition of the cross product to find the vectors $\mathbf{u} \times \mathbf{v}$, $\mathbf{u} \times \mathbf{w}$ and $\mathbf{v} \times \mathbf{w}$.

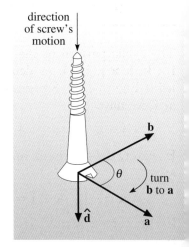

Figure 4.13

Exercise 4.13 illustrates an important property of the cross product. If two vectors **a** and **b** are parallel, then the angle θ between their directions is zero or π radians, so the cross product of **a** and **b** is the zero vector, because the magnitude of the vector, i.e. $|\mathbf{a}|\,|\mathbf{b}|\sin\theta$, is zero. The converse also holds: if **a** and **b** are two non-zero vectors such that $\mathbf{a} \times \mathbf{b} = \mathbf{0}$, then the definition of the cross product tells us that $\sin\theta = 0$; therefore $\theta = 0$ or $\theta = \pi$, and the vectors are parallel. We can also deduce that

$$\mathbf{a} \times \mathbf{a} = \mathbf{0} \quad \text{for any vector } \mathbf{a}.$$

So we can test for perpendicular vectors by using the dot product and for parallel vectors by using the cross product.

Properties of the cross product

The following are some important properties of the cross product of two vectors. They include the rules for manipulating cross products in algebraic expressions.

Properties of the cross product

Let $\mathbf{a}$, $\mathbf{b}$ and $\mathbf{c}$ be vectors, and let m be a scalar.

1   $\mathbf{a} \times \mathbf{b}$ is a vector.
2   $\mathbf{b} \times \mathbf{a} = -(\mathbf{a} \times \mathbf{b})$.
3   $\mathbf{a} \times (\mathbf{b}+\mathbf{c})=(\mathbf{a} \times \mathbf{b})+(\mathbf{a} \times \mathbf{c})$ and $(\mathbf{a}+\mathbf{b}) \times \mathbf{c}=(\mathbf{a} \times \mathbf{c})+(\mathbf{b} \times \mathbf{c})$,
   i.e. the cross product is distributive over vector addition.
4   $(m\mathbf{a}) \times \mathbf{b} = m(\mathbf{a} \times \mathbf{b}) = \mathbf{a} \times (m\mathbf{b})$, i.e. a scalar can be 'moved through' a cross product.
5   If neither $\mathbf{a}$ nor $\mathbf{b}$ is the zero vector, then $\mathbf{a} \times \mathbf{b} = \mathbf{0}$ if and only if $\mathbf{a}$ and $\mathbf{b}$ are parallel.
6   $\mathbf{a} \times \mathbf{a} = \mathbf{0}$.
7   In general, $\mathbf{a} \times (\mathbf{b} \times \mathbf{c}) \neq (\mathbf{a} \times \mathbf{b}) \times \mathbf{c}$.

These properties can all be derived from the definition of the cross product, but the derivations are not given here. Note in particular Property 2: the cross product is *not* commutative — the order does matter.

The component form of the cross product

Exercise 4.14
(a) Show that $\mathbf{i} \times \mathbf{j} = \mathbf{k}$, $\mathbf{j} \times \mathbf{k} = \mathbf{i}$ and $\mathbf{k} \times \mathbf{i} = \mathbf{j}$.
(b) Calculate $\mathbf{j} \times \mathbf{i}$, $\mathbf{k} \times \mathbf{j}$ and $\mathbf{i} \times \mathbf{k}$.
(c) Calculate $\mathbf{i} \times \mathbf{i}$, $\mathbf{j} \times \mathbf{j}$ and $\mathbf{k} \times \mathbf{k}$.
(d) Expand and simplify

$$(\mathbf{i} + \mathbf{k}) \times (\mathbf{i} + \mathbf{j} + \mathbf{k}) \quad \text{and} \quad (\mathbf{i} \times (\mathbf{i} + \mathbf{k})) - ((\mathbf{i} + \mathbf{j}) \times \mathbf{k}).$$

The cyclic pattern of the products $\mathbf{i} \times \mathbf{j}$, $\mathbf{j} \times \mathbf{k}$, $\mathbf{k} \times \mathbf{i}$ and of the products $\mathbf{i} \times \mathbf{k}$, $\mathbf{k} \times \mathbf{j}$, $\mathbf{j} \times \mathbf{i}$, as demonstrated in Exercise 4.14, can be remembered using Figure 4.14. For example, if we go round the circle clockwise starting at $\mathbf{i}$, we have

$$\mathbf{i} \times \mathbf{j} = \mathbf{k}, \quad \mathbf{j} \times \mathbf{k} = \mathbf{i}, \quad \mathbf{k} \times \mathbf{i} = \mathbf{j}.$$

However, if we go in an anticlockwise direction, the cross products are negative:

$$\mathbf{i} \times \mathbf{k} = -\mathbf{j}, \quad \mathbf{k} \times \mathbf{j} = -\mathbf{i}, \quad \mathbf{j} \times \mathbf{i} = -\mathbf{k}.$$

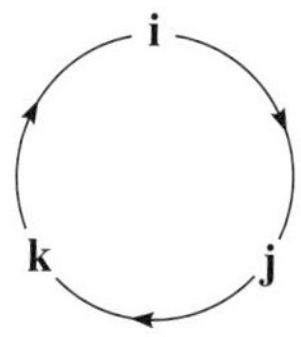

Figure 4.14

If two vectors $\mathbf{a}$ and $\mathbf{b}$ have component forms $\mathbf{a} = a_1\mathbf{i} + a_2\mathbf{j} + a_3\mathbf{k}$ and $\mathbf{b} = b_1\mathbf{i} + b_2\mathbf{j} + b_3\mathbf{k}$, then the cross product $\mathbf{a} \times \mathbf{b}$ may be written as

$$\mathbf{a} \times \mathbf{b} = (a_1\mathbf{i} + a_2\mathbf{j} + a_3\mathbf{k}) \times (b_1\mathbf{i} + b_2\mathbf{j} + b_3\mathbf{k})$$

$$= a_1\mathbf{i} \times (b_1\mathbf{i} + b_2\mathbf{j} + b_3\mathbf{k})$$
$$+ a_2\mathbf{j} \times (b_1\mathbf{i} + b_2\mathbf{j} + b_3\mathbf{k})$$
$$+ a_3\mathbf{k} \times (b_1\mathbf{i} + b_2\mathbf{j} + b_3\mathbf{k}) \qquad \text{(using Property 3)}$$

$$= a_1\mathbf{i} \times b_1\mathbf{i} + a_1\mathbf{i} \times b_2\mathbf{j} + a_1\mathbf{i} \times b_3\mathbf{k}$$
$$+ a_2\mathbf{j} \times b_1\mathbf{i} + a_2\mathbf{j} \times b_2\mathbf{j} + a_2\mathbf{j} \times b_3\mathbf{k}$$
$$+ a_3\mathbf{k} \times b_1\mathbf{i} + a_3\mathbf{k} \times b_2\mathbf{j} + a_3\mathbf{k} \times b_3\mathbf{k} \qquad \text{(using Property 3)}$$

$$= a_1 b_2(\mathbf{i} \times \mathbf{j}) + a_1 b_3(\mathbf{i} \times \mathbf{k})$$
$$+ a_2 b_1(\mathbf{j} \times \mathbf{i}) + a_2 b_3(\mathbf{j} \times \mathbf{k})$$
$$+ a_3 b_1(\mathbf{k} \times \mathbf{i}) + a_3 b_2(\mathbf{k} \times \mathbf{j}) \qquad \text{(using Properties 4 and 6)}$$

$$= (a_2 b_3 - a_3 b_2)\mathbf{i} + (a_3 b_1 - a_1 b_3)\mathbf{j} + (a_1 b_2 - a_2 b_1)\mathbf{k} \qquad \text{(using the results above).}$$

We highlight this important formula.

Component form of the cross product

If $\mathbf{a} = a_1\mathbf{i} + a_2\mathbf{j} + a_3\mathbf{k}$ and $\mathbf{b} = b_1\mathbf{i} + b_2\mathbf{j} + b_3\mathbf{k}$, then

$$\mathbf{a} \times \mathbf{b} = (a_2 b_3 - a_3 b_2)\mathbf{i} + (a_3 b_1 - a_1 b_3)\mathbf{j} + (a_1 b_2 - a_2 b_1)\mathbf{k}$$

$$= \begin{bmatrix} a_2 b_3 - a_3 b_2 \\ a_3 b_1 - a_1 b_3 \\ a_1 b_2 - a_2 b_1 \end{bmatrix}.$$

This formula is not easy to remember or use. For this reason, simpler methods have been devised, such as the following, which is known as Sarrus's Rule. Given two vectors $\mathbf{a} = [a_1 \quad a_2 \quad a_3]^T$ and $\mathbf{b} = [b_1 \quad b_2 \quad b_3]^T$, draw a tableau with $\mathbf{i}$, $\mathbf{j}$ and $\mathbf{k}$ in the top row, then repeat $\mathbf{i}$ and $\mathbf{j}$. In the second row do the same with the components of $\mathbf{a}$, and in the third row with those of $\mathbf{b}$. Then following the diagonal lines as shown, and multiplying the entries, gives the corresponding components of the cross product $\mathbf{a} \times \mathbf{b}$, which are the elements on the fourth row of the tableau.

Another quick way to evaluate cross products is to use determinants. This method is introduced in *Unit 9* when we discuss determinants. If you already know this method, then we suggest that you continue to use it.

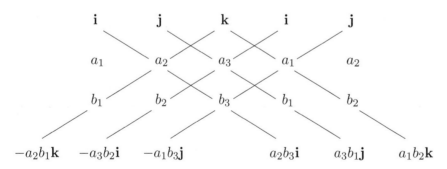

(The diagonals pointing to the right yield positive terms, while those pointing to the left have a minus sign.)

Example 4.4

If $\mathbf{a} = 2\mathbf{i} + \mathbf{j} - \mathbf{k}$ and $\mathbf{b} = \mathbf{i} - 3\mathbf{j} + 4\mathbf{k}$, find $\mathbf{a} \times \mathbf{b}$.

Solution

Since $a_1 = 2$, $a_2 = 1$, $a_3 = -1$ and $b_1 = 1$, $b_2 = -3$, $b_3 = 4$, the formula above gives

$$\mathbf{a} \times \mathbf{b} = ((1 \times 4) - (-1 \times -3))\mathbf{i}$$
$$+ ((-1 \times 1) - (2 \times 4))\mathbf{j}$$
$$+ ((2 \times -3) - (1 \times 1))\mathbf{k}$$
$$= \mathbf{i} - 9\mathbf{j} - 7\mathbf{k}.$$

Alternatively, using the tableau, we have

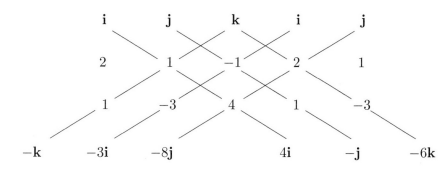

so $\mathbf{a} \times \mathbf{b} = \mathbf{i} - 9\mathbf{j} - 7\mathbf{k}$, as before. ■

Exercise 4.15

If $\mathbf{a} = 2\mathbf{i} - 3\mathbf{j} + \mathbf{k}$, $\mathbf{b} = -\mathbf{i} + 2\mathbf{j} + 4\mathbf{k}$ and $\mathbf{c} = -4\mathbf{i} + 6\mathbf{j} - 2\mathbf{k}$, find $\mathbf{a} \times \mathbf{b}$, $\mathbf{a} \times \mathbf{c}$ and $\mathbf{b} \times \mathbf{c}$. From your results, what can you say about $\mathbf{a}$ and $\mathbf{c}$?

Exercise 4.16

If $\mathbf{a} = 2\mathbf{i} + 2\mathbf{j} + \mathbf{k}$ and $\mathbf{b} = 4\mathbf{i} + 4\mathbf{j} - 7\mathbf{k}$, find a unit vector whose direction is perpendicular to the directions of both $\mathbf{a}$ and $\mathbf{b}$.

We close the section, and the unit, with some useful geometric applications of the cross product. The following example is the first step.

Example 4.5

Any two non-zero and non-parallel vectors $\mathbf{a}$ and $\mathbf{b}$ define a parallelogram, as shown in Figure 4.15. Express the area of the parallelogram in terms of $\mathbf{a} \times \mathbf{b}$.

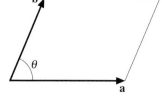

Figure 4.15

Solution

The area A of the parallelogram defined by the two vectors $\mathbf{a}$ and $\mathbf{b}$ is the same as the area of the rectangle of height $|\mathbf{b}| \sin \theta$ and width $|\mathbf{a}|$ (see Figure 4.16). Thus $A = |\mathbf{a}| \, |\mathbf{b}| \sin \theta$, and this is the magnitude of $\mathbf{a} \times \mathbf{b}$. So

$$A = |\mathbf{a} \times \mathbf{b}|. \quad \blacksquare$$

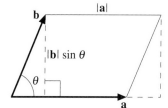

Figure 4.16

Area of a parallelogram

The area of a parallelogram with sides defined by vectors $\mathbf{a}$ and $\mathbf{b}$ is $|\mathbf{a} \times \mathbf{b}|$.

This idea is easily extended for the area of a triangle. Any two non-zero, non-parallel vectors $\mathbf{a}$ and $\mathbf{b}$ define a triangle (see Figure 4.17). The area of this triangle is half that of the corresponding parallelogram, so it is $\frac{1}{2}|\mathbf{a} \times \mathbf{b}|$.

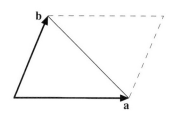

Figure 4.17

Area of a triangle

The area of a triangle with sides defined by vectors $\mathbf{a}$ and $\mathbf{b}$ is $\frac{1}{2}|\mathbf{a} \times \mathbf{b}|$.

Using the formula for the area of a parallelogram, it is easy to find the volume of a parallelepiped (see Figure 4.18). This is given by

A *parallelepiped* is like a distorted brick. All of its faces are parallelograms.

$$\text{volume of parallelepiped} = \text{base area} \times \text{vertical height } h$$
$$= |(\mathbf{a} \times \mathbf{b}) \cdot \mathbf{c}|.$$

Here we have made use of the fact that the base is a parallelogram (assumed to be in the (x, y)-plane) defined by the vectors $\mathbf{a}$ and $\mathbf{b}$. The base therefore has an area equal to the magnitude of $\mathbf{a} \times \mathbf{b}$. Now the vertical height h is the component of the vector $\mathbf{c}$ in the direction of the Cartesian unit vector $\mathbf{k}$ pointing vertically upwards, i.e. it is the z-component of $\mathbf{c}$, given by $\mathbf{c} \cdot \mathbf{k} = \mathbf{k} \cdot \mathbf{c}$. So the volume of the parallelepiped is $|\mathbf{a} \times \mathbf{b}|(\mathbf{k} \cdot \mathbf{c})$. But the vector product $\mathbf{a} \times \mathbf{b}$ points vertically upwards and can therefore be expressed as $|\mathbf{a} \times \mathbf{b}| \mathbf{k}$. Hence the volume of the parallelepiped is

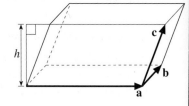

Figure 4.18

$$|\mathbf{a} \times \mathbf{b}|(\mathbf{k} \cdot \mathbf{c}) = (|\mathbf{a} \times \mathbf{b}| \mathbf{k}) \cdot \mathbf{c} = (\mathbf{a} \times \mathbf{b}) \cdot \mathbf{c}.$$

Of course, the scalar $(\mathbf{a} \times \mathbf{b}) \cdot \mathbf{c}$ can be negative if one of the defining vectors $\mathbf{a}$ or $\mathbf{b}$ is chosen to be in the opposite direction to the one chosen in Figure 4.18, or if the order of the cross product is reversed. The modulus signs in the formula $|(\mathbf{a} \times \mathbf{b}) \cdot \mathbf{c}|$ ensure that the volume comes out positive.

The scalar quantity $(\mathbf{a} \times \mathbf{b}) \cdot \mathbf{c}$ is an example of a *scalar triple product*.

End-of-section Exercises

Exercise 4.17

(a) Is $\mathbf{a} \cdot \mathbf{b}$ a vector?

(b) Can $\mathbf{a} \cdot \mathbf{b}$ be negative?

(c) What is special about $\mathbf{a}$ and $\mathbf{b}$ if $\mathbf{a} \cdot \mathbf{b} = |\mathbf{a}|\,|\mathbf{b}|$?

(d) If $\mathbf{a} \cdot \mathbf{b} = 0$, what can you say about $\mathbf{a}$ and $\mathbf{b}$?

(e) If $\mathbf{a} \times \mathbf{b} = \mathbf{0}$, what can you say about $\mathbf{a}$ and $\mathbf{b}$?

Exercise 4.18

Suppose that the vectors $\mathbf{r}$ and $\mathbf{s}$ are directed towards north and north-east, respectively, and define $\mathbf{r} \times \mathbf{s} = \mathbf{t}$.

(a) What is the direction of $\mathbf{t}$?

(b) In what direction is $\mathbf{s} \times \mathbf{r}$?

(c) In what direction is $\mathbf{t} \times \mathbf{r}$?

(d) If $|\mathbf{r}| = |\mathbf{s}| = 1$, what is $|\mathbf{t}|$?

(e) Calculate the vector $\mathbf{t} \times (\mathbf{r} \times \mathbf{s})$.

(f) If $|\mathbf{r}| = |\mathbf{s}| = 1$, what is the value of $\mathbf{r} \cdot \mathbf{s}$?

(g) If $|\mathbf{r}| = |\mathbf{s}| = 1$, what is the value of $\mathbf{s} \cdot (\mathbf{t} \times \mathbf{r})$?

Exercise 4.19

Find the value of $(\mathbf{a} \times \mathbf{b}) \cdot \mathbf{a}$ for any non-zero vectors $\mathbf{a}$ and $\mathbf{b}$.

Outcomes

After studying this unit you should be able to:

- understand the meaning of the terms scalar, vector, displacement vector, unit vector and position vector, and know what it means to say that two vectors are equal;
- use vector notation and represent vectors as arrows on diagrams;
- use the plane polar coordinate representation of the magnitude and direction of a vector, and convert between the polar coordinates and the Cartesian coordinates of the endpoint of a vector drawn from the origin;
- scale a vector by a number, and add two vectors geometrically using the triangle rule (or the parallelogram rule);
- resolve a vector into its Cartesian components, and scale and add vectors given in Cartesian component form;
- calculate the dot product (scalar product) and cross product (vector product) of two given vectors;
- determine whether or not two given vectors are perpendicular or parallel to one another;
- determine the magnitude of a vector and the angle between the directions of two vectors;
- write down the vector equation of a given straight line;
- resolve a vector in a given direction;
- manipulate vector expressions and equations involving the scaling, addition, dot product and cross product of vectors;
- use the cross product to determine the area of a parallelogram or triangle.

Solutions to the exercises

Section 1

1.1

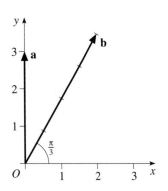

1.2

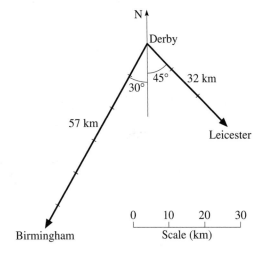

1.3

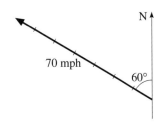

1.4 $\mathbf{f} = \mathbf{b}$, as both are of length 2 units and both point in the positive y-direction.

1.5 The completed table is as follows.

Cartesian coordinates (x, y)	Polar coordinates $\langle r, \phi \rangle$
$(0, -1)$	$\langle 1, -\frac{\pi}{2} \rangle$
$(1, 1)$	$\langle \sqrt{2}, \frac{\pi}{4} \rangle$
$(2\sqrt{2}, -2\sqrt{2})$	$\langle 4, -\frac{\pi}{4} \rangle$
$(-6, 0)$	$\langle 6, \pi \rangle$
$(-1, -1)$	$\langle \sqrt{2}, -\frac{3\pi}{4} \rangle$
	$\langle -1, \pi \rangle$
$(2.003 \times 10^7, 9.797 \times 10^7)$	$\langle 10^8, \exp(0.1\pi) \rangle$

The entry in row 6 is an invalid entry because r must be non-negative.

1.6 The most obvious choice is the Cartesian coordinate system with origin at Bristol (see Figure 1.3 on page 156), the x-axis pointing east and the y-axis pointing north. Then $r = 296$ and $\phi = \frac{\pi}{2} - \frac{15\pi}{180} = \frac{5\pi}{12}$. Hence $\mathbf{s} = \langle 296, \frac{5\pi}{12} \rangle$. Another choice would have the origin at Bristol but the x-axis pointing from Bristol to Leeds, in which case you would have $\mathbf{s} = \langle 296, 0 \rangle$. (Infinitely many other choices are possible.)

1.7 Scalar quantities: temperature, volume, energy, time.

Vector quantities: velocity, force, displacement, acceleration.

1.8 Since $(0, -3)$ lies on the negative part of the y-axis, we can immediately write down the polar coordinates of $\overrightarrow{OQ}$ as $\langle 3, -\frac{\pi}{2} \rangle$, so $|\overrightarrow{OQ}| = 3$.

Alternatively, using the formulae

$$r = (0^2 + (-3)^2)^{1/2} = 3,$$
$$\sin \phi = -3/3 = -1, \quad \cos \phi = 0$$

gives the same results.

Section 2

2.1 **(a)** Leeds to Bristol: $-\mathbf{d}$.
Leeds to Leeds: $\mathbf{0}$.

(b) **(i)** $2\mathbf{v}$ **(ii)** $-\mathbf{v}$ **(iii)** $\mathbf{0}$

(c) The vector $-1.5\mathbf{v}$ has magnitude $1.5|\mathbf{v}|$ and direction opposite to $\mathbf{v}$.

The vector $-k\mathbf{v}$ (k positive) has magnitude $k|\mathbf{v}|$ and direction opposite to $\mathbf{v}$.

(d) **(i)** The vectors $\overrightarrow{AB}$ and $\overrightarrow{DC}$ are equal in length and parallel, and point the same way (i.e. have the same direction). Thus

$$\overrightarrow{AB} = \overrightarrow{DC}.$$

(ii) The vectors $\overrightarrow{BC}$ and $\overrightarrow{DA}$ are equal in length and parallel, but point in opposite directions. Thus

$$\overrightarrow{BC} = -\overrightarrow{DA} \quad \text{(or, equivalently, } \overrightarrow{DA} = -\overrightarrow{BC}\text{).}$$

(e) $\frac{1}{|\mathbf{v}|}\mathbf{v}$ is a scaling of $\mathbf{v}$ by the positive scalar $m = \frac{1}{|\mathbf{v}|}$. The direction of $\frac{1}{|\mathbf{v}|}\mathbf{v}$ is thus the same as that of $\mathbf{v}$, and the magnitude is $m|\mathbf{v}| = \frac{1}{|\mathbf{v}|}|\mathbf{v}| = 1$.

2.2 $\mathbf{a} = 2\mathbf{i}$, $\mathbf{b} = -2.5\mathbf{i}$, $\mathbf{c} = 3\mathbf{j}$, $\mathbf{d} = -\mathbf{j}$.

2.3 (a) $-35\mathbf{j}$ (where $|\mathbf{j}|$ represents 1 km per hour).

(b) $-112\mathbf{i}$ (where $|\mathbf{i}|$ represents 1 mile).

(c) $112\mathbf{i}$ (where $|\mathbf{i}|$ represents 1 mile).

2.4 (a)

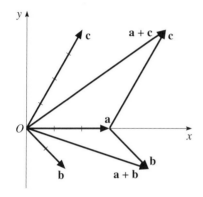

(b)

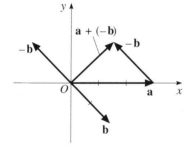

2.5

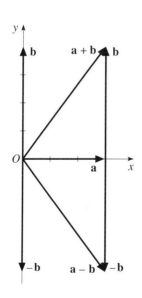

2.6 The following sketch illustrates the associative property.

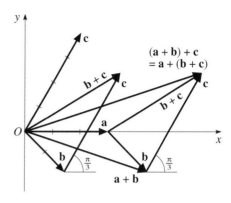

(To evaluate $(\mathbf{a} + \mathbf{b}) + \mathbf{c}$, we go first to $\mathbf{a} + \mathbf{b}$ (in the lower quadrant) and then add $\mathbf{c}$. To evaluate $\mathbf{a} + (\mathbf{b} + \mathbf{c})$, we go first to $\mathbf{a}$ (along the x-axis) and then add $\mathbf{b} + \mathbf{c}$.)

The following sketch illustrates the distributive property.

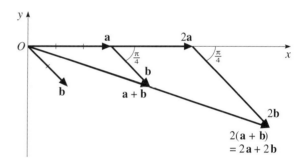

2.7 $4(\mathbf{a} - \mathbf{c}) + 3(\mathbf{c} - \mathbf{b}) + 2(2\mathbf{a} - \mathbf{b} - 3\mathbf{c})$
$\qquad = 4\mathbf{a} - 4\mathbf{c} + 3\mathbf{c} - 3\mathbf{b} + 4\mathbf{a} - 2\mathbf{b} - 6\mathbf{c}$
$\qquad = 8\mathbf{a} - 5\mathbf{b} - 7\mathbf{c}$

2.8 (a) $2\mathbf{b} + 4\mathbf{x} = 7\mathbf{a}$, therefore
$\qquad 4\mathbf{x} = 7\mathbf{a} - 2\mathbf{b}$,
so
$\qquad \mathbf{x} = \frac{7}{4}\mathbf{a} - \frac{1}{2}\mathbf{b}$.

(b) $n(\mathbf{b} - \mathbf{a}) + \mathbf{x} = m(\mathbf{a} - \mathbf{b})$, therefore
$\qquad \mathbf{x} = m(\mathbf{a} - \mathbf{b}) - n(\mathbf{b} - \mathbf{a})$
$\qquad\quad = m(\mathbf{a} - \mathbf{b}) + n(\mathbf{a} - \mathbf{b})$
$\qquad\quad = (m + n)(\mathbf{a} - \mathbf{b})$.

2.9

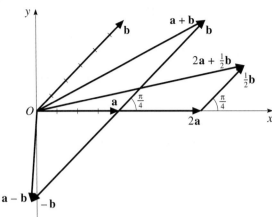

2.10 The magnitude of **v** is 4.7 times the magnitude of **u**. **v** is parallel to **u**, but the sense of **v** is opposite to the sense of **u**, i.e. **v** and **u** have opposite directions.

2.11 By the triangle rule,
$$\vec{AB} + \vec{BC} = \vec{AC},$$
$$\vec{CD} + \vec{DA} = \vec{CA}.$$
But $\vec{CA} = -\vec{AC}$, so we have
$$\vec{AB} + \vec{BC} + \vec{CD} + \vec{DA} = \vec{AC} - \vec{AC} = \mathbf{0}.$$

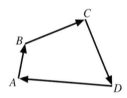

Alternatively, $\vec{AB} + \vec{BC} = \vec{AC}$. Hence
$$\vec{AB} + \vec{BC} + \vec{CD} = \vec{AC} + \vec{CD} = \vec{AD},$$
so
$$\vec{AB} + \vec{BC} + \vec{CD} + \vec{DA} = \vec{AD} + \vec{DA} = \mathbf{0},$$
since $\vec{AD} = -\vec{DA}$.

(There are various other possible arguments!)

2.12 The vectors **p**, **q** and **p** + **q** are sketched below.

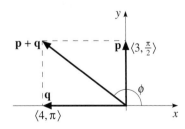

$$5\mathbf{p} = \langle 15, \tfrac{\pi}{2} \rangle, \quad -\mathbf{q} = \langle 4, 0 \rangle.$$
Since the directions of **p** and **q** are at right angles,
$|\mathbf{p} + \mathbf{q}| = \sqrt{3^2 + 4^2} = 5$ and $\phi = \tfrac{\pi}{2} + \arctan \tfrac{4}{3} = 2.498$
radians, so
$$\mathbf{p} + \mathbf{q} = \langle 5, 2.498 \rangle.$$

2.13 (a) The first rule is true and the second is false (scalar multiplication does not change direction).

(b) The proposed rule does not hold. (Consider $\mathbf{r} + \mathbf{r}$, for example, where $\mathbf{r} = \langle r, \phi \rangle$. The proposed rule gives $\mathbf{r} + \mathbf{r} = \langle 2r, 2\phi \rangle$, whereas actually $\mathbf{r} + \mathbf{r} = 2\mathbf{r} = \langle 2r, \phi \rangle$.)

(There is an algebraic rule for adding vectors in polar form, but it is rather unwieldy. This is one reason why Section 3 introduces the Cartesian representation of a vector, for which there is a simple algebraic rule for the addition of vectors.)

Section 3

3.1 $\mathbf{a} = \mathbf{i} = [1 \quad 0]^T$
$\mathbf{b} = 2\mathbf{j} = [0 \quad 2]^T$
$\mathbf{c} = \mathbf{i} = [1 \quad 0]^T \ (= \mathbf{a})$
$\mathbf{d} = -2\mathbf{i} = [-2 \quad 0]^T$
$\mathbf{e} = -\mathbf{i} + 2\mathbf{j} = [-1 \quad 2]^T$
$\mathbf{f} = 2\mathbf{j} = [0 \quad 2]^T \ (= \mathbf{b})$
$\mathbf{g} = \mathbf{i} - \mathbf{j} = [1 \quad -1]^T$
$\mathbf{h} = 3\mathbf{i} = [3 \quad 0]^T$

3.2 (a) $\mathbf{a} = 3\mathbf{i} + \mathbf{j}, \quad \mathbf{b} = -\mathbf{i} + 3\mathbf{j}, \quad \mathbf{c} = -3\mathbf{i} - 2\mathbf{j},$
$\mathbf{d} = 3\mathbf{i} + \mathbf{j} \ (= \mathbf{a}).$

(b)

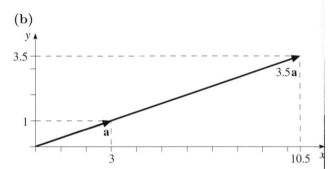

$3.5\mathbf{a} = 3.5(3\mathbf{i} + \mathbf{j}) = 10.5\mathbf{i} + 3.5\mathbf{j}$, as in the diagram.

(c)

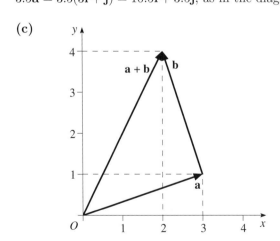

$\mathbf{a} + \mathbf{b} = (3\mathbf{i} + \mathbf{j}) + (-\mathbf{i} + 3\mathbf{j}) = 2\mathbf{i} + 4\mathbf{j}$, as in the diagram.

(d) $2\mathbf{a} + \mathbf{b} - \mathbf{c} = 2(3\mathbf{i} + \mathbf{j}) + (-\mathbf{i} + 3\mathbf{j}) - (-3\mathbf{i} - 2\mathbf{j})$
$$= 8\mathbf{i} + 7\mathbf{j}.$$
Thus $|2\mathbf{a} + \mathbf{b} - \mathbf{c}| = \sqrt{8^2 + 7^2} = \sqrt{113}$.

3.3 (a) Given $\mathbf{r} = \mathbf{s}$, we can equate the corresponding components. Thus

$$p + q = -3 \quad \text{and} \quad p - q = 7,$$

which gives $p = 2$ and $q = -5$.

(b) $\mathbf{t} = \mathbf{u} + \mathbf{v} = \dfrac{1}{\sqrt{2}}\left(\begin{bmatrix} 1 \\ 1 \end{bmatrix} + \begin{bmatrix} 1 \\ -1 \end{bmatrix}\right)$

$$= \frac{1}{\sqrt{2}}\begin{bmatrix} 2 \\ 0 \end{bmatrix} = \begin{bmatrix} \sqrt{2} \\ 0 \end{bmatrix}.$$

Hence $|\mathbf{t}| = \sqrt{2}$.

3.4 (a) $|\mathbf{a}| = 2$, $|\mathbf{b}| = 3$, $|\mathbf{c}| = 1$.

(b) Use the formulae $x = r\cos\phi$ and $y = r\sin\phi$ (see Subsection 1.5).

First consider the vector $\mathbf{a}$. The Cartesian components of $\mathbf{a}$ are the numbers a_1 and a_2 given by

$$a_1 = 2\cos\tfrac{\pi}{3} = 1, \quad a_2 = 2\sin\tfrac{\pi}{3} = \sqrt{3}.$$

Thus

$$\mathbf{a} = a_1\mathbf{i} + a_2\mathbf{j} = \mathbf{i} + \sqrt{3}\mathbf{j}.$$

Similarly for $\mathbf{b}$ and $\mathbf{c}$:

$$\mathbf{b} = \left(3\cos\tfrac{3\pi}{4}\right)\mathbf{i} + \left(3\sin\tfrac{3\pi}{4}\right)\mathbf{j} = -\tfrac{3}{\sqrt{2}}\mathbf{i} + \tfrac{3}{\sqrt{2}}\mathbf{j},$$

$$\mathbf{c} = \left(\cos\tfrac{\pi}{6}\right)\mathbf{i} + \left(\sin\tfrac{\pi}{6}\right)\mathbf{j} = \tfrac{\sqrt{3}}{2}\mathbf{i} + \tfrac{1}{2}\mathbf{j}.$$

(c) We now have

$$\mathbf{a} + \mathbf{c} = \left(\mathbf{i} + \sqrt{3}\mathbf{j}\right) + \left(\tfrac{\sqrt{3}}{2}\mathbf{i} + \tfrac{1}{2}\mathbf{j}\right)$$

$$= \left(1 + \tfrac{\sqrt{3}}{2}\right)\mathbf{i} + \left(\sqrt{3} + \tfrac{1}{2}\right)\mathbf{j}$$

$$\simeq 1.866\mathbf{i} + 2.232\mathbf{j}.$$

3.5 (a) The components are

$$v_1 = 5\cos\tfrac{5\pi}{18} \simeq 3.214,$$

$$v_2 = 5\sin\tfrac{5\pi}{18} \simeq 3.83.$$

(b) The magnitudes are

$$|\mathbf{a}| = ((\sqrt{3})^2 + (-1)^2)^{1/2} = 2,$$

$$|\mathbf{b}| = ((-3)^2 + 3^2)^{1/2} = 3\sqrt{2} \simeq 4.243.$$

To specify the directions, we need a reference direction. Using the plane polar coordinate convention, we can specify the angle ϕ with respect to the positive x-axis. Thus, for vector $\mathbf{a}$,

$$\cos\phi = a_1/|\mathbf{a}| = \sqrt{3}/2,$$

$$\sin\phi = a_2/|\mathbf{a}| = -1/2,$$

hence $\phi = -\tfrac{\pi}{6}$.

For vector $\mathbf{b}$,

$$\cos\phi = -3/(3\sqrt{2}) = -1/\sqrt{2},$$

$$\sin\phi = 3/(3\sqrt{2}) = 1/\sqrt{2},$$

hence $\phi = \tfrac{3\pi}{4}$.

3.6 Systems (b), (c) and (d) are right-handed.

3.7 (a) $\mathbf{d} = 2(\mathbf{i} + \mathbf{j} + \mathbf{k}) - 3(2\mathbf{i} - 3\mathbf{j} - \mathbf{k})$

$$= -4\mathbf{i} + 11\mathbf{j} + 5\mathbf{k},$$

$\mathbf{e} = (\mathbf{i} + \mathbf{j} + \mathbf{k}) - 2(2\mathbf{i} - 3\mathbf{j} - \mathbf{k}) + 4(3\mathbf{i} + \mathbf{k})$

$$= 9\mathbf{i} + 7\mathbf{j} + 7\mathbf{k}.$$

(b) $|\mathbf{d}| = \sqrt{(-4)^2 + 11^2 + 5^2} = \sqrt{162}\ (= 9\sqrt{2})$,

$$|\mathbf{e}| = \sqrt{9^2 + 7^2 + 7^2} = \sqrt{179}.$$

(c) $|\mathbf{a}| = \sqrt{1^2 + 1^2 + 1^2} = \sqrt{3}$.

A unit vector in the direction of $\mathbf{a}$ is

$$\frac{1}{|\mathbf{a}|}\mathbf{a} = \frac{1}{\sqrt{3}}(\mathbf{i} + \mathbf{j} + \mathbf{k}).$$

(d) If $\mathbf{a} + \mathbf{x} = \mathbf{b}$, then

$$\mathbf{x} = \mathbf{b} - \mathbf{a} = (2\mathbf{i} - 3\mathbf{j} - \mathbf{k}) - (\mathbf{i} + \mathbf{j} + \mathbf{k})$$

$$= \mathbf{i} - 4\mathbf{j} - 2\mathbf{k}.$$

Thus the components of $\mathbf{x}$ are 1, -4 and -2.

3.8 $\mathbf{p} = \begin{bmatrix} 3 \\ 0 \\ 18 \end{bmatrix} - \begin{bmatrix} 2 \\ 3 \\ -1 \end{bmatrix} = \begin{bmatrix} 1 \\ -3 \\ 19 \end{bmatrix}$, so

$$|\mathbf{p}| = (1^2 + (-3)^2 + 19^2)^{1/2} = 371^{1/2}\ (\simeq 19.26).$$

3.9 Relative to the origin of the Cartesian coordinate system, the two points have position vectors $\mathbf{i} + \mathbf{j} + 2\mathbf{k}$ and $2\mathbf{i} + 3\mathbf{j} + \mathbf{k}$. Thus the vector equation of the line is

$$\mathbf{t} = (1 - s)(\mathbf{i} + \mathbf{j} + 2\mathbf{k}) + s(2\mathbf{i} + 3\mathbf{j} + \mathbf{k})$$

$$= (1 + s)\mathbf{i} + (1 + 2s)\mathbf{j} + (2 - s)\mathbf{k},$$

where $-\infty < s < \infty$.

3.10 (a) $|\mathbf{a}| = \sqrt{2^2 + (-1)^2} = \sqrt{5}$,

$$|\mathbf{b}| = \sqrt{1^2 + 3^2 + 5^2} = \sqrt{35}.$$

The vector $\mathbf{a}$ lies in the (x, y)-plane, and the angle ϕ that it makes with the x-axis is given by $\cos\phi = 2/\sqrt{5}$ and $\sin\phi = -1/\sqrt{5}$. Hence $\phi \simeq -0.4636$ radians.

(b) $\mathbf{a} + \mathbf{b} = 3\mathbf{i} + 2\mathbf{j} + 5\mathbf{k}$,

$$2\mathbf{a} - \mathbf{b} = 3\mathbf{i} - 5\mathbf{j} - 5\mathbf{k},$$

$$\mathbf{c} + 2\mathbf{b} - 3\mathbf{a} = -4\mathbf{i} + 10\mathbf{j} + 8\mathbf{k}.$$

(c) The vector $\overrightarrow{PQ}$ is equal to $2\mathbf{a} - \mathbf{b}$. The point Q is the end of the vector $\overrightarrow{OQ}$, which is given by

$$\overrightarrow{OQ} = \overrightarrow{OP} + \overrightarrow{PQ}$$

$$= (2\mathbf{j} + 3\mathbf{k}) + (3\mathbf{i} - 5\mathbf{j} - 5\mathbf{k})$$

$$= 3\mathbf{i} - 3\mathbf{j} - 2\mathbf{k},$$

so Q is the point $(3, -3, -2)$.

3.11 $\mathbf{0} = [0 \ \ 0 \ \ 0]^T$,

$$\mathbf{i} = [1 \ \ 0 \ \ 0]^T,$$

$$\mathbf{j} = [0 \ \ 1 \ \ 0]^T,$$

$$\mathbf{k} = [0 \ \ 0 \ \ 1]^T.$$

Section 4

4.1 $\mathbf{a} \cdot \mathbf{b} = |\mathbf{a}|\,|\mathbf{b}| \cos\theta = 2 \times 4 \times \cos\frac{\pi}{3} = 4,$

$\mathbf{b} \cdot \mathbf{c} = |\mathbf{b}|\,|\mathbf{c}| \cos\theta = 4 \times 1 \times \cos\frac{\pi}{6} = 2\sqrt{3},$

$\mathbf{a} \cdot \mathbf{c} = |\mathbf{a}|\,|\mathbf{c}| \cos\theta = 2 \times 1 \times \cos\left(\frac{\pi}{3} + \frac{\pi}{6}\right)$

$= 2 \cos\frac{\pi}{2} = 0,$

$\mathbf{b} \cdot \mathbf{b} = |\mathbf{b}|\,|\mathbf{b}| \cos\theta = 4 \times 4 \times \cos 0 = 16.$

4.2 (a) $(\mathbf{a} + \mathbf{b}) \cdot (\mathbf{a} - \mathbf{b}) = \mathbf{a} \cdot (\mathbf{a} - \mathbf{b}) + \mathbf{b} \cdot (\mathbf{a} - \mathbf{b})$

$= \mathbf{a} \cdot \mathbf{a} - \mathbf{a} \cdot \mathbf{b} + \mathbf{b} \cdot \mathbf{a} - \mathbf{b} \cdot \mathbf{b}$

$= \mathbf{a} \cdot \mathbf{a} - \mathbf{a} \cdot \mathbf{b} + \mathbf{a} \cdot \mathbf{b} - \mathbf{b} \cdot \mathbf{b}$

$= \mathbf{a} \cdot \mathbf{a} - \mathbf{b} \cdot \mathbf{b}$

(b) $|\mathbf{a} + \mathbf{b}|^2 = (\mathbf{a} + \mathbf{b}) \cdot (\mathbf{a} + \mathbf{b})$

$= \mathbf{a} \cdot (\mathbf{a} + \mathbf{b}) + \mathbf{b} \cdot (\mathbf{a} + \mathbf{b})$

$= \mathbf{a} \cdot \mathbf{a} + \mathbf{a} \cdot \mathbf{b} + \mathbf{b} \cdot \mathbf{a} + \mathbf{b} \cdot \mathbf{b}$

$= \mathbf{a} \cdot \mathbf{a} + \mathbf{a} \cdot \mathbf{b} + \mathbf{a} \cdot \mathbf{b} + \mathbf{b} \cdot \mathbf{b}$

$= \mathbf{a} \cdot \mathbf{a} + 2\mathbf{a} \cdot \mathbf{b} + \mathbf{b} \cdot \mathbf{b}$

4.3 (a) If $2\mathbf{a} + 3\mathbf{b}$ and $m\mathbf{a} + \mathbf{b}$ are perpendicular, then

$(2\mathbf{a} + 3\mathbf{b}) \cdot (m\mathbf{a} + \mathbf{b}) = 0.$

Expanding this expression,

$2m\mathbf{a} \cdot \mathbf{a} + 2\mathbf{a} \cdot \mathbf{b} + 3m\mathbf{b} \cdot \mathbf{a} + 3\mathbf{b} \cdot \mathbf{b} = 0.$

Now $\mathbf{a}$ and $\mathbf{b}$ are perpendicular, so $\mathbf{a} \cdot \mathbf{b} = \mathbf{b} \cdot \mathbf{a} = 0$, and they are unit vectors, so $\mathbf{a} \cdot \mathbf{a} = \mathbf{b} \cdot \mathbf{b} = 1$. Thus

$2m + 3 = 0,$

so $m = -1.5$.

(b) $|\mathbf{c}|^2 = \mathbf{c} \cdot \mathbf{c}$

$= (3\mathbf{a} + 5\mathbf{b}) \cdot (3\mathbf{a} + 5\mathbf{b})$

$= 9\mathbf{a} \cdot \mathbf{a} + 15\mathbf{a} \cdot \mathbf{b} + 15\mathbf{b} \cdot \mathbf{a} + 25\mathbf{b} \cdot \mathbf{b}.$

Thus, since $\mathbf{a}$ and $\mathbf{b}$ are perpendicular unit vectors,

$|\mathbf{c}|^2 = 9 + 25 = 34,$

so $|\mathbf{c}| = \sqrt{34} \; (\simeq 5.831)$.

4.4 $\mathbf{a} \cdot \mathbf{b} = (4 \times 1) + (1 \times -3) + (-5 \times 1) = -4.$

The negative sign tells us that the angle between $\mathbf{a}$ and $\mathbf{b}$ is between $\frac{\pi}{2}$ and π radians, i.e. it is an obtuse angle.

4.5 $|\mathbf{a}| = \sqrt{2^2 + (-3)^2 + 1^2} = \sqrt{14},$

$|\mathbf{b}| = \sqrt{(-1)^2 + 2^2 + 4^2} = \sqrt{21}.$

Also,

$\mathbf{a} \cdot \mathbf{b} = (2 \times -1) + (-3 \times 2) + (1 \times 4) = -4,$

so if θ is the angle between $\mathbf{a}$ and $\mathbf{b}$, then

$\cos\theta = \dfrac{\mathbf{a} \cdot \mathbf{b}}{|\mathbf{a}|\,|\mathbf{b}|} = \dfrac{-4}{\sqrt{14} \times \sqrt{21}} = -\dfrac{4}{7\sqrt{6}}.$

The negative sign means that θ is obtuse, so $\theta \simeq 1.806$ radians.

4.6 $\mathbf{a} \cdot \mathbf{i} = (a_1\mathbf{i} + a_2\mathbf{j} + a_3\mathbf{k}) \cdot \mathbf{i}$

$= a_1\mathbf{i} \cdot \mathbf{i} + a_2\mathbf{j} \cdot \mathbf{i} + a_3\mathbf{k} \cdot \mathbf{i}$

$= a_1.$

Similarly,

$\mathbf{a} \cdot \mathbf{j} = a_2 \quad \text{and} \quad \mathbf{a} \cdot \mathbf{k} = a_3.$

(Notice that this means that the components of a vector are given by the dot products of the vector with the Cartesian unit vectors $\mathbf{i}$, $\mathbf{j}$, $\mathbf{k}$.)

4.7 (a) $\mathbf{a} \cdot \mathbf{c} = -2$, $\mathbf{a} \cdot \mathbf{d} = -3$, $\mathbf{a} \cdot \mathbf{e} = 0$.

Thus only $\mathbf{e}$ is perpendicular to $\mathbf{a}$.

(b) First,

$\mathbf{a} + 2\mathbf{b} = \mathbf{j} + 9\mathbf{k}.$

Now a suitable vector along the line joining the origin to the point $(1, 1, 1)$ is $\mathbf{i} + \mathbf{j} + \mathbf{k}$. The corresponding unit vector is $\mathbf{u} = \frac{1}{\sqrt{3}}(\mathbf{i} + \mathbf{j} + \mathbf{k})$. The component of $\mathbf{a} + 2\mathbf{b}$ in the direction of this line is

$\mathbf{u} \cdot (\mathbf{a} + 2\mathbf{b}) = \frac{1}{\sqrt{3}}(\mathbf{i} + \mathbf{j} + \mathbf{k}) \cdot (\mathbf{j} + 9\mathbf{k})$

$= \frac{10}{\sqrt{3}}.$

4.8 The angle between $\mathbf{i}$ and $\mathbf{v}$ is $\frac{\pi}{6}$, and that between $\mathbf{j}$ and $\mathbf{v}$ is $\frac{\pi}{2} - \frac{\pi}{6} = \frac{\pi}{3}$. Also, $|\mathbf{v}| = 1.5$. So the $\mathbf{i}$-component of $\mathbf{v}$ is

$|\mathbf{v}| \cos\frac{\pi}{6} = \frac{3}{2} \times \frac{\sqrt{3}}{2} = \frac{3\sqrt{3}}{4},$

and the $\mathbf{j}$-component of $\mathbf{v}$ is

$|\mathbf{v}| \cos\frac{\pi}{3} = \frac{3}{2} \times \frac{1}{2} = \frac{3}{4}.$

The angle between $\mathbf{i}$ and $\mathbf{w}$ is $\frac{\pi}{2} + \frac{\pi}{6} = \frac{2\pi}{3}$, and that between $\mathbf{j}$ and $\mathbf{w}$ is $\pi - \frac{\pi}{6} = \frac{5\pi}{6}$. Also, $|\mathbf{w}| = 2$. Moreover, using the formulae from the Handbook,

$\cos\frac{2\pi}{3} = \cos(\pi - \frac{\pi}{3})$

$= \cos\pi \cos\frac{\pi}{3} + \sin\pi \sin\frac{\pi}{3}$

$= -\cos\frac{\pi}{3}$

$= -\frac{1}{2}$

and

$\cos\frac{5\pi}{6} = \cos(\pi - \frac{\pi}{6})$

$= \cos\pi \cos\frac{\pi}{6} + \sin\pi \sin\frac{\pi}{6}$

$= -\cos\frac{\pi}{6}$

$= -\frac{\sqrt{3}}{2}.$

The $\mathbf{i}$-component of $\mathbf{w}$ is therefore

$|\mathbf{w}| \cos\frac{2\pi}{3} = -2 \times \frac{1}{2} = -1,$

and the $\mathbf{j}$-component of $\mathbf{w}$ is

$|\mathbf{w}| \cos\frac{5\pi}{6} = -2 \times \frac{\sqrt{3}}{2} = -\sqrt{3}.$

In summary,

$\mathbf{v} = \frac{3\sqrt{3}}{4}\mathbf{i} + \frac{3}{4}\mathbf{j} \quad \text{and} \quad \mathbf{w} = -\mathbf{i} - \sqrt{3}\mathbf{j}.$

4.9 The technique here is the same for all the vectors. One must find the angle between the vector in question and the unit vectors **i** and **j**.

Vector **a** points vertically downwards, in the direction −**j**. Hence **i** and **a** are perpendicular, and

$$\mathbf{a} = 0\mathbf{i} - \mathbf{j} = -\mathbf{j}.$$

The angle between **i** and **b** is α, and the angle between **j** and **b** is $\frac{\pi}{2} - \alpha$. Hence the **i**-component of **b** is

$$|\mathbf{b}| \cos \alpha = 1.5 \cos \alpha,$$

and the **j**-component of **b** is

$$|\mathbf{b}| \cos(\tfrac{\pi}{2} - \alpha) = 1.5 \sin \alpha,$$

where we have used the formula

$$\cos(\beta - \alpha) = \cos \beta \cos \alpha + \sin \beta \sin \alpha$$

to evaluate $\cos(\frac{\pi}{2} - \alpha)$ (see the Handbook). So

$$\mathbf{b} = 1.5 \cos \alpha \, \mathbf{i} + 1.5 \sin \alpha \, \mathbf{j}.$$

The angle between **i** and **c** is $\frac{\pi}{2} + \alpha$, and the angle between **j** and **c** is α.

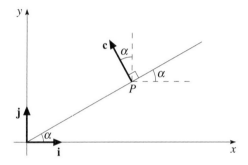

Therefore the **i**-component of **c** is

$$|\mathbf{c}| \cos(\tfrac{\pi}{2} + \alpha) = -1.5 \sin \alpha,$$

where we have used the formula

$$\cos(\beta + \alpha) = \cos \beta \cos \alpha - \sin \beta \sin \alpha$$

to evaluate $\cos(\frac{\pi}{2} + \alpha)$ (see the Handbook). The **j**-component of **c** is

$$|\mathbf{c}| \cos \alpha = 1.5 \cos \alpha,$$

so

$$\mathbf{c} = -1.5 \sin \alpha \, \mathbf{i} + 1.5 \cos \alpha \, \mathbf{j}.$$

Finally, the angle between **i** and **d** is $\pi - \alpha$, and the angle between **j** and **d** is $\frac{\pi}{2} + \alpha$.

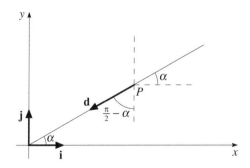

Thus the **i**-component of **d** is

$$|\mathbf{d}| \cos(\pi - \alpha) = -2 \cos \alpha,$$

and the **j**-component of **d** is

$$|\mathbf{d}| \cos(\tfrac{\pi}{2} + \alpha) = -2 \sin \alpha$$

(using the usual trigonometric formulae). So

$$\mathbf{d} = -2 \cos \alpha \, \mathbf{i} - 2 \sin \alpha \, \mathbf{j}.$$

4.10 As in the previous exercise, we must find the angles between **a**, **b**, **c**, **d** and the unit vectors **i** and **j**. First notice that **b** points in the direction **i**, so $\mathbf{b} = 1.5\mathbf{i}$. Similarly, **d** points in the direction −**i**, so $\mathbf{d} = -2\mathbf{i}$. Also, **c** points in the direction **j**, so $\mathbf{c} = 1.5\mathbf{j}$.

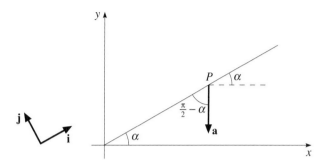

The remaining vector, **a**, makes an angle $\frac{\pi}{2} + \alpha$ with **i**, and an angle $\pi - \alpha$ with **j**. Hence the **i**-component of **a** is

$$|\mathbf{a}| \cos(\tfrac{\pi}{2} + \alpha) = -\sin \alpha,$$

and the **j**-component of **a** is

$$|\mathbf{a}| \cos(\pi - \alpha) = -\cos \alpha.$$

Therefore

$$\mathbf{a} = -\sin \alpha \, \mathbf{i} - \cos \alpha \, \mathbf{j}.$$

4.11 Here the angle between **i** and **p** is $\pi - \alpha$, and the angle between **j** and **p** is $\frac{\pi}{2} - \alpha$. Therefore the **i**-component of **p** is

$$|\mathbf{p}| \cos(\pi - \alpha) = -2.5 \cos \alpha,$$

and the **j**-component of **p** is

$$|\mathbf{p}| \cos(\tfrac{\pi}{2} - \alpha) = 2.5 \sin \alpha.$$

Thus

$$\mathbf{p} = -2.5 \cos \alpha \, \mathbf{i} + 2.5 \sin \alpha \, \mathbf{j}.$$

The angle between **i** and **q** is $\pi - \beta$, and the angle between **j** and **q** is $\frac{\pi}{2} + \beta$. Therefore the **i**-component of **q** is

$$|\mathbf{q}| \cos(\pi - \beta) = -3 \cos \beta,$$

and the **j**-component of **q** is

$$|\mathbf{q}| \cos(\tfrac{\pi}{2} + \beta) = -3 \sin \beta.$$

Hence

$$\mathbf{q} = -3 \cos \beta \, \mathbf{i} - 3 \sin \beta \, \mathbf{j}.$$

Finally, the angle between **i** and **r** is γ, and the angle between **j** and **r** is $\frac{\pi}{2} + \gamma$. Thus the **i**-component of **r** is

$$|\mathbf{r}| \cos \gamma = 2.5 \cos \gamma,$$

and the **j**-component of **r** is

$$|\mathbf{r}| \cos(\tfrac{\pi}{2} + \gamma) = -2.5 \sin \gamma.$$

So

$$\mathbf{r} = 2.5 \cos \gamma \, \mathbf{i} - 2.5 \sin \gamma \, \mathbf{j}.$$

4.12 The **i**-component of **a** is clearly zero, while the **j**-component is simply $|\mathbf{a}|$. Similarly, the **i**-component of **b** is $-|\mathbf{b}|$ while the **j**-component is zero. Hence

$\mathbf{a} = |\mathbf{a}|\,\mathbf{j}$ and $\mathbf{b} = -|\mathbf{b}|\,\mathbf{i}$.

The **i**- and **j**-components of **c** are, respectively,

$|\mathbf{c}|\cos\frac{\pi}{4} = 2 \times \frac{1}{\sqrt{2}} = \sqrt{2}$

and

$|\mathbf{c}|\cos(\frac{\pi}{2} + \frac{\pi}{4}) = -2\sin\frac{\pi}{4} = -\sqrt{2},$

so

$\mathbf{c} = \sqrt{2}\mathbf{i} - \sqrt{2}\mathbf{j}.$

Given that $\mathbf{a} + \mathbf{b} + \mathbf{c} = \mathbf{0}$, the sum of all the **i**-components of $\mathbf{a} + \mathbf{b} + \mathbf{c}$ must be zero, and so must the sum of all the **j**-components. Therefore (**i**-components)

$0 - |\mathbf{b}| + \sqrt{2} = 0$

and (**j**-components)

$|\mathbf{a}| + 0 - \sqrt{2} = 0.$

Thus we see that $|\mathbf{a}| = |\mathbf{b}| = \sqrt{2}$.

4.13 For the sake of clarity, here is a diagram showing **u**, **v** and **w** (where all three vectors start at O) drawn in the (x, y)-plane. (The z-axis points out of the page.)

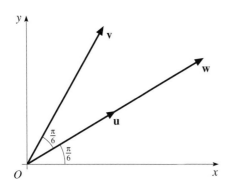

The cross products are all perpendicular to the (x, y)-plane.

A unit vector in the direction of $\mathbf{u} \times \mathbf{v}$ is **k**, so

$\mathbf{u} \times \mathbf{v} = \left(|\mathbf{u}|\,|\mathbf{v}|\sin\frac{\pi}{6}\right)\mathbf{k} = (2 \times 3 \times \frac{1}{2})\mathbf{k} = 3\mathbf{k}.$

The angle between **u** and **w** is zero, so

$\mathbf{u} \times \mathbf{w} = \left(|\mathbf{u}|\,|\mathbf{w}|\sin 0\right)\widehat{\mathbf{c}} = (2 \times 4 \times 0)\widehat{\mathbf{c}} = 0\widehat{\mathbf{c}} = \mathbf{0}.$

A unit vector in the direction of $\mathbf{v} \times \mathbf{w}$ is $-\mathbf{k}$, so

$\mathbf{v} \times \mathbf{w} = \left(|\mathbf{v}|\,|\mathbf{w}|\sin\frac{\pi}{6}\right)(-\mathbf{k}) = (3 \times 4 \times \frac{1}{2})(-\mathbf{k})$
$= -6\mathbf{k}.$

4.14 (a) **i**, **j** and **k** are unit vectors forming a right-handed system.

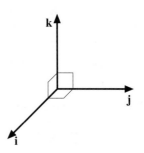

Thus, using the definition of the cross product,

$\mathbf{i} \times \mathbf{j} = (|\mathbf{i}|\,|\mathbf{j}|\sin\frac{\pi}{2})\mathbf{k} = \mathbf{k}.$

Similarly,

$\mathbf{j} \times \mathbf{k} = \mathbf{i}$ and $\mathbf{k} \times \mathbf{i} = \mathbf{j}.$

(b) Since $(\mathbf{a} \times \mathbf{b}) = -(\mathbf{b} \times \mathbf{a})$ for any vectors **a** and **b**, we have

$\mathbf{j} \times \mathbf{i} = -\mathbf{k},$ $\mathbf{k} \times \mathbf{j} = -\mathbf{i}$ and $\mathbf{i} \times \mathbf{k} = -\mathbf{j}.$

(c) Since $\mathbf{a} \times \mathbf{a} = \mathbf{0}$ for any vector **a**, we have

$\mathbf{i} \times \mathbf{i} = \mathbf{j} \times \mathbf{j} = \mathbf{k} \times \mathbf{k} = \mathbf{0}.$

(d) $(\mathbf{i} + \mathbf{k}) \times (\mathbf{i} + \mathbf{j} + \mathbf{k})$
$= (\mathbf{i} \times (\mathbf{i} + \mathbf{j} + \mathbf{k})) + (\mathbf{k} \times (\mathbf{i} + \mathbf{j} + \mathbf{k}))$
$= (\mathbf{0} + \mathbf{k} + (-\mathbf{j})) + (\mathbf{j} + (-\mathbf{i}) + \mathbf{0})$
$= -\mathbf{i} + \mathbf{k},$

$(\mathbf{i} \times (\mathbf{i} + \mathbf{k})) - ((\mathbf{i} + \mathbf{j}) \times \mathbf{k})$
$= (\mathbf{0} + (-\mathbf{j})) - (-\mathbf{j} + \mathbf{i})$
$= -\mathbf{i}.$

4.15 To compute $\mathbf{a} \times \mathbf{b}$, we use Sarrus's Rule:

	i	**j**	**k**	**i**	**j**	
	2	-3	1	2	-3	
	-1	2	4	-1	2	
$-3\mathbf{k}$	$-2\mathbf{i}$	$-8\mathbf{j}$		$-12\mathbf{i}$	$-\mathbf{j}$	$4\mathbf{k}$

so $\mathbf{a} \times \mathbf{b} = -14\mathbf{i} - 9\mathbf{j} + \mathbf{k}.$

Similarly for $\mathbf{a} \times \mathbf{c}$:

	i	**j**	**k**	**i**	**j**	
	2	-3	1	2	-3	
	-4	6	-2	-4	6	
$-12\mathbf{k}$	$-6\mathbf{i}$	$4\mathbf{j}$		$6\mathbf{i}$	$-4\mathbf{j}$	$12\mathbf{k}$

so $\mathbf{a} \times \mathbf{c} = \mathbf{0}.$

Finally, for $\mathbf{b} \times \mathbf{c}$:

	i	**j**	**k**	**i**	**j**	
	-1	2	4	-1	2	
	-4	6	-2	-4	6	
$8\mathbf{k}$	$-24\mathbf{i}$	$-2\mathbf{j}$		$-4\mathbf{i}$	$-16\mathbf{j}$	$-6\mathbf{k}$

so $\mathbf{b} \times \mathbf{c} = -28\mathbf{i} - 18\mathbf{j} + 2\mathbf{k}.$

Since $\mathbf{a} \times \mathbf{c} = \mathbf{0}$, and neither vector is zero, the vectors **a** and **c** are parallel. In fact, $\mathbf{c} = -2\mathbf{a}.$

4.16 A vector perpendicular to **a** and **b** is **a** × **b**, which we can compute using Sarrus's Rule:

	i	**j**	**k**	**i**	**j**	
	2	2	1	2	2	
	4	4	−7	4	4	
−8**k**	−4**i**	14**j**		−14**i**	4**j**	8**k**

so **a** × **b** = −18**i** + 18**j**.

We are asked for a unit vector, so the obvious choice is

$$\frac{1}{|\mathbf{a} \times \mathbf{b}|}(\mathbf{a} \times \mathbf{b}) = \frac{-18\mathbf{i} + 18\mathbf{j}}{18\sqrt{2}}$$
$$= \tfrac{1}{\sqrt{2}}(-\mathbf{i} + \mathbf{j}).$$

(Note that $\tfrac{1}{\sqrt{2}}(\mathbf{i} - \mathbf{j})$ is also a unit vector perpendicular to **a** and **b**. This can be obtained by considering **b** × **a** rather than **a** × **b**.)

4.17 (a) No, it is a scalar.

(b) Yes, if the angle between **a** and **b** is between $\frac{\pi}{2}$ and π radians.

(c) If either **a** = **0** or **b** = **0**, then indeed **a** · **b** = $|\mathbf{a}|\,|\mathbf{b}|$ (= 0). So assume that **a** and **b** are both non-zero. If **a** · **b** = $|\mathbf{a}|\,|\mathbf{b}|\cos\theta = |\mathbf{a}|\,|\mathbf{b}|$, then $\cos\theta = 1$, so $\theta = 0$, i.e. **a** and **b** are in the same direction.

(d) If **a** · **b** = 0, then either **a** = **0** or **b** = **0** (or both), or **a** and **b** are perpendicular.

(e) If **a** × **b** = **0**, then either **a** = **0** or **b** = **0** (or both), or **a** and **b** are parallel (but may have opposite senses).

4.18 (a) **t** is perpendicular to both **r** and **s**, and its sense is vertically down, i.e. into the ground.

(b) Conversely, the sense of **s** × **r** is vertically up.

(c) **t** × **r** is perpendicular to **t** (and thus in the horizontal plane) and perpendicular to **r**, and by the screw rule its sense is due east.

(d) $|\mathbf{t}| = |\mathbf{r}|\,|\mathbf{s}|\sin\frac{\pi}{4} = \frac{1}{\sqrt{2}}$

(e) **t** × (**r** × **s**) = **t** × **t** = **0**

(f) $\mathbf{r} \cdot \mathbf{s} = |\mathbf{r}|\,|\mathbf{s}|\cos\frac{\pi}{4} = \frac{1}{\sqrt{2}}$

(g) $\mathbf{s} \cdot (\mathbf{t} \times \mathbf{r}) = |\mathbf{s}|\,|\mathbf{t} \times \mathbf{r}|\cos\frac{\pi}{4}$ (by part (c))
$$= |\mathbf{s}|\left(|\mathbf{t}|\,|\mathbf{r}|\sin\frac{\pi}{2}\right)\cos\frac{\pi}{4}$$
$$= 1 \times \tfrac{1}{\sqrt{2}} \times 1 \times 1 \times \tfrac{1}{\sqrt{2}} = \tfrac{1}{2}$$

4.19 (**a** × **b**) · **a** = 0 for any non-zero vectors **a** and **b**, because **a** × **b** is perpendicular to **a**, and the dot product of perpendicular vectors is zero.

(If **a** and/or **b** is the zero vector, then the answer is still zero.)

Index